The Wonderf

Authoritative, up-to-d[illegible] illustrated, this handy unique guide to more than 125 of the most important minerals and rocks offers the beginner or amateur collector a fascinating introduction to a pleasureable and profitable hobby.

Richard M. Pearl, a leading authority in this field, has devised four keys to recognizing rocks and seven keys to recognizing minerals that will enable anyone to identify quickly and correctly typical specimens and their distinguishing features.

Including 46 beautiful full color illustrations, as well as a drawing of each rock and mineral, this book also provides interesting information on the use, origin, chemical content, and geographic location of each of the specimens described. In addition, Mr. Pearl gives many useful tips for hobbyists, tells how to label, classify, and display specimens and recommends a list of books and magazines for further reading in the field.

Conveniently indexed, easy to use, *How To Know The Minerals and Rocks* will provide many hours of informative relaxation at home or in the field.

"Recommended . . . a readable, useful book. . . ."

—*Library Journal*

THIS IS A REPRINT OF A HARDCOVER EDITION ORIGINALLY PUBLISHED BY THE MC GRAW-HILL BOOK COMPANY.

SIGNET KEY and MENTOR Books of Related Interest

HOW TO KNOW
the Minerals and Rocks

by RICHARD M. PEARL
Department of Geology
Colorado College, Colorado Springs, Colorado

A SIGNET KEY BOOK
Published by THE NEW AMERICAN LIBRARY

Published as a SIGNET KEY BOOK
By Arrangement with McGraw-Hill Book Company, Inc.

FIRST PRINTING, FEBRUARY, 1957
SECOND PRINTING, JUNE, 1957
THIRD PRINTING, JANUARY, 1958
FOURTH PRINTING, OCTOBER, 1958
FIFTH PRINTING, APRIL, 1959
SIXTH PRINTING, MAY, 1961
SEVENTH PRINTING, FEBRUARY, 1962

Dedicated in gratitude and affection
to Lillian Drews Garvin

SIGNET KEY BOOKS are published by
The New American Library of World Literature, Inc.
501 Madison Avenue, New York 22, New York

PRINTED IN THE UNITED STATES OF AMERICA

Preface

How to Know the Minerals and Rocks is a practical field guide to more than 125 of the most important minerals and rocks, including gems, ores, native metals, meteorites, and other interesting members of the mineral kingdom. It is simplified, authoritative, and up to date—written for the layman and for the beginning and amateur collector. With it you can identify for yourself the better-quality typical specimens you are most likely to find, as well as others of outstanding interest to collectors, prospectors, and scientists.

Even many fairly advanced collectors of minerals are unable to recognize by name the commonest rocks, because of their diverse appearance and the lack of definite tests for them. The Four Keys to Recognizing Rocks make it easy to identify the chief types by a simple but systematic procedure.

Similarly, the Seven Keys to Recognizing Minerals enable the new collector to become acquainted quickly with the important minerals which make up the majority of those he will come across in this fascinating and fast-growing hobby. Moreover, no special skill is needed to make the tests, and no equipment other than a pocketknife, a common magnet, a piece of broken porcelain, a piece of glass, a copper coin, a piece of quartz, and some vinegar.

Although the author believes wholeheartedly in the value of the standard blowpipe methods for testing minerals and has taught them to many students, they are not employed in this book because of the proved reluctance of most collectors to attempt their use without personal instruction. A few other kinds of tests are mentioned, but the minerals can be identified without them.

Besides the Keys for mineral and rock identification, this book has two unique features. Each description of a mineral and rock is accompanied by a drawing which brings out clearly the typical appearance and the characteristics by which the mineral and rock can be recognized. These well-labeled drawings, based upon sketches that were made especially for this book by the author's wife and were prepared in close collaboration with his writing of the text, will prove more valuable to the collector than pages of explanation.

The description of certain minerals includes handy tips on collecting, handling, cleaning, preserving, or displaying them—information not readily available elsewhere. The descriptions also cover the chemical composition, occurrence, uses, historical lore, and a range of other entertaining and informative background material on each mineral and rock.

Simplified information is given for learning how to read the chemical formulas of minerals. A list is presented of all the national magazines in the United States devoted to mineral and rock collecting and related hobbies. A selected reading list of books on these subjects is given, with brief descriptions to aid you in purchasing them.

Other distinctive features of this book include careful attention to scientific words so that all such words are explained when first used; emphasis of technical words by italics; thoughtful selection of photographs to tie in with the text and illustrate the discussion; and a complete Index.

Richard M. Pearl

COLORADO SPRINGS, COLO.

Contents

Acknowledgments

In addition to preparing preliminary sketches for almost all the drawings, my wife, Mignon W. Pearl, has given careful attention to the rest of the manuscript, and her advice has been extremely helpful. Eva L. Keller, of Colorado Springs, designed one of the difficult illustrations. Dr. Don B. Gould, of Colorado College, helpfully supplied a needed item of information. Nordis Felland, Librarian of the American Geographic Society, New York, checked some geographic names.

Stephen J. Voorhies prepared the line drawings that appear throughout this book.

I wish to express my gratitude to the following for color illustrations: Henry L. Gresham of Ward's Natural Science Establishment, Rochester, N. Y., who made available the photographs of minerals from the Harvard University Collection; Harry B. Groom, Jr., Assistant Professor of Geology, Louisiana Polytechnic Institute, whose photographs of minerals in the Harvard Collection appear on the jacket; and *Leica Photography Magazine,* in the pages of which Professor Groom's photographs were first reproduced.

R. M. P.

CHAPTER 1

This Fascinating Mineral Hobby

Collectors of minerals and rocks are rapidly becoming more numerous all over the world, especially in the United States and Canada. This has been true for nearly twenty years, yet mineral collecting is still young and vigorous enough to offer rewarding opportunities for those who join the fastest-growing collecting hobby in America.

Enthusiastic "rockhounds" are to be met today in practically every community. Tens of thousands of adults and youngsters have been attracted to this exciting activity within recent years. You may become a member of a mineral or gem society in almost every state and province, attend regular meetings, and go on conducted field trips to obtain specimens from many interesting localities. Over ninety such clubs exist in California alone, many of them providing junior memberships for boys and girls to encourage them in this wholesome and profitable hobby. Most local and state societies are banded together into one of the six regional federations—Eastern, Midwest, Rocky Mountain, Texas, California, and Northwest—which in turn are affiliated with the American Federation of Mineralogical Societies. These federations sponsor annual conventions, which attract a large attendance to see the extensive exhibits of fellow collectors and dealers who display the newest discoveries and latest equipment. Such a convention is a thrilling spectacle. And there are thousands of equally ardent collectors who do not belong to an organized group but enjoy hunting rocks and minerals just the same.

A hobby that is expanding this fast, appealing to people of all ages and occupations, must possess some strong points. Indeed, mineral collecting does have exceptional advantages to recommend it.

First of all, it is carried on primarily out of doors, where you become acquainted with the wonders and beauties of Nature at her best and learn to understand the expressive face of the earth in its manifold aspects. Scenery is ever-changing, in response to the weathering and erosion of minerals which constitute the rocks of the earth's crust. We find out from a study of minerals why cliffs wear down and how soils originate, why the walls of the Grand Canyon show such vivid hues, why the sands of the Florida beach are so varied in size and shape and color. As the noted English artist and author John Ruskin wrote, "There are no natural objects out of which more can be learned than out of stones. They seem to have been created especially to reward a patient observer. For a stone, when it is examined, will be found a mountain in miniature. The surface of a stone is more interesting than the surface of an ordinary hill, more fantastic in form, and incomparably richer in color."

Fig. 1 Emblem of American Federation of Mineralogical Societies

Mineral collecting, furthermore, has its indoor opportunities, even for the shut-in, who can acquire desirable specimens by trading with other collectors and buying from dealers. Splendid selections of minerals are prominently shown in museums in most of the larger cities and in numerous smaller ones, as well as in many colleges and universities. No more pleasant way to spend an evening can be found than in examining the collections of others in your own community or while traveling.

The art of amateur gem cutting, beginning as an off-

Fig. 2 Faceted and cabochon gem cuts

shoot of mineral collecting, has become a major hobby in itself as thousands of home craftsmen are attaining results superior to those of commercial lapidaries, because they are eager enough to experiment and persevering enough to bring their work to a high degree of perfection. A few of them, endowed with the gift of artistic expression, turn out carvings of surpassing beauty. Some of them are able to cut *faceted* stones, having flat surfaces or "faces" at different angles, while others prefer to make *cabochons,* which are simpler because they need only a rounded top. Enterprising boys, and girls too, using inexpensive equipment, have developed a skill equal to that of their elders. If you would like to transform stones into flashing gems, here is the hobby for you.

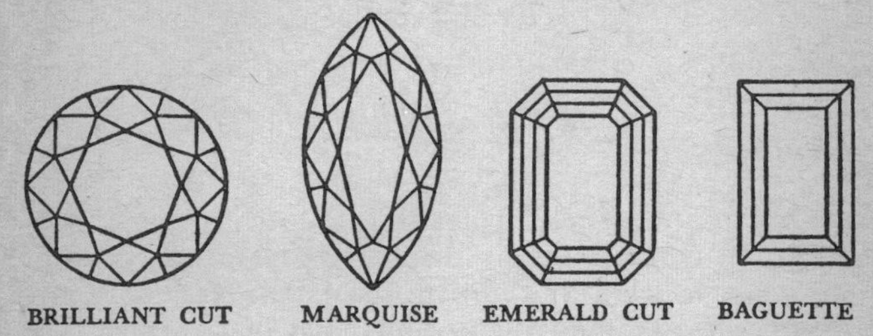

Fig. 3 Popular faceted cuts of gems

Crystals, which Abbé Haüy called the "flowers of the mineral kingdom," are the chief delight of a large proportion of mineral collectors. Smooth and shining faces, bright hues, and intriguing forms combine to make crystals outstandingly interesting to those who admire beautiful things. Though scarcely any two crystals seem alike, we are able to classify them all into six types known as *crystal systems.* These are named below, with a model of

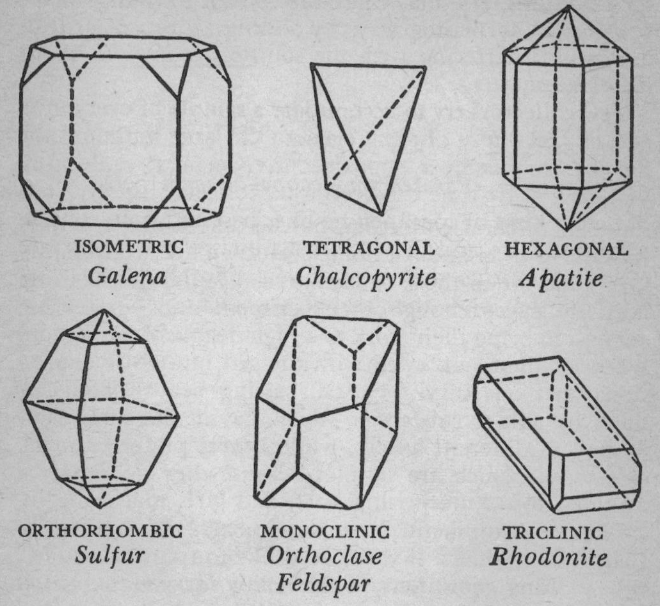

Fig. 4 The six crystal systems

A common crystal form or combination of forms is shown for each system. Countless modifications are possible.

an important mineral belonging to each system. They differ from one another in the length and arrangement of the *axes* which run through them; the axes are only imaginary, like the equator and poles of the earth, but are extremely useful in describing crystals.

The most perfect crystals are the smallest ones, because they have been protected by their very smallness. A collection of such miniature crystals or *micromounts,* which are tiny clusters delicately mounted in a box and viewed through a magnifying glass or microscope, reveals a fairyland of breath-taking sparkle and color.

Another phase of mineral collecting that can be carried on indoors is the growing of crystals from saturated chemical solutions. You may cause the crystals to change shape or color in surprising ways by adding a drop of acid or otherwise interfering with the solution as it gives up its dissolved matter.

Few collectors try to accumulate a sample of every mineral or rock; most of them leave to the large museums the task of gathering a comprehensive general collection. Within a short time the beginning collector usually finds out what kind of specimen he likes best and then concentrates on that kind. The most distinctive collections are made by limiting the scope of your efforts and focusing on those that have the greatest appeal to you.

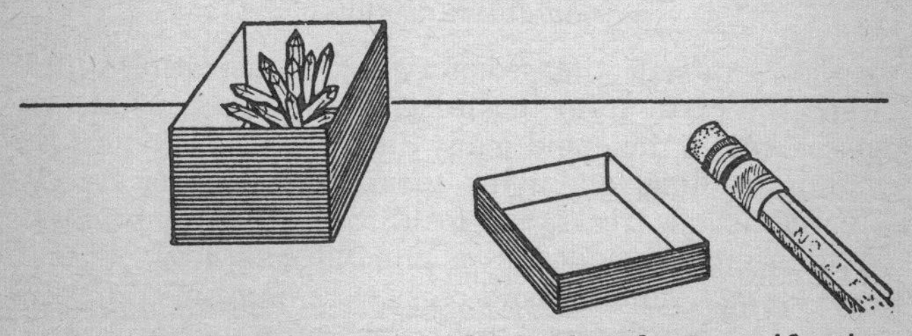

Fig. 5 Micromount, to be observed under magnification

For instance, a collector may specialize in a single mineral—perhaps calcite, which comes in more than 300 different crystal forms; or perhaps quartz, which is abundant everywhere and is found in astonishing variety. Another collector may lean heavily toward ore minerals, of interest particularly to miners and prospectors. Ores of common metals such as iron and copper may be emphasized, or of precious metals such as gold and silver. Minerals from one state or region (perhaps the Rocky Mountains, Death Valley, or New England) or from your home county; minerals of your favorite color; minerals that are finely crystallized; or gem minerals—these likewise are all worthwhile subjects for specialized collections.

An enviable collection might also feature unusual occurrences of minerals, such as *geodes,* which are nodules lined with crystals; or altered minerals called *pseudomorphs* (petrified wood is a good example, the original wood having turned to stone); or sand from rivers and

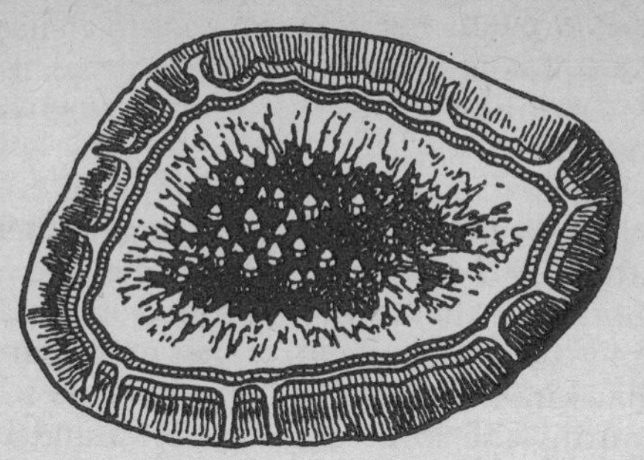

Fig. 6 Geode from Brazil, showing inside lined with amethyst crystals

seashores, or stalactites from caverns, or meteorites which reach the earth from the mysterious vastness of cosmic space. Any of these and many others can be obtained by finding, trading, or buying them. Rocks, either typical ones or curious freaks, and fossils buried in the rocks are appropriately included in a mineral collection. At one time, in fact, minerals and rocks were both called fossils, which in Latin meant "to dig," because they are taken from the earth.

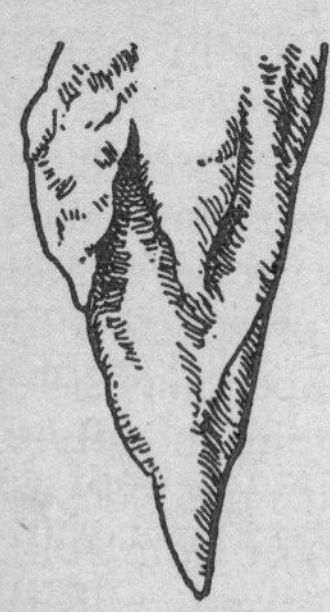

Fig. 7 Stalactite from Mammoth Cave, Kentucky

Mineral collecting can be more than outdoor or indoor fun. It can lead to an acquaintance with one of the most vital sources of human wealth. Mining ranks with farming, fishing, and lumbering as a primary producer of basic raw materials. Man has become dependent upon the mineral industries for the existence of both his peaceful and his military civilizations. Yielding metals, nonmetallic substances, and fuels, our mineral resources largely create the conditions of present-day life on this planet. In addition, minerals have always played an important part in the development of chemistry, physics, and other sciences.

By exposure to the weather, rocks and their minerals decay and fall apart to become soil. Plants are thus able to grow, in turn providing food for animals. Water, which is the most essential of all foods, is also an integral part of the mineral kingdom, being either a rock or a mineral, according to even the most precise definitions.

It is hard to decide which are the most important mineral products besides soil and water. Salt must be included, because it is a mineral indispensable to life—the location of salt licks has marked the route of caravans throughout the centuries. The lure of gems has encouraged trade and transportation since the dawn of history. Flint, a member of the quartz group, was highly prized for weapons, which became the first manufactured articles. Clay, used for pottery, started the earliest large-scale mineral industry. Building stones, as were used in the pyramids, contributed a good deal to the expanding service of earth materials.

Those mentioned above belong among the *nonmetallic* or so-called *industrial minerals and rocks.* The list is seemingly endless, hundreds of them being used in thousands of ways. Consider some more of them—pumice from the Lipari Islands to polish your teeth or from California to insulate your home; potash from New Mexico to fertilize the soil and make farming a scientific employment; emery from Greece to grind away metal in an airplane; asbestos from Quebec to be woven into fireproof clothing; feldspar from North Carolina to glaze chinaware; mica from South Dakota to be flaked into Christmas-tree "snow"; sulfur from Texas to make possible the heavy-chemical industry. Specimens of them all should be represented in your mineral collection.

Coal and petroleum are mineral fuels. Though not so attractive to most collectors, their importance should not be overlooked. Coal is the very foundation of modern industrial economy; countries that lack ample reserves of suitable coal cannot hope to do a large share of the world's manufacturing. Armies, navies, and air forces ride, float, and fly to victory on petroleum.

The *metallic minerals* are the ores from which metals are extracted. These metals may be gold, silver, or platinum—the *precious metals;* or copper, lead, or zinc, which are known as *base metals;* or iron and the so-called *ferro-alloy metals,* which are mixed or alloyed with iron to make steel. Discovery of the art of smelting ores revolutionized man's life, enabling him to obtain useful metals from otherwise worthless rock. He could then also melt two or more metals together to produce brass, bronze, and other alloys.

So significant are the mineral products to civilized beings that human history itself is divided into the Old Stone Age, the New Stone Age, the Bronze Age, and the Iron Age. Perhaps we have now moved into the Uranium Age—only the future can tell. As a mineral collector you will be playing your part in the thrilling drama of man.

The amateur collector will probably not come into the fortune of a Texas oilman or of Dr. Williamson, the African diamond magnate, whose faith in his knowledge of the rocks during years of fruitless search was finally repaid by his discovery of the world's largest diamond mine. Nevertheless, the amateur will surely find many fine minerals, perhaps some of satisfying value, and possibly even a new one unknown to science. He will at the same time learn more about his natural environment. Such knowledge is one of the marks of a broadly educated person. And in doing so he will vastly enjoy himself in this vital, many-sided hobby.

More frequently than in the past, hobbyists are turning mineral collecting into a business, selling at a profit to museums, other dealers, and private collectors. Occasionally someone does this as a full-time vocation. The personal experiences of capable professional collectors such as Edwin W. Over, Jr., of Manitou Springs, Colo., and Dr. Harvey H. Nininger, the Arizona meteorite expert, in out-of-the-way places ranging from Baja California to Prince of Wales Island off the coast of Alaska, would make entertaining adventure stories.

CHAPTER 2

How Rocks and Minerals Are Formed

The difference between a rock and a mineral should be clearly understood. Rocks are the essential building materials of which the earth is constructed, whereas minerals are the individual substances that go to make up the rocks. Most rocks, therefore, are aggregates of two or more minerals. Thus, granite (a rock) is composed of at least two minerals (quartz and feldspar), though others are almost certain to be present.

If a single mineral exists on a large enough scale, it may also be considered as a rock, because it may then be regarded as an integral part of the structure of the earth. Thus, a pure sandstone or quartzite rock contains only one mineral, quartz, distributed over a wide area. Other single minerals which are described in this book and are regarded also as rocks by this definition include anhydrite, dolomite, gypsum, magnesite, serpentine, and sulfur —all of which occur in huge beds or masses. Some rocks of this type have a different name from that of the mineral composing them. Thus, the mineral halite makes rock salt; calcite is the constituent of the rock called limestone; and either calcite or dolomite can make up the rock called marble. Kaolinite composes many of the rocks we know as clay. Bauxite has been proved to be really a rocky mixture of several minerals, but many geologists still prefer to call it a mineral.

In addition to these two classifications, rocks include natural glass, though it may be devoid of any actual mineral components. Obsidian, an abundant rock in Mexico and Iceland, is natural volcanic glass. Organic products of the earth, which cannot be called minerals because they are formed from plants and animals, are properly known as rocks. Coal, derived from partly decomposed vegetation, is a rock of this kind.

Seldom will you find a single species of mineral occurring entirely by itself. Like people, minerals have a tendency to be found in the company of others of the same kind, having formed under the same conditions. This is a fact which proves most helpful to the collector, who soon discovers that often the best way to recognize a mineral is by its associations.

Thus, feldspar and quartz occur together in the rock called pegmatite because they originate in the same manner, that is, by the cooling of molten rock of a certain chemical composition and within the limited range of temperature required to form pegmatite. Again, no one can fail to know at a glance that he has a specimen of the zinc ore from Franklin, N. J., when he sees the distinctive combination of red zincite, yellowish-green willemite, black franklinite, and white calcite. These minerals are not found together anywhere else in the world, and each mineral immediately suggests the presence of the others. As another instance, in 1870 a man named DeKlerk was led to the first diamond ever recovered from its original rock when he saw some pebbles of garnet in a dry stream bed in South Africa and realized that the two gems often occur side by side.

Moreover, each group of minerals is related naturally to definite types of rock. This enables us to identify the rock more readily than otherwise. Rocks are not so easy to name as minerals because they grade imperceptibly into one another, but this principle of mineral association is very helpful.

The many rocks which constitute the earth's crust are the result of geologic processes acting during long ages, building up some rocks and breaking down others. The normal rock cycle leads from molten rock to igneous rock, then to sediment and sedimentary rock, followed or preceded by a metamorphic stage. Countless bypaths to this cycle give rocks an infinite variety and prevent them from becoming monotonous to anyone who has gained a speaking acquaintance with them and even a slight knowledge of geology.

Igneous Rocks

All minerals and rocks have their primary origin in a body of molten rock called *magma,* which is believed to exist in local pockets deep within the crust of the earth. This magma eventually becomes the igneous rocks and minerals. The name igneous, related to the word *ignite,* suggests fire and heat.

Seismologists, who are the scientists who study earthquake waves, tell us that the earth beneath its relatively thin surface layers is not liquid, as it was formerly thought to be, nor is there anywhere a complete zone of molten rock. Probably the hot rock is prevented from melting by the enormous pressure upon it, which maintains it in a semiplastic condition. When the pressure is relieved anywhere by cracks in the solid rock above, or heat due to radioactivity reaches the melting temperature, the rock slowly begins to rise in a molten state.

As this magma comes to rest in a cooler place, but still within the earth's crust, it starts to solidify; and thus the igneous rocks are born. They are known as *intrusive* rocks because they have intruded or forced their way into other rocks which were there already. This process has been going on ever since the beginning of geologic time, and so igneous rocks are presumably being formed in the same way today as they have been throughout the long history of our planet.

The intrusive igneous rocks common and important enough to be described in this book are porphyry, granite, pegmatite, syenite, monzonite, gabbro, and peridotite. Constituting the core of mighty mountain chains, these rocks are revealed for observation only after millions of years of prolonged weathering and erosion by the wind and rain and other agents of the atmosphere.

When the molten rock actually breaks through to the surface and wells out as a lava flow, or is blown out as volcanic fragments, the resulting igneous rock is called *extrusive.* We usually have in mind a volcano such as Vesuvius or Mauna Loa when we refer to this sort of igneous rock, but lava can issue quietly from open fissures in the earth without building up a cone or crater, as it still does in Iceland.

More than 500 volcanoes have erupted within recorded history. It is hardly safe to say that a volcano is extinct, for it may only be dormant, waiting for an occasion to awaken once again. Lassen Peak, sleeping in the California Sierras, surprised the nation in 1914 by becoming the only active volcano in the United States. When Vesuvius sprang to life in A.D. 79, suffocating Pompeii and Herculaneum in its grip, it had been so long quiescent that its old activity had been forgotten by the Roman people.

Although volcanoes are widespread throughout the world, the most striking feature of their distribution is the so-called ring of fire surrounding the Pacific Ocean basin, from the tip of South America north to Alaska and back down to New Zealand. Another belt of volcanoes roughly follows the equator from the West Indies to the Mediterranean and on to the East Indies.

The extrusive igneous rocks included in this book are obsidian, pumice, felsite, and basalt. Formed upon the surface or at a shallow depth beneath a light covering, these rocks need not wait long before weathering and erosion set in upon them. The term *volcanism,* however, includes the behavior of all molten rock, whether it takes place on the surface or far below and whether or not it builds up a typical volcanic mountain with an opening in the center. The originator of this extensive activity was thought to be the Roman god of fire, Vulcan, who operated his workshop underneath glowing Etna, one of the natural lighthouses of the Mediterranean.

Intrusive and extrusive igneous rocks are unlike chiefly because they have cooled at different rates. Intrusive rocks, losing their heat slowly while beneath the ground, acquire a coarse texture as the individual minerals have time to grow to a considerable size. Observe, for instance, the conspicuous pink feldspar, white quartz, and black hornblende in the granite from Pikes Peak. The slowest-cooling igneous rock is pegmatite, and its constituent minerals may be enormous—single crystals of spodumene 20 feet long and muscovite mica 10 feet across.

On the other hand, extrusive rocks cool rapidly; many grains get started, but each is small. Compare even the normal texture of granite, as described above, with the dense basaltic lava of the Columbia Plateau in Oregon, Washington, and Idaho.

In extreme cases of sudden chilling, no minerals are visible at all, the only product being a natural glass. Obsidian Cliff in Yellowstone National Park, seen by a million tourists annually, is a world-famous example of volcanic glass which originated in this fashion. A porous texture, especially of pumice, results from the escape of gas as it bubbles into the air.

Igneous rocks, such as granite and felsite, that are rich in silicon tend to be light-colored and relatively light in weight. As the amount of silicon is reduced and the proportion of iron and magnesium increases, the igneous rocks become darker and heavier, as gabbro and basalt are.

The cooling of magma to form an igneous rock is accompanied by shrinkage and the development of parallel open cracks called *joints.*

Shrinkage also causes cavities or pockets, and these may later be filled or lined with crystals projecting toward the center. Some of the man-sized pockets of this sort yield large gemmy crystals of quartz, feldspar, and other minerals.

Another phase of igneous activity that concerns the mineral collector has to do with ore deposits. Metal-bearing solutions of many kinds accompany the rise of magmas. As the molten rock cools and becomes solid, large quantities of liquid and gas, charged with mineral matter, are given off. Leaving the igneous rocks behind them, they make their way slowly toward the surface, forming mineral deposits wherever conditions are favorable. Thus, lower temperature, reduced pressure, the presence of limestone and other easily changed rocks are conducive to the deposition of ore minerals.

During the long-distance migration of the solutions that have been expelled from the magma, ore deposits of gold, silver, lead, zinc, and other metals are produced. These are referred to as *veins* because they run through

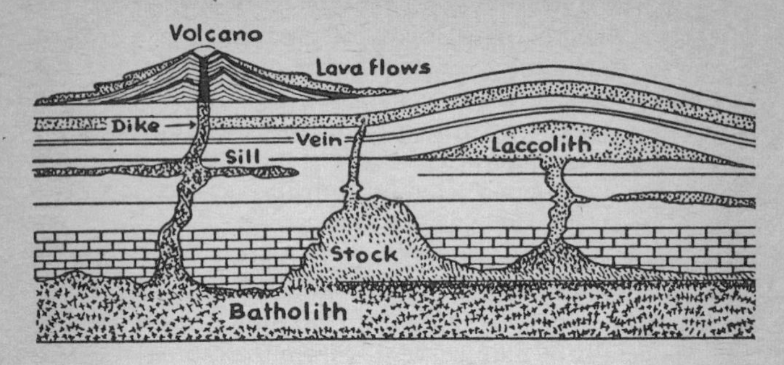

Fig. 8 Cross section through the earth, showing bodies in which igneous rock occurs

the enclosing rock like veins within the skin. They are classified according to the temperature and pressure at which they came into existence, which in turn depend upon the distance they have traveled from the magma.

Eventually, if not used up by one of the processes just described, the mineral matter that is left may appear at the surface of the earth in a volcano, gas vent, geyser, or hot spring. Around the volcanoes of the Mediterranean shore, for instance, are coatings of such minerals as native sulfur, realgar, and hematite, which are described in this book. Amidst the spectacular *fumaroles* or gas vents of the Valley of Ten Thousand Smokes in Alaska are magnetite, pyrite, galena, and other minerals in large amounts. The geysers of New Zealand carry gold, silver, and mercury. Hot water at Steamboat Springs, Nev., is depositing cinnabar today as in the past. There are numerous similar examples of each of these mineral occurrences, representing the final stages of igneous activity.

Sedimentary Rocks

Even the most deeply buried igneous rock will someday be exposed by erosion. The age of the earth, determined by the measurement of radioactivity in igneous rocks to be more than two and one-half billion years old, allows ample time for very extensive erosion to have occurred almost everywhere. The forces of weathering will then begin to attack the rock, causing it to crumble and decompose. Some of the fine particles may be dissolved by rain water as it seeps through the soil and into the pores of the bedrock underneath. The rest may be washed away bodily by streams, or wafted by the wind, or carried in the frozen grip of giant glaciers.

When either the dissolved rock matter or the transported sediment is deposited somewhere else and afterward hardens into firm rock, we have a sedimentary rock, the second of the two major kinds of rock. Two types of sedimentary rock are possible, according to whether the original material had been dissolved in water or had been moved in the form of fragments.

In the first case—represented by such rocks as rock salt in Kansas and Michigan and beds of borax in Death Valley, Calif.—the minerals are deposited when the dissolving power of the solution is reduced. This may happen because the water gets cooler or some of it evaporates or because of the action of certain plants and animals which extract chemicals from the water. In the same fashion sugar settles at the bottom of the cup when coffee cools, and salt incrusts the sides of a pan when salty water or brine is evaporated.

The second type of sedimentary rock is built up by the accumulation of separate grains of mud, sand, or gravel. Thus, mud becomes shale, sand becomes sandstone, and gravel becomes conglomerate. These sediments vary considerably in their mineral composition, and they grade into one another in the size of their particles.

Although the importance of wind and glaciers as transporting agents cannot be denied, most sedimentary material is nevertheless carried by streams. Rivers are therefore not only the great sculptors of the landscape and the chief creators of scenery, but they likewise play the major role in transporting the products of the earth that are to become the sedimentary minerals and rocks.

Probably the most intriguing sedimentary deposits are the ones known as *placers,* in which are concentrated gold, gems, and other heavy, durable minerals. The bearded Western prospector, equipped with gold pan and accompanied by his faithful burro, is the symbol of placer mining. Resisting chemical decay and physical damage alike, heavy minerals that will end in placers are washed from the higher elevations and taken downstream, until the force of the water is no longer sufficient to move them any farther. A slight obstruction in the channel or change in the current may be enough to cause them to drop to the bottom.

Billions of dollars' worth of native gold has been recovered from the bonanza placers of California, the Klondike, and elsewhere. Besides gold and a number of valuable gem stones—such as diamond, corundum (ruby and sapphire), spinel, and zircon—the most likely constituents of placers include magnetite, chromite, ilmenite, and cassiterite. Quartz, of course, is ever-present.

A special kind of placer is laid down along ocean beaches by waves and shore currents, which effectively separate the heavy minerals from the light ones. At Nome, Alaska, two submerged beaches and four now elevated above sea level have yielded a good deal of gold in very tiny grains. Vast accumulations of ilmenite, rutile, and zircon line the beaches of India, Brazil, Australia, and Florida. So-called *black sands,* containing magnetite, ilmenite, and chromite, are extensively developed on the coasts of California, Oregon, and Japan. A most extraordinary representative of beach placers is the rich diamond bed near Alexander Bay in Namaqualand, South Africa, where diamonds brought down by the Orange River were distributed along the beach, in close association with oyster shells.

Wind often blows the smaller rock fragments into heaps called *dunes*. A single sample of dune sand may contain several dozen different minerals, but they are not of specimen interest except to collectors of sand who must study them under magnification.

Owing to their bulk, glaciers are effective agents in transporting and depositing sediments. Unlike streams and wind, they are not selective in their action, so that a glacier embraces in its icy grasp boulders the size of a house, surrounded by particles that have been ground so relentlessly as to deserve the name "rock flour." With equal disregard for size, a glacier dumps the large and small material at the same time, with no attempt at sorting it. Such accumulations, common in every area glaciated during the recent Ice Age, are called *moraines.* Incorporated in moraines are minerals and rocks of foreign extraction which have been pushed, dragged, or carried bodily from their place of origin, in some cases hundreds of miles away. Chunks of native copper, brought down from the Upper Peninsula of Michigan, are strewn across the state of Wisconsin. Masses of chalcocite are frozen in a moraine at Kennecott, Alaska.

Fig. 9 Stratification (horizontal) and joints (vertical) in sedimentary rock, limestone in Indiana

Loose sediment, whatever its origin, eventually becomes solid—"as hard as a rock"—because mineralized underground water cements together the individual grains and the weight of later sediments squeezes down upon them more and more tightly. At a fairly shallow depth, except in arid climates, the ground is saturated with water which fills all pore spaces of the soil and bedrock. This water drains into streams or soaks out at the surface as seeps and springs. In caverns stalactites hang from the roofs, while stalagmites build up from the floors—both the result of evaporation of underground water as it percolates into the earth.

The distinctive property of most sedimentary rocks is their *stratification,* which refers to the layers or beds as each one is deposited on top of the earlier ones. Just as

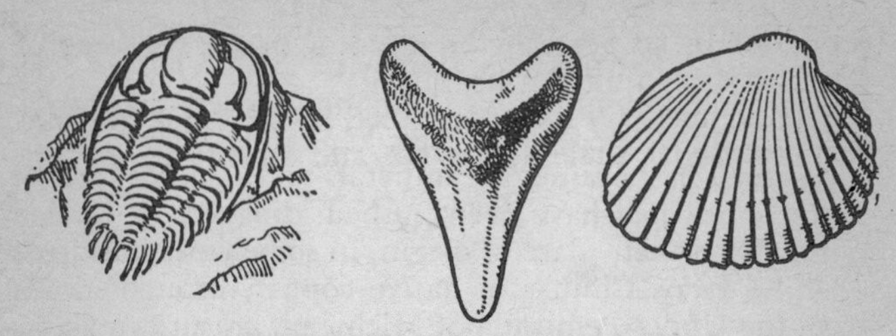

TRILOBITE TOOTH OF ANCIENT SHARK PELECYPOD SHELL

Fig. 10 Common fossils in sedimentary rock

the bottom book in a pile must have been the first one put down, so the lowest bed was the first one deposited, and each successive bed was formed at a later time.

Only in sedimentary rocks are fossils found. Obviously the heat of an igneous rock would consume any evidence of animal or plant life that might have existed.

Another characteristic of sedimentary rocks is the presence of foreign lumps or nodules called *concretions*. In the white cliffs of Dover are numerous odd-shaped pieces of flint, perhaps secreted by ancient sponges when the chalk that now makes up the cliffs was deposited in a shallow sea.

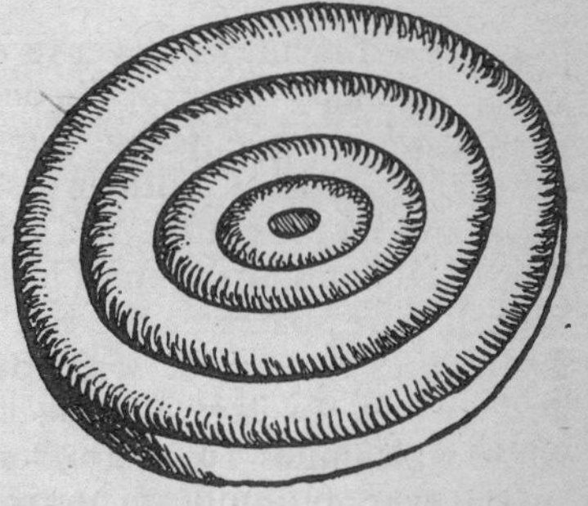

Fig. 11 Concretion from shale bed, Virginia

Joints are as abundant in sedimentary rocks as they are in igneous rocks, but the shrinkage which causes them is the result of drying instead of cooling. Most sediments are laid down in water—streams, lakes, the ocean—and may contain 50 per cent or more of moisture, some of which is driven off during burial.

The sedimentary rocks described in this book are conglomerate, coal, shale, limestone, and sandstone.

Metamorphic Rocks

The third main kind of rock, called *metamorphic,* is the result of drastic changes in either an igneous or a sedimentary rock. The new rock has been changed so much from its original state that practically all signs of ancient life are gone, and so fossils are almost never present. Even most of the evidence as to the nature of the original rock has been lost, and often it is impossible to tell whether the preexisting rock was igneous or sedimentary.

Heat from an invading magma that forces its way toward the surface of the earth is one of the factors that produces a metamorphic rock by creating new textures or entirely new minerals from the old rock. Another factor is pressure resulting from deep burial or slow movement in the earth's crust, pressure of the sort that ultimately bends rocks into mountain ranges. The chemical action of liquids and gases is also effective.

Limestone, for example, turns from a sedimentary rock into marble as the grains of calcite recrystallize under the influence of the agents of metamorphism. Because of the recrystallization, marble usually has a more glistening appearance than limestone. New minerals may be formed in the process, giving marble the swirled patterns that are so attractive a feature of colored marble. The collector may expect to find garnet, idocrase, and epidote, among many other minerals characteristic of this type of occurrence. Scheelite, an ore of tungsten, is perhaps the most valuable metallic mineral originating in this manner.

Joints are prominent in metamorphic rocks, for the gradual but irresistible application of natural forces strains them past the breaking point.

The metamorphic rocks described in this book are gneiss, schist, slate, marble, and quartzite.

Soils and Scenery

The weathering of any of these three major types of rock leads to the formation of soil. In addition to broken fragments of decomposing rock, soil consists of decayed plant material. With continued weathering, the soil zone becomes deeper and the bedrock further concealed. New minerals are created in this process, but with few exceptions they are scarcely suitable as specimens. Some of the chemical elements in the soil combine into various soluble compounds which, when they are washed out of the ground, leave the soil depleted of elements essential to plant growth.

As important to the natural history of rocks and minerals as the making of soil and the production of ore deposits is the creation of the scenery that beautifies and diversifies our terrestrial environment. The inhabitants of the earth during much of geologic time—if there had been any thinking beings prior to our own brief age—would have lived on a monotonous globe. Often devoid of mountains and hills, glaciers and volcanoes, the earth throughout a large part of its existence has been a desolate place. When the seas inundated the low-lying continents, they spread widely over the dreary landscape. When they retreated, they left behind an even more barren scene. At irregular intervals, of course, majestic mountain ranges pushed their way into the sky, thick masses of glacial ice inched precarious paths down the frosty slopes, and volcanoes spewed forth flaming debris upon the horizon.

But these momentous events only made the dismalness of the intervening periods seem the more uninspiring by contrast. We are more fortunate than perhaps we deserve to live in a world only lately having suffered the paroxysms of mountain building, only recently emerging from an Ice Age which has crowned its higher elevations with shining diadems of white.

What scenery comes into view in any given place at any given time depends upon the underlying rock and

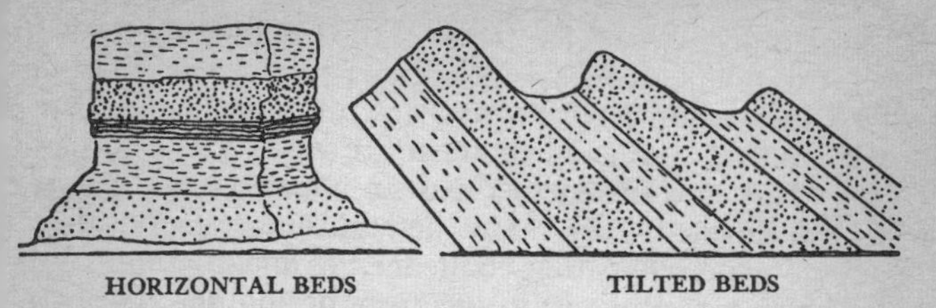

Fig. 12 Difference in topography caused by structure

the kind of geologic agent acting upon it. Hard limestone, for instance, may stand erect as a sharp cliff, while a crumbly shale next to it will disintegrate into a rolling valley. Whereas flat layers of durable sandstone will protect from erosion the softer beds between them, thereby forming a mesa or butte, the same association of rocks will appear as alternating hills and valleys if the layers have been tilted on edge.

Blowing sand fashions scenery in a desert region unlike that of underground water in an area noted for its caves. Ocean breakers are responsible for scenic effects very different from those caused by the pull of gravity as it sets into motion landslides and avalanches.

Fig. 13 Stream cycle of erosion

Even the same agent of erosion or deposition avoids uniformity by taking its scenery through a cycle. Rivers, for instance, go from a youthful stage to one of maturity, then into old age. As the cycle progresses, the valley assumes new characteristics which enable the experienced observer to recognize the relative age of that particular stream. The sharp V-shaped valley of a youthful stream gives way to one having a flatter profile as the river cuts its way downward and sideward. The development of meanders accentuates the swing of the stream until, in old age, it wanders across a wide valley between low hills.

To the person with a vivid and inquiring mind, the rocks and the minerals in them are never static things. They come into the earth's crust in numerous ways, they are transformed into many new substances, and they undergo experiences that challenge the imagination. And they never cease to exist in one form or another. To such an alert person who also knows the dramatic story of the rocks and minerals, they are not only seen in three dimensions and in color but they acquire the fourth dimension of time.

CHAPTER 3

Building a Mineral Collection

A mineral and rock collection is as near as your back yard and as distant as the far corners of the world. Specimens of some members of the mineral kingdom may be secured with little trouble and less cost, while others require the initiative of a globe-trotter and the purse of a merchant prince. Minerals are to be found in garden soil, in road cuts and building excavations, under cliffs and in stream beds, on beaches and sand dunes, in quarries and mines. Heaps of waste rock called *dumps* are a prolific source of specimens. Everywhere around us, in fact, minerals are present.

Cavities in rock are especially favorable spots for finding choice crystals, for in such open spaces they have a chance to grow freely to substantial sizes. Ordinary-looking boulders known as geodes, when broken open, often reveal rows of glistening crystals lining the inner walls, like the inside of a treasure cave in a storybook. Mammoth crystal-filled geodes, outwardly resembling the eggs of some prehistoric beast, are picked up by the thousands around Keokuk, Iowa, and elsewhere in the central Mississippi Valley.

A small number of minerals can be sifted as pebbles from the soil in one's own yard. Sand and clay pits and other diggings in soft rock will yield additional interesting minerals, among them fine specimens of gypsum, pyrite, and marcasite. Near exposed cliffs and rock outcrops, road and railway cuts and tunnels in solid rock, and excavations made for the construction of buildings are promising places to search for minerals. Quarries and coal mines are common, and their waste piles may be surprisingly productive. An intriguing feature of coal deposits is the abundance of fossils—the remains or impressions of plants and animals that once lived on the earth. Monument works, which are often situated in the vicinity of quarries, are worth a visit, and so are smelters.

The best sources of minerals are, of course, mines and their dumps. In the United States, mines are not limited, as you may have believed, to the open spaces of the West. On the contrary, Pennsylvania, West Virginia, Illinois, Kentucky, and Ohio stand among the eight leading mineral-producing states. The second-largest zinc mine in the country, at Franklin and Sterling Hill, N.J., is within 40 miles of the metropolis of New York, and the fourth-largest is in up-State St. Lawrence County.

The loose sand and sagebrush areas of deserts yield—besides agate and other minerals usually expected there—flowerlike groups of crystals, including the attractive "desert roses" and "barite roses." The temporary lakes in arid regions give up halite, borax, and many other saline minerals, which form when the water evaporates. Beach sands may contain a multitude of heavy minerals brought together by waves and currents from widespread localities. Owing their origin to the uplift of a mountain range, the explosion of a volcano, the flow of lava, the bubbling of a hot spring, even the crash of a shooting star, the products of the mineral kingdom are on every hand.

Mineral localities consequently are world-wide. Many specimens are available on public land, especially in the national forests; the national parks and monuments, except Death Valley, are closed to collecting. Others can often be obtained on private property by asking permission and taking care to close gates and respect the rights of the owners or residents.

You might consider seriously the size of the specimens you want to collect. Some collectors, having unlimited space, feature large and showy specimens, whereas others are obliged to restrict themselves to micromounts, the exquisite miniature crystals which occupy little more room than a stamp or coin collection. Either extreme is perfectly acceptable, though the average collector acquires whatever pleases his fancy, regardless of size, and seems always to need more room than is available. The number of specimens of the same kind to be taken is also a matter of decision. It is true that duplicate ones can usually be traded off, and even sold, but it is the excessively greedy collector who gives the hobby a bad name—he and the fellow who despoils other people's property.

If the specimens finally admitted to your collection are chosen with discrimination, the result will be a genuinely valuable asset. Each of the kinds of materials described in this book—minerals, gems, ores, crystals, rocks, meteorites—can be assembled into a handsome, interesting, and profitable collection. Sands, pebbles, concretions, geodes, stalactites and stalagmites, and many other forms are also proper specialties around which to build a collection. The list is extensive, making possible enough variety to suit the taste of almost every person who has an interest in the wonders of inorganic nature.

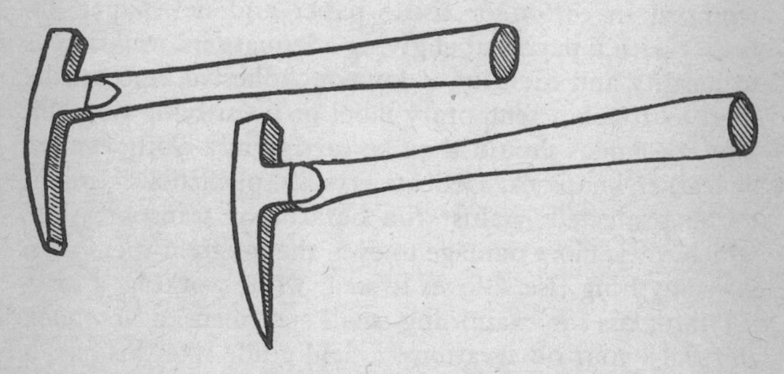

Fig. 14 Prospector's hammer and pick

A mineral collector does not require elaborate equipment, but he may make or buy as much as he needs for certain purposes. The one essential item in the field is a prospector's hammer, with either a pick or a chisel opposite the hammer head. A sledge hammer, light or heavy, will sometimes be worth taking along, especially if it does not need to be carried far. A separate cold chisel is also useful for wedging rock apart or freeing crystals from crevices. Square-pointed and diamond-pointed steel tools are additional equipment for extracting specimens. Excess rock may be trimmed away with the same sudden but carefully planned blows used in the mining operation itself; a succession of light taps is usually as effective as one hard blow and is more easily controlled.

Fig. 15 Collector's knapsack

Minerals, and especially crystals, should be well wrapped in cotton or tissue paper and newspaper, together with a paper label giving adequate information as to locality and identity, if known. Adhesive tape can be used to attach a temporary label or identifying number. The specimens should then be carried in a cloth, canvas, or leather knapsack. Delicate crystals, particularly, ought to be protected against the hazards of transportation, which cause more damage to even the toughest rocks than does anything else. Gloves to wear while working, a magnifying glass for examining small specimens, a notebook to record your observations, a field guide like this one, a camera, and a pocketknife are other desirable articles to have. Inexpensive things such as an ice pick, a file, and a ruler often come in handy. Adequate clothing should be

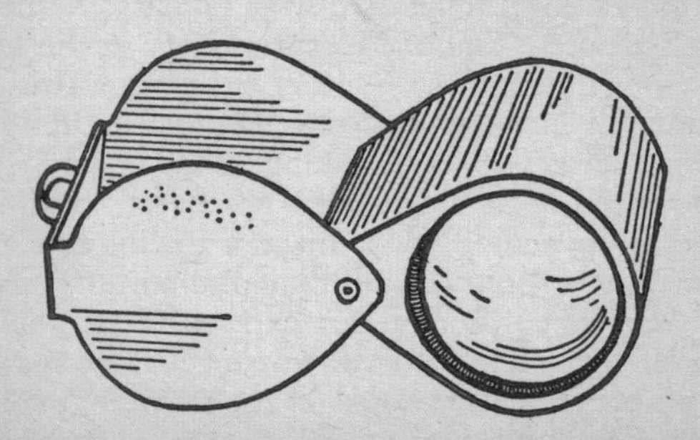

Fig. 16 Collector's pocket magnifying lens

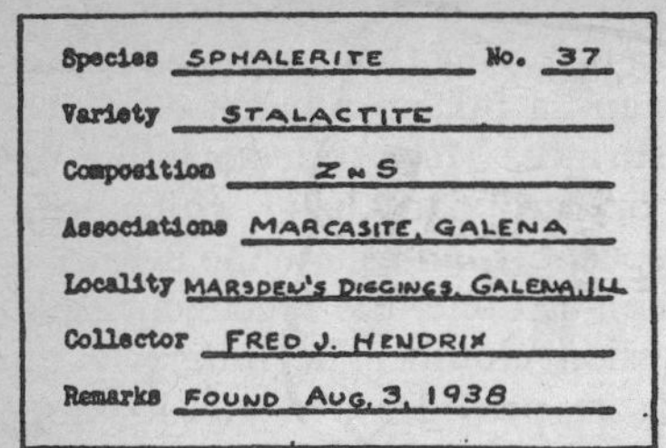
Species SPHALERITE No. 37
Variety STALACTITE
Composition ZnS
Associations MARCASITE, GALENA
Locality MARSDEN'S DIGGINGS, GALENA, ILL.
Collector FRED J. HENDRIX
Remarks FOUND AUG. 3, 1938

Fig. 17 Mineral label

Name RHYOLITE PORPHYRY No. 16
Occurrence SIDE OF MESA
Locality HOLDEN GULCH, NEAR BELMONT, NEV
Collector WILLIAM BURNS
Remarks EXCHANGED FOR JASPER

Fig. 18 Rock label

worn, just as for any type of outing or camp life. Testing apparatus is described later in this book, but identification is usually best made at your leisure at home or in a laboratory.

Specimens should be trimmed carefully to size, but without destroying the surrounding matrix of a crystal; a pink topaz crystal in light-gray rhyolite from the Thomas Range of Utah, for instance, is of more interest and brings a higher price than the loose crystal, because it shows the natural occurrence and associations. Another reason for the greater value of a matrix specimen of topaz is that it is less common than an isolated crystal. This is true of nearly every mineral.

Good grooming will improve a mineral specimen. Most specimens can be cleaned in soapy warm water applied with a soft brush. Soluble minerals, such as halite (table salt), cannot, of course, be immersed in water, but alcohol will rinse them. A blast of air will remove dust from fragile specimens such as the hairlike zeolites. A coating of clear lacquer may aid in protecting specimens from soil or tarnish. Each mineral has an individuality of its own, and the technique of cleaning and preserving mineral specimens may require some time to learn.

After cleaning them, you may give your specimens a permanent label by writing or typing the data on adhesive tape or lettering them in india ink on a patch of white enamel painted on the surface. Most collectors like to prepare a simple paper or cardboard label which will stand or lie next to each specimen and show the essential information about it. If this is done, the specimen itself need bear only an accession number beginning with 1; a small label of this sort provides a neater-looking specimen but makes necessary some kind of cataloguing system. Therefore, the specimens are finally enumerated and described in a notebook or card file. An index or cross-reference list is desirable for finding quickly all specimens of a given kind or from a given locality. The sample labels on page 35 tell the least that should generally be known about a mineral or a rock.

Fig. 19 Mineral cabinet with partitioned drawers

At first you may use simple storage boxes until your collection expands and you feel the need of a good case to set off some of your really beautiful specimens. M. F. Wasson, a Denver attorney, has demonstrated an example of the ingenuity possible in displaying minerals to the best advantage, by illuminating an old china cabinet with concealed strings of white Christmas-tree lights. Some collectors who are wealthy or skilled in carpentry have built-in wall cases in their homes or have bought standard metal floor cases of the kind seen in museums. Portable outfits resembling a traveling salesman's sample case and consisting of removable sliding trays, which can

Fig. 20 Riker mount with glass top

be set on a table, are popular with collectors who own them.

Gems and small crystals are easy to exhibit in Riker mounts, which are frames that come in various dimensions; being paper-bound and glass-covered, they can be handled without danger of damaging the contents and can be suspended from a wall like pictures. Attractive plastic boxes and more elaborate wood frames are coming into the market, as interest in the mineral hobby expands. Larger specimens can be mounted on individual stands of metal, wood, glass, or plastic; besides being transparent, plastic can be attractively lettered with a vibrating electric tool. There is no end to the possibilities in housing,

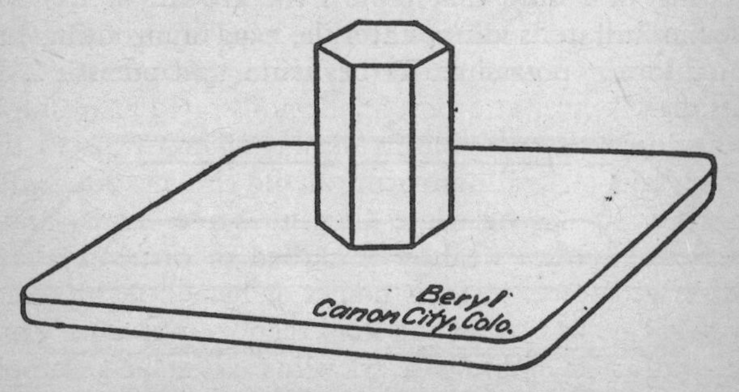

Fig. 21 Plastic specimen mount

lighting, mounting, arranging, and labeling a mineral collection for display.

Unless you are fortunate enough to be able to travel extensively on every continent and collect all the specimens you want, you will sooner or later realize the benefit to your collection of well-selected purchases. Dealers who advertise in the magazines named on page 187 have world-wide connections, enabling you to have eventually a thoroughly representative collection. Also, you will learn faster by having at hand an inexpensive selection of named samples to study and test. An increasing number of dealers maintain regular stores in which browsing and shopping can conveniently be done.

Specimens that you do not find yourself or buy from a dealer may be secured by exchanging with fellow collectors; this is one of the benefits of membership in a club devoted to the mineral hobby. Material to be traded should be clean and well labeled, accompanied by a list giving the pertinent information and particularly the locality. Packages to be shipped by parcel post or express should be well packed, for minerals often prove to be disappointingly fragile.

Growing crystals artificially is becoming increasingly popular. This is a creative activity which is in some ways as satisfying as collecting in the field. It also has its scientific aspects, for it helps us understand the conditions existing in nature that govern the growth of minerals. Copper sulfate, sodium chloride, potassium alum, barium chloride, potassium ferrocyanide, and potassium fer-

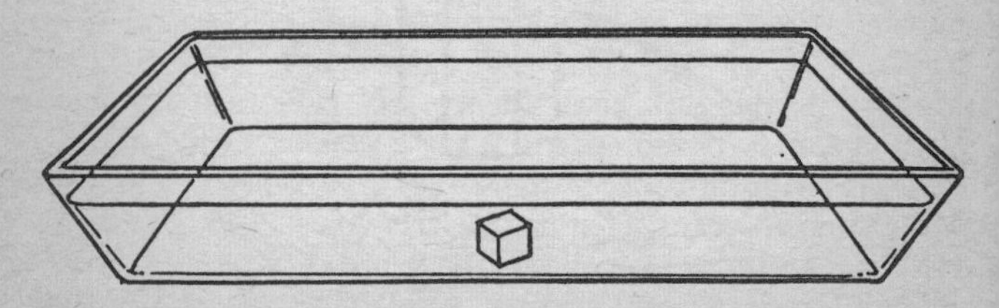

Fig. 22 Growing artificial crystal

ricyanide are among the chemical salts that will crystallize readily, requiring only a saturated solution in a covered flat dish, kept where the temperature is constant and outside interference is at a minimum.

As the solution slowly evaporates, the upper part becomes supersaturated with the dissolved salt. Being denser, it sinks to the bottom of the dish, where it adds its excess salt to the crystal that has already started to grow. Perhaps a seed crystal of the same substance has been placed in the dish for the purpose of encouraging growth. Then the liquid rises again and the process continues over and over, while the crystal increases in size. Larger and more symmetrical crystals are made by suspending a seed crystal on a wire to serve as a nucleus, though the solution may need to be stirred from time to time.

The color of the crystal is often very pretty in itself, such as the deep blue of copper sulfate, the lemon yellow of potassium ferrocyanide, and the ruby red of potassium ferricyanide. It can be varied by adding a small amount of pigment, and wholly colorless crystals take on delicate hues when a drop of ink or dye is put into the solution.

Changes in the shape of the crystal can be effected by adding almost any foreign substance. Small crystals attach themselves to the main one and may have to be removed, after which the larger crystal heals over. A lifetime of interesting experiments awaits the grower of artificial crystals, with something new revealed every day.

Visits to museums are strongly encouraged as a means of becoming familiar with choice specimens. Almost every college and university has a geological museum, and some cities boast truly magnificent exhibits. Among the finest mineral collections on the North American continent are those in the American Museum of Natural History (New York), Harvard University (Cambridge, Mass.), Philadelphia Academy of Natural Sciences, United States National Museum (Washington), Royal Ontario Museum of Mineralogy (Toronto), Chicago Museum of Natural History, Denver Museum of Natural History, and Los Angeles County Museum of History, Science, and Art. In mining regions, especially in the West, local material is often shown in the county courthouses and in the windows of assayers. Before collecting in a given locality, it is wise to look first at specimens of minerals and rocks that have already been found there, in order to be sure of their appearance and names.

At the end of the descriptive section you will find brief notes about books especially recommended for further reading. A small personal library is a source of much satisfaction to the collector as he grows in experience and knowledge. These books contain information on many subjects of interest to mineral and rock collectors, and the locality guides furnish detailed instructions for reaching productive deposits in many states. These and more detailed books can be borrowed through nearly every public and school library, whether or not they actually are on the shelves.

A list of the national magazines dealing with this hobby is also given in this book. A good suggestion is that every serious-minded collector, whether beginner or advanced, should subscribe to one of these periodicals. The instruction and inspiration you will receive will more than repay the small cost.

CHAPTER 4

Seven Keys to Recognizing Minerals

The secret of identifying minerals quickly and successfully is to become familiar with their common physical properties. A property of a substance is any quality typical of it, or anything pertaining to its appearance. Thus, a sweet taste is a property of sugar, a white color is a property of snow, and heaviness is a property of lead.

Unless we can recognize a mineral by sight alone, it may seem to be any one of many minerals, but as soon as we are able to determine one or two definite properties, we have immediately reduced the long list of possible minerals to the names of a few probable ones. With only these to choose from, we can much more easily decide the true identity of the unknown specimen. The convenient arrangement of the Seven Keys used in this book ought to enable you to recognize the most important minerals by an easy step-by-step procedure.

MINERAL KEY NO. 1 LUSTER

Light is reflected from the surface of minerals in various ways, producing a number of different types of luster. First of all, every mineral has either a *metallic* or a *nonmetallic* luster, according to whether or not it resembles the surface of a metal. This serves to put any unknown mineral into one of two main groups without further delay.

A metallic luster, though difficult to describe, is simple to recognize, being the luster of a typical metal—gold, silver, lead, copper, aluminum, and the rest. Minerals having this luster are opaque, and when crushed they yield a powder which is black or darker in color than the mineral itself. (This powder is referred to as *streak* and is described in Key No. 4.)

A nonmetallic luster is more complex, because several kinds can be recognized. Minerals having a nonmetallic luster become transparent on a thin edge, and when crushed they give a powder which is white or lighter in color than the solid mineral.

Perhaps the most common of the nonmetallic lusters is *vitreous,* which means glassy; it is how ordinary glass looks in reflected light. Quartz and many other minerals have this sort of luster. Minerals such as mica that display cleavage (described in Key No. 5) have a *pearly* luster, which is due to closely parallel layers' trapping the light and breaking it up into tiny rainbows. Diamond and non-metallic lead minerals reflect a brilliant luster called *adamantine,* which means diamondlike. Sphalerite is one of the few minerals which shows a *resinous* luster, like that of rosin from trees. A *silky* luster is displayed by fibrous minerals such as gypsum of the satin-spar variety. *Greasy, oily,* and other lusters may be described in common words just as they appear to the observer.

MINERAL KEY NO. 2 HARDNESS

A rock is often called soft because the individual particles, which may be hard in themselves, are loosely held together and readily fall apart. In speaking of minerals, however, hardness means the resistance of the whole surface to being scratched.

A century ago a mineralogist named Friedrich Mohs devised a scale of hardness which is still in use and known as the *Mohs scale.* He placed talc, the softest of all minerals (soft enough to be made into talcum powder), as No. 1 in this series, and diamond, the hardest of all known substances, as No. 10. The complete scale is given below.

10	Diamond	5	Apatite
9	Corundum	4	Fluorite
8	Topaz	3	Calcite
7	Quartz	2	Gypsum
6	Feldspar	1	Talc

The Mohs scale does not indicate any exact hardness; thus, No. 9 is not three times as hard as No. 3. It means only that any mineral can scratch all those beneath it in

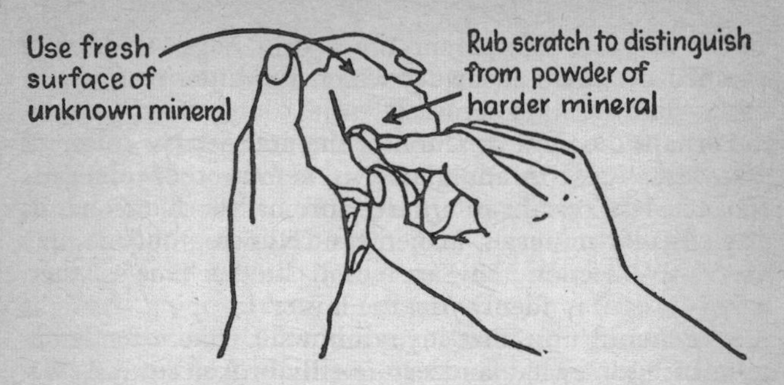

Fig. 23 Testing hardness

the scale and in turn will be scratched by those above it. Two minerals of the same hardness will scratch each other. For convenience, some familiar objects, which enable us to make tests quickly in the field, have been included in the scale, as follows:

2½	Fingernail
3	Copper coin
5½	Knife blade, window glass
6½	Steel file

Minerals under 2½ will leave a mark on paper; those under 5½ can be scratched by a knife; those over 5½ will scratch glass.

MINERAL KEY NO. 3 COLOR

Nature field guides customarily use color as a basis of classification. This is generally true of those dealing with birds, flowers, butterflies, etc., in which color plays a chief part in identification. Minerals, however, are so variable that we can scarcely rely upon color as a satisfactory means of recognizing them.

Some minerals, it is true, are reasonably constant in their color, such as yellow sulfur, pink rhodochrosite, blue azurite, and green malachite. Most minerals, however, are colored by chemical elements that are really minor impurities and that produce a bewildering array of colors without changing the essential composition. Quartz, for instance, occurs in almost every imaginable color, as do tourmaline, corundum, and numerous other minerals. Nevertheless, certain colors are more or less characteristic of particular minerals, and in the following outline and descriptive section they are emphasized whenever they may be useful in identifying the mineral.

You should note that many minerals have a tendency to tarnish somewhat, and so a freshly broken surface may have to be exposed to reveal the true color. This is so dominant a property of the mineral bornite, which miners often call peacock ore and purple copper ore, that bornite is listed here under the usual purple color of its tarnish.

MINERAL KEY NO. 4 STREAK

Most minerals lose their color entirely when they are finely crushed. Some, however, still show a pale color, similar to that of the whole mineral, but lighter. A few

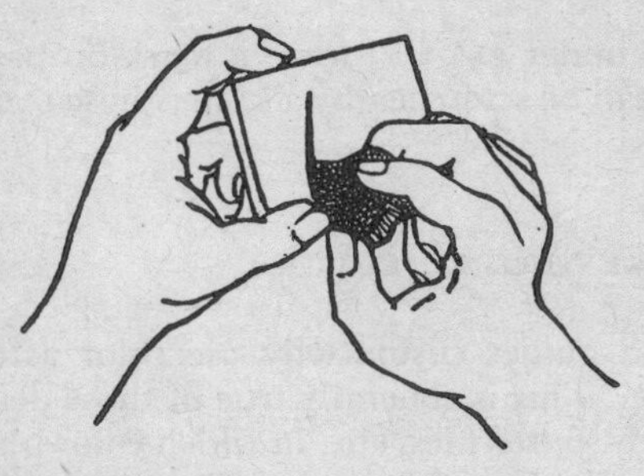

Fig. 24 Testing streak of mineral on streak plate

mineral powders give a fairly vivid color, which may even be rather different from the original one seen before crushing.

The color of a powdered mineral is called its streak because it is usually obtained by rubbing it against a piece of unglazed porcelain. For this purpose ordinary pieces of untreated tile are sold for a few cents as *streak plates,* but the edge of a broken china cup or dish is adequate though not so convenient to handle. One mineral for which streak is a useful property in identification is hematite. No matter how black or steely it may look at first, every piece of hematite gives an Indian-red streak; the name of the mineral, which means "bloodstone," was derived from this fact.

MINERAL KEY NO. 5 CLEAVAGE

Crystalline minerals are said to cleave or have cleavage when they break in definite directions along smooth surfaces. This interesting property is the result of a precise pattern of atoms in regular layers, whose cohesion is weaker in certain directions than in others. A piece of mica will flake into thinner and thinner sheets because it can be so readily cleaved in a single direction. Other minerals have two, three, four, or as many as six directions of cleavage.

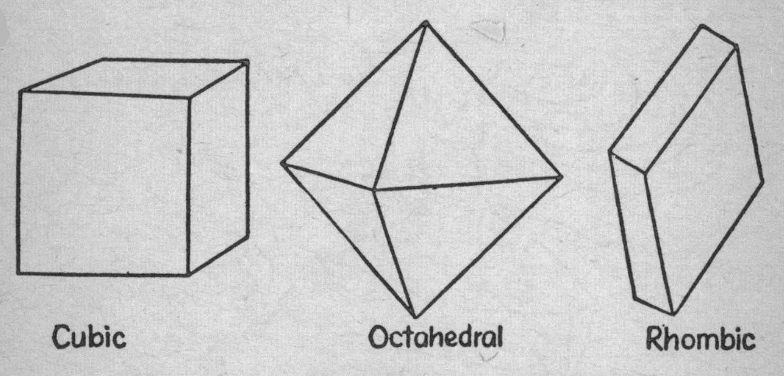

Fig. 25 Important kinds of cleavage

Cleavage is often confused with an original crystal face, though the pearly luster of the cleavage surface is a helpful clue. We describe cleavage according to how easily it is obtained and what its crystal direction is. Diamond, for example, has a "perfect octahedral" cleavage, which is used by diamond cutters to remove flawed parts of a crystal merely by splitting them away with a sharp blow.

Cleavage is a constant enough property to serve as an excellent means of identifying minerals. It can best be recognized by small steplike surfaces on the outside in preference to internal cracks, because these may be due to other causes.

When a mineral breaks with smooth surfaces like those of cleavage but only in certain favored places and on only a few specimens, it is said to show pseudocleavage, or *parting*. Because true cleavage and parting resemble each other so closely, they are included together in the outline and descriptive section of this book, though mentioned separately under the individual minerals.

MINERAL KEY NO. 6 FRACTURE

Minerals that break in irregular directions, like shattered glass, are said to fracture instead of cleave. The particular kind of fracture depends upon the appearance of the new surface. When it has a series of arcs, typical of the growth pattern of shells, it is known as *conchoidal,* meaning shell-like. Quartz and a host of other minerals have this con-

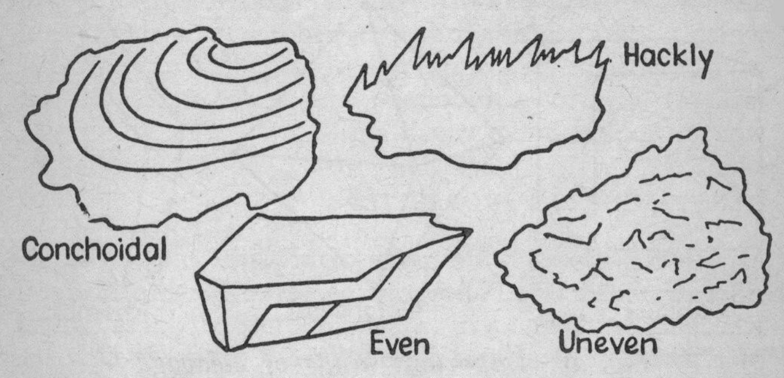

Fig. 26 Important kinds of fracture

choidal fracture, which is also seen on chipped glass. Native metals such as copper and silver have a *hackly* fracture, which gives a jagged surface uncomfortable to touch. Other kinds of fracture are called simply *even, uneven, earthy,* and so forth—ordinary words that describe their appearance.

MINERAL KEY NO. 7 SPECIFIC GRAVITY

Minerals vary considerably in weight, some being heavy for their size, others light. The relative weight of a mineral is known as its specific gravity, which is a number that gives a direct comparison with the weight of an equal volume of water. For instance, a specimen of corundum having a specific gravity of 4.0 weighs four times as much as the same volume of water.

Methods for determining specific gravity are beyond the scope of this book, but experience in handling specimens will give you a surprising ability to estimate it closely. A typical metallic mineral such as pyrite or hematite has a specific gravity of about 5. A typical nonmetallic mineral has a specific gravity between 2.6 and 2.8, a range which covers the common minerals quartz, feldspar, and calcite. Minerals appreciably above or below these values seem noticeably heavy or light when lifted. These average figures are used as the basis of distinction in the outline and descriptive section of this book. Thus, a specimen which might be of medium weight for a metallic mineral would perhaps be considered heavy for a nonmetallic mineral—your own judgment and experience tell you what to expect when you lift it.

OTHER MINERAL PROPERTIES

Minerals possess a wide range of physical properties besides those described above as the Seven Keys to Mineral Recognition. Whenever any of these properties is typical of a given mineral and is therefore a valuable clue for identifying it, you will find the property described or illustrated in the descriptive section of this book. The more common and useful of these miscellaneous properties are discussed here now.

Many minerals belonging to the carbonate class will effervesce, or fizz, in acid, a reaction involving the escape of carbon dioxide gas. Household vinegar is sufficiently strong, though you will often find it helpful to scratch the specimen with a knife blade to form a powder which reacts more quickly. Dilute hydrochloric (muriatic) acid is the standard acid for this purpose. Of the minerals described in this book, the following are carbonates: aragonite, azurite, calcite, cerussite, dolomite, magnesite, malachite, rhodochrosite, siderite, smithsonite, strontianite. Some of these react more slowly than others, and some satisfactorily only when the solution is warmed. The only one that needs a different acid to dissolve it is cerussite, which requires nitric acid to give the proper effect. If anything stronger than vinegar is used, it should be handled carefully and carried in a bottle having an eye dropper or glass rod attached to the stopper for convenience in touching it to the specimen.

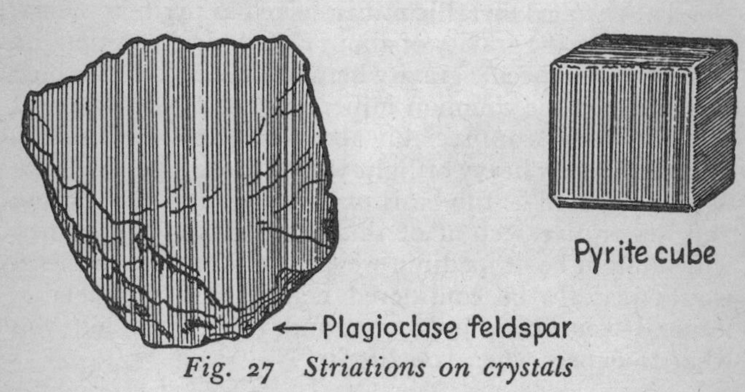

Fig. 27 Striations on crystals

Striations are parallel straight lines resembling a grating. They come about in several different ways. Some mark the boundary between the parts of twin crystals, where the twinning is repeated over and over again. This sort of striation is seen on plagioclase feldspar. Others, as shown on pyrite and quartz, result from a conflict between two kinds of crystal faces, each controlling the growth for a while and one of them finally winning out.

Flexible minerals, such as chlorite, can be bent in your fingers and will stay bent until forced in another direction. *Elastic* minerals, on the contrary, will snap back to their original position unless they have actually been broken; the mica minerals are typical examples of this interesting property.

Malleable minerals are those which can be hammered flat without falling to powder. The native metals—gold, silver, copper—are malleable, though loosely held fragments sometimes crumble or come apart. *Sectile* minerals can be cut with a knife, like horn or dry cheese, without powdering, but they will pulverize if pounded with a hammer. A few minerals described in this book, such as gypsum, are somewhat sectile.

Magnetic minerals are those which can be attracted by a common horseshoe or bar magnet. After being heated, or when tested with an electromagnet, hundreds of minerals are magnetic, but only two of the common minerals—magnetite and pyrrhotite—can be picked up before such treatment.

Fig. 28 Short-wave ultraviolet lamp

Fluorescent minerals glow in the dark when exposed to invisible radiation, such as ultraviolet light, X rays, and cathode rays. The most practicable source for such radiation is an *ultraviolet lamp,* which may be of two main types. The long-wave lamp emits a good deal of heat. The short-wave lamp, though more expensive, is cool and it is effective with a larger number of minerals. Either one causes colors to appear that were not perceptible before. A glass filter is employed to screen out the undesirable visible light, but a dull purple almost always comes through. Some of the most spectacular optical effects in the mineral kingdom are obtained by fluorescence.

When the glow continues after the lamp is turned off, the mineral is said to be *phosphorescent*. Other kinds of so-called *luminescence* can be produced by heating or striking certain minerals in the dark. Although fluorite is the mineral which gave its name to the property, it does not show fluorescence as well as some others. Of the ones described in this book, scheelite and willemite can be most relied upon to show fluorescence. Many diamonds fluoresce, and so do many specimens of calcite and opal. Battery-powered portable lamps have been a popular item of equipment for prospecting for scheelite, an important ore of tungsten.

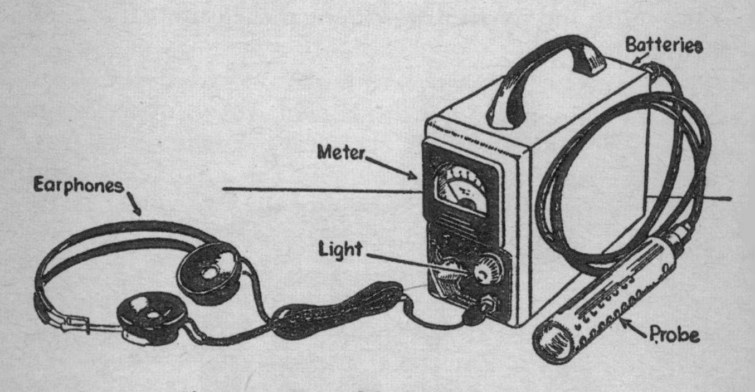

Fig. 29 Portable Geiger counter

Radioactive minerals break down spontaneously and at a uniform rate. As the atoms disintegrate and change to other elements, they give off energy. Although various kinds of equipment will detect this radiation, the instrument most generally in use is the *Geiger counter*. By means of a click, a flashing bulb, or a dial, the presence of the invisible radiation is revealed. Portable models have become common among prospectors, both professional and amateur. Uraninite and its cousin, pitchblende, are the radioactive minerals described in this book, although zircon and a few others often possess this vital property to a minor extent.

The ability of some minerals such as enargite and stibnite to *fuse* or melt in the flame of a match or candle is worth remarking upon. Cryolite is unique among the minerals included in this book in its property of becoming virtually invisible when immersed in water, because there is very little difference in the light-bending power of the mineral and the liquid.

Final identification of a difficult mineral might require blowpipe tests, chemical tests or analyses, optical examination with a petrographic microscope, or X-ray photography. Such procedures are explained in the more advanced textbooks on mineralogy.

How to Read Chemical Formulas

The chemical composition of minerals is written in a special shorthand called a formula, which is really quite simple to read. It tells which chemical elements go to make up the mineral and how many atoms there are of each kind. For example, the formula of quartz is SiO_2, denoting that this mineral is composed of silicon (Si) and oxygen (O), the proportion being one atom of silicon to two atoms of oxygen. Every chemical element is given a symbol which is an abbreviation of either the English or the Latin name. Thus, C stands for carbon, Ca for calcium, and Fe for *ferrum,* which means iron. The symbols of forty of the most common elements occurring in minerals are included in the following list. Those marked with an asterisk (*) are able to exist by themselves as native elements or minerals in the earth's crust; more than half of them are common or important enough to be described in this book. The rest of the elements listed below are combined with other elements in the form of mineral compounds.

* Ag	Silver	Ba	Barium
Al	Aluminum	Be	Beryllium
* As	Arsenic	* Bi	Bismuth
* Au	Gold	* C	Carbon
B	Boron	Ca	Calcium

Cl	Chlorine	Ni	Nickel
Cr	Chromium	O	Oxygen
Co	Cobalt	P	Phosphorus
* Cu	Copper	* S	Sulfur
F	Fluorine	Si	Silicon
* Fe	Iron	* Sb	Antimony
H	Hydrogen	Sn	Tin
* Hg	Mercury	Sr	Strontium
K	Potassium	Te	Tellurium
Li	Lithium	Ti	Titanium
* Pb	Lead	U	Uranium
Mg	Magnesium	V	Vanadium
Mn	Manganese	W	Tungsten
Mo	Molybdenum	Zn	Zinc
Na	Sodium	Zr	Zirconium

Certain *compounds,* or combinations of elements, are especially frequent in minerals. These belong to various major chemical classes, of which the most important are listed here, with an example of each, taken from this book.

Al_2O_4	Aluminate	Spinel
B_4O_7, etc.	Borate	Borax
CO_3	Carbonate	Calcite
Cr_2O_4	Chromite	Chromite
MoO_4	Molybdate	Wulfenite
PO_4	Phosphate	Apatite
SO_4	Sulfate	Barite
SiO_4, Si_2O_6, Si_3O_8, etc.	Silicate	Zircon
TiO_3	Titanate	Ilmenite
VO_4	Vanadate	Vanadinite
WO_4	Tungstate	Scheelite

Other chemical classes, consisting of a single element, which combines with one or more different elements, include the following:

As	Arsenide	Niccolite
Cl	Chloride	Halite
F	Fluoride	Fluorite
O_2	Oxide	Hematite
S	Sulfide	Galena

Water may be present in the form of H_2O, as in gypsum, or as hydroxyl (OH), as in topaz. The oxide of silicon (SiO_2) is referred to simply as silica. When a formula includes a comma, as (Fe,Al), it means that the given atom may be of either element (here, iron or aluminum, as in epidote). The letter *n*, as nH_2O in opal, indicates a variable number of groups of atoms.

How to Use the Outlines

Through a step-by-step process of eliminating the classifications that do not apply to the specimen you are trying to name, you ought to arrive at the section which includes the right mineral. A few precautions, however, may prove of value.

If you are not certain about the existence of any one of the properties upon which the outline is based, you will be wise to examine either the opposite section or the adjacent ones. For example, if the cleavage is probably present but appears indistinct, try the sections headed "Shows good cleavage" and "Does not show good cleavage." If the other properties are sure but the hardness is doubtful, examine the sections varying in hardness from the one you have almost decided upon. This technique holds good for luster, color, and streak as well—of these, the streak is most apt to cause uncertainty.

Each section begins with the minerals that are generally most easily recognized by their typical color or other readily observed characteristics. This facilitates identifying the more difficult minerals, because once the simpler ones are eliminated, attention can be confined to the details of the less obvious ones.

A magnifying glass should be used to examine the cleavage, striations, inclusions, or other features shown in the drawings because they may be present on too small a scale to be visible otherwise.

The color is indicated in the illustrations for those minerals which belong to groups whose color is used as a key for classifying them. For the rest the chief colors are given in the scientific data above the illustrations.

Bornite is placed according to the purple color of its tarnish, which is the hue almost always seen. The other minerals are classified by the color of their fresh surface, although the outside of the specimen is often somewhat darkened or made iridescent by a film of tarnish. Hence a newly broken surface should be exposed before deciding the color, especially of a metallic mineral.

Identifying the Minerals. Outline of Keys

3. Cannot be scratched by copper coin, but can be scratched by knife blade *Page* 108
4. Can scratch glass and be scratched by quartz *Page* 124
5. Cannot be scratched by quartz *Page* 126

b. Does not show good cleavage *Page* 129

1. Can be scratched by fingernail *Page* 129
2. Cannot be scratched by fingernail, but can be scratched by copper coin *Page* 132
3. Cannot be scratched by copper coin, but can be scratched by knife blade *Page* 136
4. Can scratch glass and be scratched by quartz *Page* 146
5. Cannot be scratched by quartz *Page* 154

COVELLITE

KEYS: Metallic luster. Can mark paper. Blue color.
Streak: Gray or black. **Cleavage:** 1 direction.
Specific Gravity: 4.6–4.8 (medium weight).

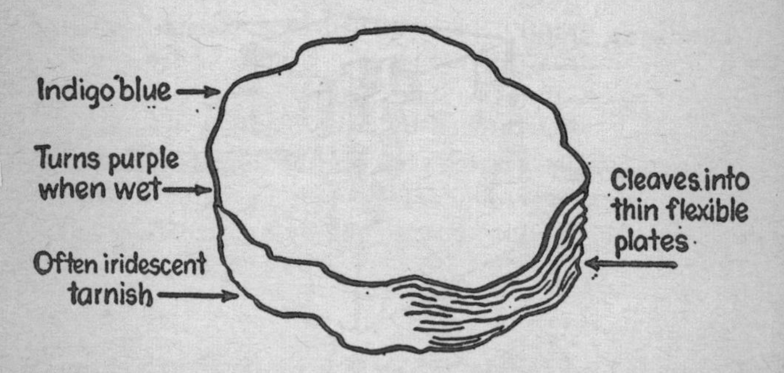

Named after N. Covelli (1790–1829), the man who discovered it on Mount Vesuvius, covellite is copper sulfide (CuS). It is not too common a mineral, but a number of good localities have been described, and it serves as a minor ore of copper. It is associated with other copper minerals, often in the richest part of the vein, and seems to have altered from them. Most covellite does not occur in crystals but rather in irregular pieces. Large crystals, singly and in groups, beautifully surfaced with an iridescent coating, have come from the Calabona mine at Alghero on the Mediterranean island of Sardinia. Similar specimens occur at Butte, Mont.—"the richest hill on earth"—where covellite is fairly abundant. It is found on Luzon Island in the Philippines and was formerly mined at Kennecott, Alaska, in large masses of the distinctive indigo-blue color that identifies this attractive metallic mineral. Several places in Colorado and a few in Wyoming and Utah have furnished some covellite. Argentina and other countries in South America also produce it. Bor, Yugoslavia, and Leogang, Austria, are among the chief European sources.

GALENA

KEYS: Metallic luster. Can mark paper. Gray or black color.
Streak: Lead-gray. **Cleavage:** 3 directions.
Specific Gravity: 7.4–7.6 (heavy).

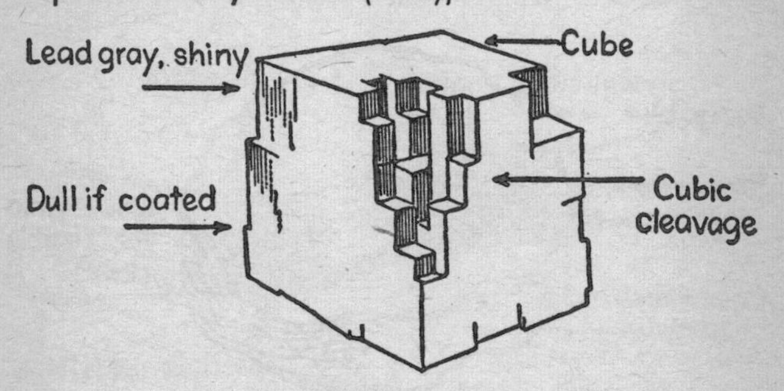

Galena is lead sulfide (PbS). It is by far the chief ore of lead, as well as an important ore of silver, which is present as a valuable "impurity." Silver is especially apt to be found by assaying the fine-grained variety known as steel galena, in which the right-angled cleavage that is so characteristic of the mineral may not be readily visible. World-wide in distribution, galena is noteworthy in places as separated as Broken Hill, Australia; Freiberg and the Harz Mountains, Germany; the mining districts of Cornwall, Cumberland, and Derbyshire, England; and Leadville, Colo. In the United States galena can be found in metal-bearing veins and in limestone at many localities. It is particularly abundant in the Mississippi Valley from Wisconsin to Missouri, in the Tri-state area where Kansas, Oklahoma, and Missouri come together, and in the Rocky Mountain states of Idaho, Utah, and Colorado. The otherwise shiny surface of galena becomes dull when coated with a film of other substances; and, upon oxidizing, galena alters to anglesite and cerussite. Interesting combinations of galena with other minerals are often found in various rocks. Such an occurrence is the one at the Sullivan mine, Kimberley, B. C.

STIBNITE

KEYS: Metallic luster. Can mark paper. Gray or black color.
Streak: Lead-gray. **Cleavage:** 1 direction.
Specific Gravity: 4.6 (medium weight).

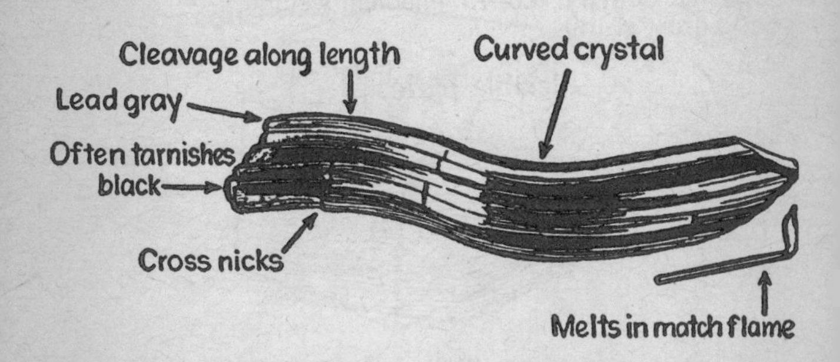

Antimony sulfide in chemical composition (Sb_2S_3), stibnite is the most important ore of antimony. From the extensive mines at Ichinokawa on the island of Shikoku, Japan, have come truly magnificent crystals, nearly 2 feet long and possessing many brilliant terminal faces. Groups of these are in the proud ownership of leading museums. An unusual feature of stibnite crystals is their curved or twisted appearance, as though they had been warped. The excellent crystals from Felsöbánya, Rumania, sometimes penetrate tabular specimens of barite. At Bau, in Borneo, large crystals are also found. Some well-crystallized material occurs near Hollister and elsewhere in California. Massive stibnite is produced in quantity in Hunan Province, China, where the world's largest deposits are situated. Stibnite is fusible enough to be melted in a match flame. White and yellow oxides of antimony often coat its surface, and stibnite loses its brightness when exposed to light. The dark powder was used by the ancients to blacken their eyebrows. Today stibnite enters directly into the manufacture of fireworks, vulcanized rubber, and medicines.

MOLYBDENITE

KEYS: Metallic luster. Can mark paper. Gray or black color.
Streak: Dark-gray, with greenish tinge.
Cleavage: 1 direction.
Specific Gravity: 4.6–4.7 (medium weight).

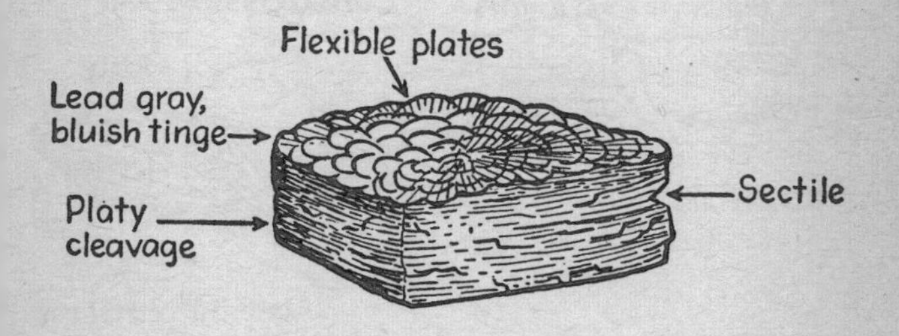

A sulfide of molybdenum (MoS_2) and the principal ore of that strategic industrial and military metal, molybdenite is so tricky to pronounce that miners simply call it "molly." Crisscrossed throughout with thin veins of it is Bartlett Mountain, rising behind Climax, Colo., to an altitude of 11,300 feet—the greatest concentration of molybdenite on this planet. For large crystals, however, the collector would have to go to such places as Bluehill Bay, Me.; Edison, N.J.; Renfrew County, Ont.; or as distant as Kingsgate, New South Wales. Thick sheets of the mineral have been taken from the very old rocks that underlie New York City. The resemblance between molybdenite and graphite is strong; perhaps the bluish tone to its color and the greenish tinge to its streak on porcelain will help you recognize molybdenite, and also it is heavier. Molybdenite is commonly found in granite and quartz, which are not the typical host rocks for graphite. The yellow dust on the top and in cracks is an alteration product, ferrimolybdite, which might easily be mistaken for sulfur or one of the secondary uranium minerals.

GRAPHITE

KEYS: Metallic luster. Can mark paper. Gray or black color.
Streak: Black. **Cleavage:** 1 direction.
Specific Gravity: 2.1–2.2 (light).

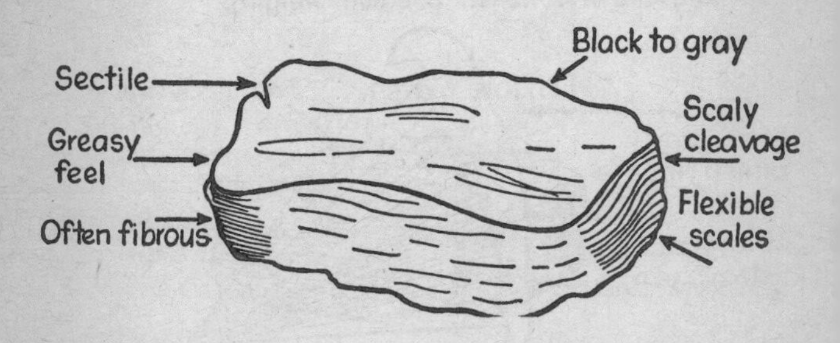

Like diamond, graphite consists solely of crystallized carbon (C). The extraordinary difference between these two minerals in color, hardness, conductivity, and crystallization is the most remarkable contrast in all mineralogy. Whereas diamond is a nonconductor of electricity, graphite is a good conductor; whereas diamond crystals are common, graphite crystals are scarce and poorly developed. A curious fact is that graphite is really the more stable form of carbon, for diamond will change to it when heated. The greasy feel of graphite and the way it soils the fingers indicate its uses as a lubricant for machinery, a protective coating for metals, and the so-called lead for pencils. This last use, its original one, gave graphite its name, from the Greek word for "to write." Fine crystals come from Sterling Hill, N.J. The best-known occurrence in the United States is near the Revolutionary War fort of Ticonderoga, N.Y. Graphite is also found with coal in Rhode Island. Korea, however, has produced more commercial graphite in one year than any other country. A more consistent output comes from Madagascar, Ceylon, Mexico, Siberia, and Central Europe.

PYROLUSITE

Keys: Metallic luster. Can mark paper. Gray or black color.
Streak: Black. **Cleavage:** 2 directions.
Specific Gravity: 4.4–4.5 (medium weight).

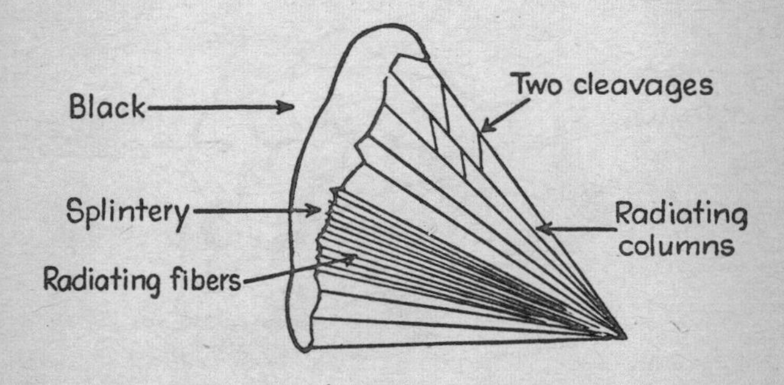

An oxide of manganese (MnO_2) and the most abundant ore of that metal, pyrolusite is a widespread mineral. When in well-developed crystals, such as those of Horni Blatna, Czechoslovakia, it is termed polianite, which is very different from the common massive pyrolusite, being hard enough then to scratch glass. Most frequently the crystals are actually those of another manganese mineral called manganite, which have changed chemically, losing water but retaining their original shape. Pyrolusite is at its charming best when it assumes fanciful scenic patterns in chalcedony quartz, turning it into moss agate. Similar plantlike designs are developed on slabs of sandstone and limestone. Ordinary pyrolusite, on the contrary, which is often soft enough to soil the hands a dirty black, is scarcely attractive. Sometimes it takes on a characteristic bluish cast. Usually pyrolusite is mixed with other manganese ores, all of them being mined together under the name *wad.* The most extensive deposits are in the Soviet Union, Central India, Union of South Africa, Gold Coast, and Brazil. Pyrolusite acts as a decolorizing agent in glass and is used in batteries.

GOLD

KEYS: Metallic luster. Cannot mark paper, but can be scratched by knife blade. Copper color.

Fracture: Hackly.

Specific Gravity: 15.6–19.3 (very heavy).

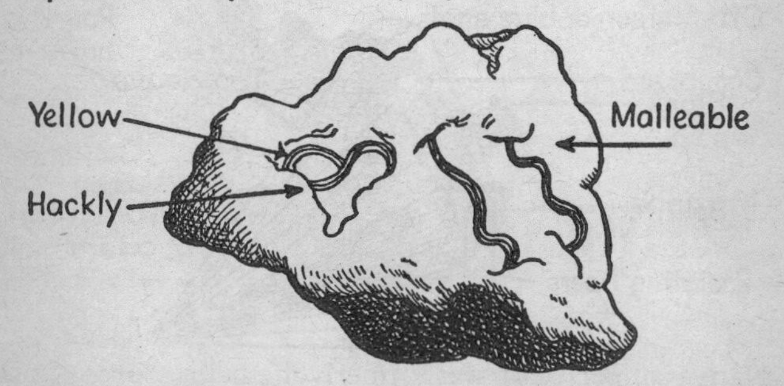

Native gold (Au) is never found entirely pure. A varying proportion of silver is always present; when the percentage is high, the alloy is called electrum. Gold from Australia is noted for its low silver content. Well-developed crystals are extremely rare, making their appealing beauty all the more tantalizing. Exquisite, indeed, are the dendritic or fernlike groups. In public museums in Denver and nearby Golden, Colo., are displayed two vaults of wonderful specimens from that state. Gold ranges in size from the Welcome Stranger nugget found at Ballarat, Australia, which weighed 2,280 ounces, down to the "flour gold" in the Snake River, Ore., which requires about 5,000 of the minute particles to be worth one cent. Gold can be distinguished from the various kinds of "fool's gold"—pyrite, chalcopyrite, mica—by its heaviness and malleability. Since 1886 the South African district of Witwatersrand, familiarly called the Rand, has produced over 16,000 tons of gold valued at more than 12 billion dollars, from dozens of mines centering around Johannesburg. The ranking gold mine of the Western Hemisphere is the Homestake mine at Lead, S.D.

COPPER

KEYS: Metallic luster. Cannot mark paper, but can be scratched by knife blade. Copper color.

Fracture: Hackly. **Specific Gravity:** 8.9 (heavy).

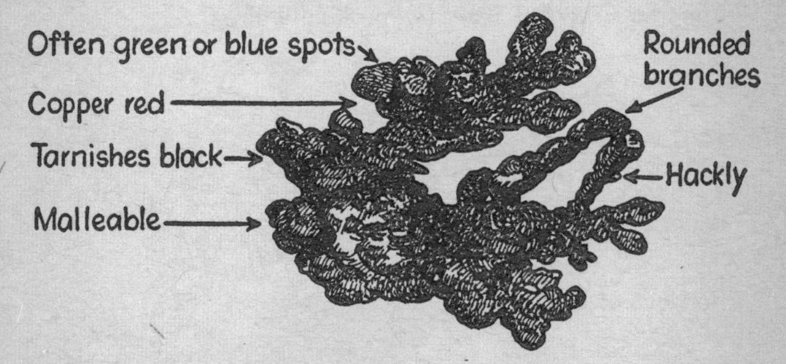

Native copper (Cu) was formerly the main source of copper, but various sulfide minerals now provide most of our needs for this indispensable metal. The native mineral is still a favorite of collectors, however, because of the interesting shapes it assumes. The stupendous deposits on the Keweenaw Peninsula in northern Michigan dwarf everything else of their kind in existence. Here, for more than a mile in depth, native copper, from great masses to tiny specks, has been mined. Branching skeletons, tiny scales, twisted wires, hollow shells shaped like human skulls, stream-worn pebbles—these are all typical of the Michigan copper. One enormous piece weighing 420 tons was found in 1857. Combinations of copper and native silver are called "half-breeds"; both minerals soon become tarnished and look alike, but when cleaned they stand in striking contrast to each other. Another Michigan occurrence consists of copper enclosed in transparent calcite; unaffected by tarnish, the copper gleams in its pristine state like gold. Native copper is also found at Corocoro, Bolivia, and in small amounts in other countries. The island of Cyprus, an early source of copper, gave its name to it.

MILLERITE

KEYS: Metallic luster. Cannot mark paper, but can be scratched by knife blade. Copper color.

Streak: Greenish-black. **Cleavage:** 3 directions.
Specific Gravity: 5.3–5.7 (medium weight).

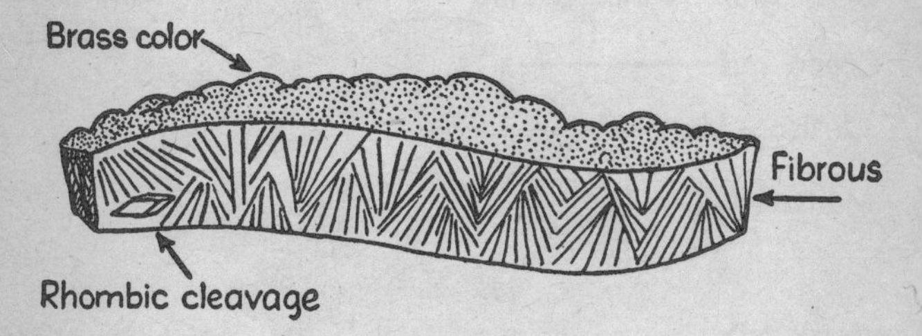

Millerite, a subordinate nickel ore, is a sulfide of nickel (NiS). The German mineralogist Abraham Gottlob Werner first described millerite in 1789 and called it Haarkies. Given its present name for William Hallowes Miller, an English mineralogist (1801-1880), it is unusual among metallic minerals in consisting of slender brassy crystals which are often matted together like a wad of hair. Crystals of capillary texture occur in Wales at Merthyr Tydfil. Delicately tangled tufts are found in the crystal-lined rocks, known as geodes, which can be collected at Milwaukee, Wis.; St. Louis, Mo.; and Keokuk, Iowa. Velvety coatings of millerite come from the Gap mine in Lancaster County, Pa. Various localities in Germany yield needles of millerite. Interesting occurrences of millerite include sublimates from volcanic fumes at Mount Vesuvius, coal beds in the Saar, and the 25-ton Santa Catharina (Brazil) meteorite. Millerite is never found in large quantities. It is generally formed at low temperatures and may alter from other nickel minerals. The bright-scarlet chemical test for nickel will distinguish closely fibrous millerite from fibrous marcasite.

CHALCOPYRITE

KEYS: Metallic luster. Cannot mark paper, but can be scratched by knife blade. Copper color.

Streak: Greenish-black. **Fracture:** Uneven.

Specific Gravity: 4.1–4.3 (medium weight).

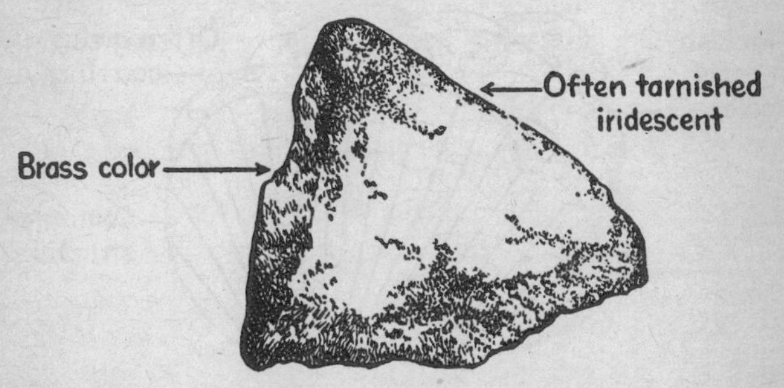

A copper–iron sulfide ($CuFeS_2$), chalcopyrite was so named in 1725 to distinguish it from regular pyrite, which does not contain copper except as an impurity. Like pyrite, it is one of the minerals referred to as fool's gold, and its brassy color resembles gold more than that of pyrite does. Chalcopyrite may also tarnish to give an iridescent appearance. Unlike pyrite it can be scratched by a knife, and unlike true gold it is brittle. It is not only the most common of all copper minerals, but it also frequently carries valuable amounts of gold or silver. It is associated with nickel deposits in a number of places. Rich pieces occur in the Noranda gold mine in the Rouyn district of Quebec. The mines at Ducktown, Tenn., should be mentioned for the quality of their chalcopyrite. Large perfect and sharp crystals have been obtained at Ellenville, N.Y., and in Chester County, Pa. A curious massive type, found in some mines in Cornwall, England, has a rounded surface and is known as blistered copper ore. Distributed throughout a huge ore body at Rio Tinto, Spain, chalcopyrite has long been mined there for copper and gold.

NICCOLITE

KEYS: Metallic luster. Cannot mark paper, but can be scratched by knife blade. Copper color.

Streak: Brownish-black. **Fracture:** Uneven.
Specific Gravity: 7.8 (heavy).

A nickel arsenide (NiAs), niccolite is unusually attractive for a metallic mineral. Many times called copper nickel by miners because of its coppery color and nickel content, it is one of the lesser ores of nickel. As early as 1694 it was known in Germany as *Kupfernickel,* and from this name was taken our word for the white metal. Concentric shells a foot in diameter, alternating with zones of arsenopyrite, come from Natsume, Japan. Crystals are exceedingly rare, a few having been found at Richelsdorf and Eisleben, Germany. The typical occurrence of niccolite is with silver, cobalt, and other nickel ores. These associations are important in Germany, Czechoslovakia, and Canada. In the United States some niccolite has been reported from New Jersey and Colorado. A thin green crust of annabergite often covers specimens of niccolite and may be a useful clue for determining the presence of niccolite beneath the ground. The reddish tinge of niccolite is different from the color of any of the other minerals described in this book, though it is similar to that of certain copper arsenides, and so a test for nickel might be necessary.

PYRRHOTITE

KEYS: Metallic luster. Cannot mark paper, but can be scratched by knife blade. Copper color.

Streak: Dark grayish-black. **Fracture:** Uneven.

Specific Gravity: 4.6 (medium weight).

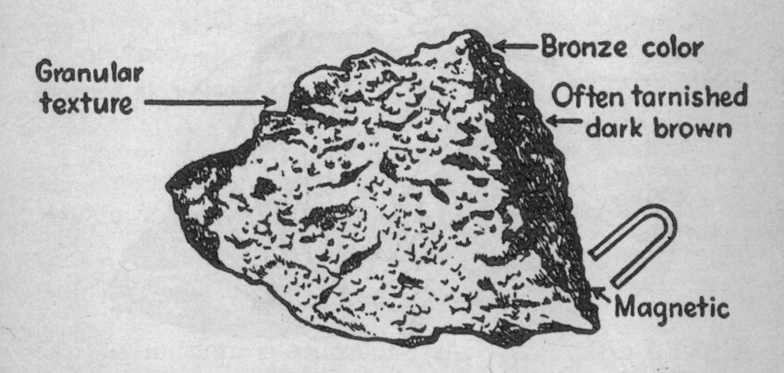

Pyrrhotite is iron sulfide (FeS), with always a slight deficiency of iron that puzzled mineralogists for a long while. It has been called magnetic pyrite because it somewhat resembles pyrite and it is the only common mineral except magnetite to be noticeably magnetic. Thick crystals have been collected at the Morro Velho gold mine in Brazil. Smaller but good crystals have come from Kongsberg, Norway, and Andreasberg, Germany. Large crystal groups are known at Loben, Austria, and elsewhere in Central Europe. Great amounts of massive material are mined at Sudbury, Ont., where they are intimately mixed with pentlandite, a nickel sulfide that resembles pyrrhotite but is not magnetic. Ducktown, Tenn., is an important locality for ordinary pyrrhotite. The Western states yield this mineral in a moderate quantity. The word pyrrhotite, with its so difficult spelling, means reddish. The variety called troilite has been known in meteorites since 1766 and comes close to being pure iron sulfide. Troilite of terrestrial origin has been found in Del Norte County, Calif.

BORNITE

KEYS: Metallic luster. Cannot mark paper, but can be scratched by knife blade. Purple color.

Streak: Gray-black. **Fracture:** Uneven.

Specific Gravity: 5.1 (medium weight).

This copper–iron sulfide (Cu_5FeS_4) is a significant ore of copper. Although bornite is a common enough mineral, crystals of it are rare, and so only irregular masses are usually found. Even these pieces, which should be readily recognized by their brownish-bronzy color on a freshly fractured surface, are disguised by the purplish tarnish which steals over them, covering them with a bright iridescence and giving bornite the miners' names of peacock ore, purple copper ore, and horseflesh ore. Any specimen suspected of being bornite should be broken open to expose a new area for observation, to see if the tarnish gives way to a bronze hue. The color of the bornite from Androka, Madagascar, is very choice. Large amounts of bornite are mined in a number of countries of Latin America and at Butte, Mont. It is also important at Mt. Lyell, Tasmania. The rare crystals used to be found in the United States at Bristol, Conn. This mineral was named in 1832 after Ignaz von Born, an eminent Austrian mineralogist who lived from 1742 to 1791.

CUPRITE

KEYS: Metallic luster. Cannot mark paper, but can be scratched by knife blade. Red or brown color.

Streak: Brownish-red. **Fracture:** Uneven.

Specific Gravity: 6.0 (medium weight).

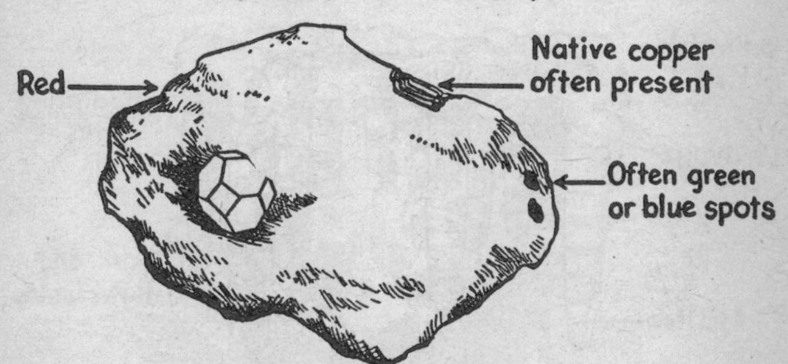

Copper oxide (Cu_2O) in composition, cuprite is an ore of copper; its name refers to this metal. The crystal forms of cuprite are highly interesting to the mineral collector. The most fascinating of the forms consists of a brilliant red mat of hairlike crystals, drawn out to needle length; this variety is called chalcotrichite (meaning "hair copper") and is much in demand for its exceptional beauty. The best specimens come from Morenci, Ariz., and from old copper mines near Gwennap, England. Fine crystals of the usual types of cuprite occur in several mines in Cornwall, England, and even larger ones come from Chessy, France. The name ruby copper suggests the appearance of the more desirable specimens. At Gumeschevsk in the Ural Mountains pieces of cuprite are perforated by cavities lined with later crystals of the same mineral. Cuprite is an important source of copper at Bisbee, Ariz. It is associated with other copper minerals, and some native copper is almost always present and aids in its identification. Ancient bronze and copper objects of art show tiny crystals of cuprite which have grown upon them during the passage of centuries.

GOETHITE

KEYS: Metallic luster. Cannot mark paper, but can be scratched by knife blade. Red or brown color.

Streak: Brownish-yellow. **Cleavage:** 1 direction.
Specific Gravity: 3.3–4.3 (medium weight).

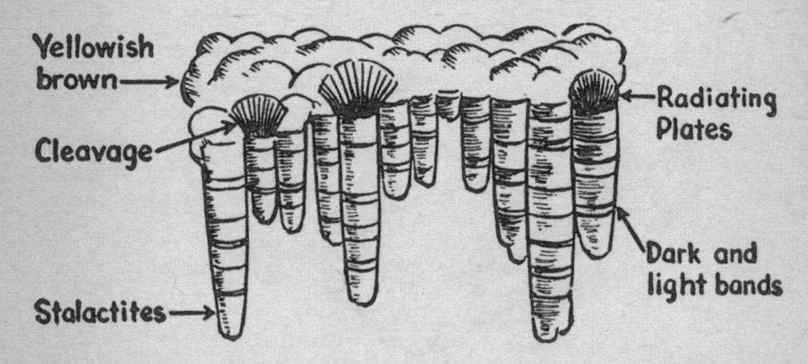

Iron hydroxide with the chemical formula $HFeO_2$ was named goethite after the German poet and philosopher Johann Wolfgang von Goethe (1749-1832), who was a student and collector of minerals. It has undergone the strange experience of a mineral which was one day believed to be an uncommon one and almost the next day was learned to be one of the most abundant minerals. This odd development was the result of X-ray examinations which revealed that most of the iron ore that had always been known as limonite was actually crystalline in its atomic structure and therefore should really be called goethite instead. Fine crystallized specimens are found in cavities in granite in the Pikes Peak region of Colorado. The large cubes of goethite found at Pelican Point on the shore of Great Salt Lake, Utah, were originally pyrite and have changed chemically. Lostwithiel, England, is a classic locality for splendid crystals of goethite. This mineral is the main constituent of the important iron ores of Alsace-Lorraine, and it is widely distributed in Cuba. Goethite is found among the other iron minerals of the Lake Superior deposits, especially at Negaunee, Mich.

SILVER

KEYS: Metallic luster. Cannot mark paper, but can be scratched by knife blade. Gray or black color.

Streak: Silver-white. **Fracture:** Hackly.

Specific Gravity: 10.5 (very heavy).

When free of tarnish, silver (symbol, Ag) can be a handsome mineral. With its fernlike designs, network patterns, and crystal groups it resembles copper and gold except in color. Wire silver and crystals of unsurpassed beauty were produced for hundreds of years at Kongsberg, Norway, some of the masses weighing as much as 750 pounds. At Freiberg and Schneeberg, Germany, are situated other silver mines of considerable age. Aspen, Colo., is famous for its twisted masses of wire silver, and for the largest silver nuggets ever found, one of which, weighing 1,840 pounds, was too large to be hauled from the Mollie Gibson mine in an ore bucket. The fabulous "silver sidewalk" of the La Rose mine at Cobalt, Ont., was a slab of almost solid metal 100 feet long and 60 feet thick. Another Canadian silver locality is in the pitchblende deposits at Great Bear Lake. The Coeur d'Alene district in Idaho is also a prominent place for native silver. Mexico is the world's leading producer of silver, which may well be regarded as a Western Hemisphere metal, even though known to prehistoric man on the other continents.

ENARGITE

KEYS: Metallic luster. Cannot mark paper, but can be scratched by knife blade. Gray or black color.

Streak: Grayish-black. **Cleavage:** 2 directions.

Specific Gravity: 4.4 (medium weight).

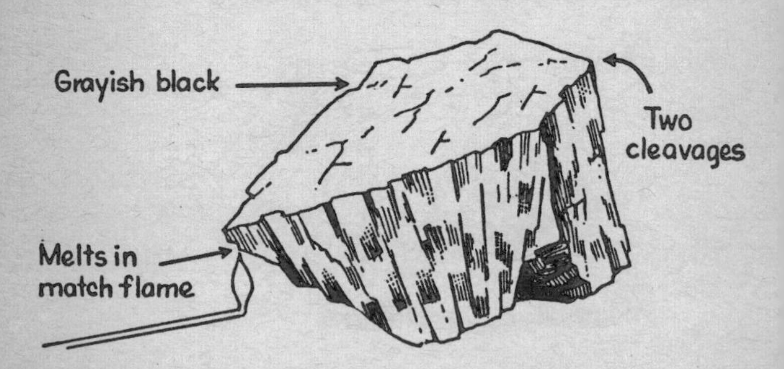

A sulfide of copper and arsenic (Cu_3AsS_4), enargite is an ore of copper, closely resembling stibnite except for its somewhat darker color—a test for copper is the easiest way to distinguish between them with certainty. Enargite is particularly important at Butte, Mont., where it also yields arsenic oxide ("white arsenic") for the chemical industry. The deposits in Utah at Bingham Canyon and Tintic also produce substantial amounts of enargite. California, Nevada, and Colorado furnish small quantities, especially the silver mines in the San Juan Mountains of Colorado. Outside of the United States the main sources of enargite are in South America, in the noted copper mines at Cerro de Pasco and Morococha, both in Peru, and at Chuquicamata, Chile. A large deposit exists at Bor, Yugoslavia, but otherwise enargite is not common in Europe. The name of this mineral comes from a Greek word meaning distinct, because of its definite cleavage, and was applied to it in 1850. As antimony replaces the arsenic, enargite grades into famatinite, which was named after the Sierra de Famatina, Argentina.

PYRITE

KEYS: Metallic luster. Can scratch glass. Brass color.
Streak: Greenish- to brownish-black. **Fracture:** Uneven.
Specific Gravity: 5.0–5.1 (medium weight).

The most familiar form of iron sulfide (FeS_2) is pyrite. Its name alludes to the sparks that fly when it is struck with a hammer. More abundant than marcasite, which has the same chemical composition, it ranks as one of the commonest of minerals. Pyrite, in fact, is referred to as a persistent mineral because it occurs under almost every geologic condition. It is one of the minerals called fool's gold. Huge crystals of pyrite have come, among other places, from Leadville, Colo.; Ubina, Bolivia; and the island of Elba. The well-shaped crystals from Chester, Vt., are attractively embedded in a green rock. So-called iron-cross twins come from Schoharie, N.Y. At Sparta, Ill., are the "pyrite suns," which are radiating disks of the mineral. Of little value for its iron content, pyrite is often rich in gold and copper, as well as being a source of sulfur. Very large deposits occur at Rio Tinto, Spain, where they have been worked since the days of the Phoenicians. Some of the most interesting occurrences of pyrite are those in which it has replaced the organic matter of fossils; a few localities for such specimens are Holland Patent, N.Y., and Lyme Regis, England.

MARCASITE

KEYS: Metallic luster. Can scratch glass. Brass color.
Streak: Greenish-black. **Fracture:** Uneven.
Specific Gravity: 4.9 (medium weight).

Having exactly the same composition as pyrite, though not nearly so common, marcasite is iron sulfide (FeS_2). The curious spear and cockscomb forms of marcasite are actually twin crystals; at Dover, England, the spear-shaped specimens are believed locally to be relics of Roman weapons. Marcasite often grows as stalactites covered with pyramid-shaped crystals projecting outward like spikes on a war club. Rounded lumps of various sizes occur embedded in shale. In the former state of Württemberg, Germany, fossils from the age of dinosaurs are found to be replaced by marcasite. Leading localities for marcasite in the United States include Mineral Point, Wis., Galena, Ill., and the zinc and lead mines around Joplin, Mo. The name marcasite used to be applied to pyrite until a distinction was made between the two minerals, which have different atomic structures. Marcasite is much less apt than pyrite to be present as individual crystals, tending instead toward fibrous and radiating aggregates, especially in nodules. Because marcasite decomposes so readily, specimens fall to pieces quickly; unless they are kept in a dry atmosphere, they become covered with white powder.

CHROMITE

KEYS: Metallic luster. Can scratch glass. Gray or black color.

Streak: Dark-brown. **Fracture:** Uneven.

Specific Gravity: 4.6 (medium weight).

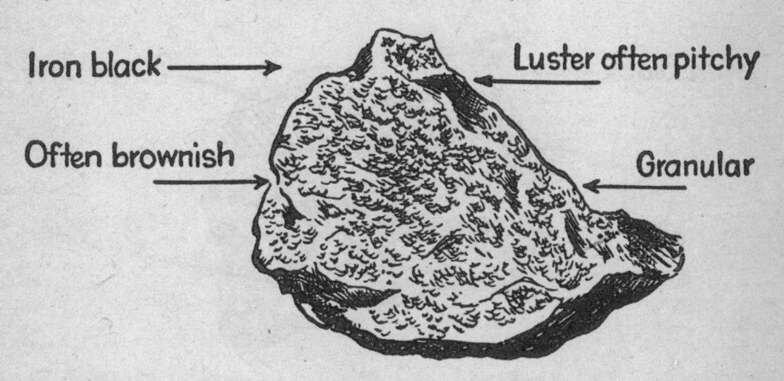

In composition an iron chromite ($FeCr_2O_4$) and in use the only ore of chromium, this mineral has an easy name to remember. Good crystals, which resemble those of magnetite and franklinite, are small and scarce; they are found, for instance, on the northern islands of Unst and Fetlar in the Shetland Islands. Chromite may be slightly magnetic but not enough to be mistaken for magnetite. A pitchy luster and a brownish cast to the color, while not necessarily present, are frequent enough to aid in recognizing chromite when you see it. Though hardly to be called a North American mineral, some of it has been mined along both coasts from Alaska to California and from Newfoundland to North Carolina. Meteorites sometimes contain chromite, which is typically a high-temperature mineral. Bricks made from it are so heat-resistant that they are used to line the walls of furnaces in which metals are melted. Chromite is extremely tough and hard to break, and it is more than durable enough to become a constituent of placer gravels, especially those that contain platinum, for the two minerals are formed and preserved under similar conditions.

ILMENITE

KEYS: Metallic luster. Can scratch glass. Gray or black color.

Streak: Black or brownish-red. **Fracture.** Even.
Specific Gravity: 4.7 (medium weight).

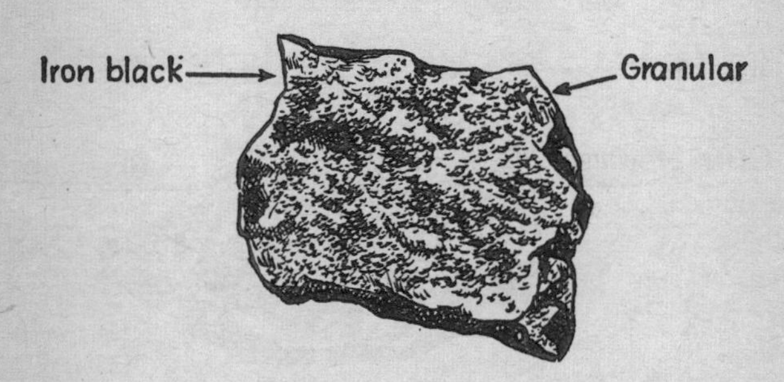

An iron titanate ($FeTiO_3$), ilmenite was named after the Ilmen Mountains, Russia, the original locality. It has come a long way from being an undesirable impurity in iron ore to its present status as one of the most promising industrial minerals of our time. The enormous new deposit at Allard Lake, Que., contains enough ilmenite to supply the whole world. Interestingly, this very black mineral makes the whitest of all paints and the white smoke used for skywriting and smoke screens. Crystals of ilmenite that are bright or well-shaped are rare; they may look like dark hematite. Some occur in Orange County, N.Y., and crystals weighing over 16 pounds have been found at Kragerö, Norway. Crystals are also found at Chester, Mass., and at St. Christophe, France. The black sand of certain beaches contains large amounts of ilmenite; for example, at Pablo Beach, Florida, and on the extraordinary beaches, one of which extends for 15 miles, in Travancore, India. Massive ilmenite resembles magnetite but is nonmagnetic, although the two minerals are often intergrown so that they must be separated magnetically before they can be used.

MALACHITE

KEYS: Nonmetallic luster. Leaves colored mark on streak plate. Green or blue mineral color.

Hardness: 3½–4. **Fracture:** Conchoidal.

Specific Gravity: 3.9–4.1 (heavy).

Malachite is a basic copper carbonate [$Cu_2(OH)_2(CO_3)$], and fizzes when touched by acid. Over one-half million pounds of the choice green mineral were taken from one pure mass of malachite in the Demidoff copper mine at Nizhni Tagil, in the Ural Mountains of Siberia. It was extensively used in Czarist Russia for table tops and other ornamental purposes. Another form of Russian malachite occurs in fibrous nodules having a silky luster; these were carved into exquisitely fashioned objects of art. The best crystals are found at Betzdorf, Germany, and the finest of those that have changed over from blue azurite come from Tsumeb, South-West Africa. The largest deposit of malachite is in the Katanga district of the Belgian Congo and Northern Rhodesia, where valuable copper ore is mined, as well as superb pieces of banded malachite well suited to being cut and polished. New Mexico and Arizona are the main producing states in the United States, although malachite can be found in the upper levels of almost every copper mine in the West. The green patina that appears on copper and bronze is in reality a thin tarnish of malachite.

AZURITE

KEYS: Nonmetallic luster. Leaves colored mark on streak plate. Green or blue mineral color.

Hardness: 3½–4. **Fracture:** Conchoidal.

Specific Gravity: 3.7–3.8 (heavy).

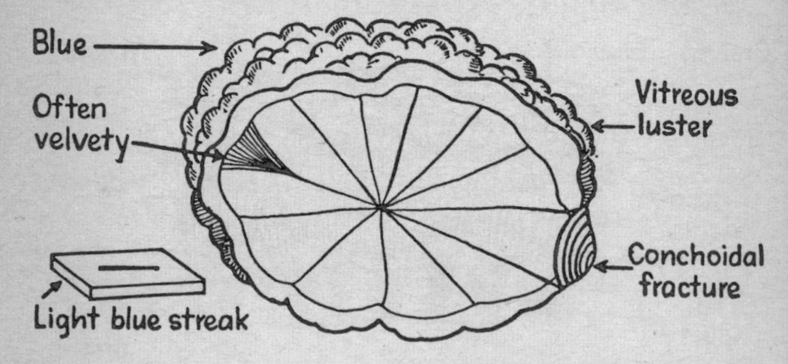

Azurite, like malachite, is a basic copper carbonate $[Cu_3$ ([illegible]$)_2 (CO_3)_2]$. It fizzes similarly in contact with acid. Its rich blue color, from which it receives its name, is as distinctive as the equally deep green of malachite; the two minerals often occur together in a wonderfully appealing combination of contrasting colors. Inasmuch as azurite readily changes to malachite, the result may be a crystal which retains the original shape of the azurite but which now has the green color and all the other properties of malachite. The perfect and lustrous crystals of azurite from Chessy, France, are the finest ever known, though Tsumeb, South-West Africa, has more recently become the chief locality for crystals of remarkable size and beauty. Arizona is the leading American state, but unfortunately most of the Bisbee copper mines that produced splendid crystals, singly and in groups, have now been deepened below the zone in which azurite exists. During the fifteenth and sixteenth centuries azurite was the most popular blue pigment among European painters, and it had been employed for the ancient wall paintings of the Orient.

CHRYSOCOLLA

KEYS: Nonmetallic luster. Leaves colored mark on streak plate. Green or blue mineral color.

Hardness: 2–4. **Fracture:** Conchoidal.
Specific Gravity: 2.0–2.2 (light).

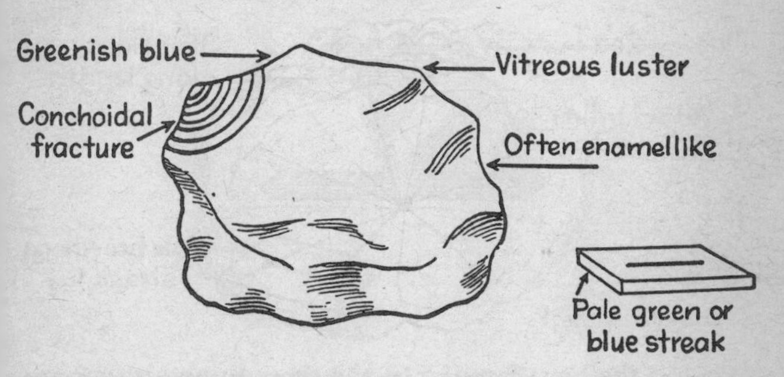

A hydrous copper silicate of indefinite composition [$(CuSiO_3 . nH_2O)$], chrysocolla is a minor ore of copper. It is used as an ornamental stone, substituting for turquoise, which likewise varies between greenish and bluish hues. Although softer and not so well known or so valuable as turquoise, it is in some ways more durable because its delicate color is permanent, and the shining enamel-like surface which it often shows is quite attractive. Chrysocolla occurs in the upper part of copper mines, associated with other colorful minerals containing that metal. Excellent specimens come from various localities in Arizona, New Mexico, Chile, England, and the Belgian Congo. The only crystals that have ever been found were from Mackay, Idaho, and are of microscopic size. The word chrysocolla, meaning "gold glue," was given to a similar-looking mineral used in olden times to solder gold, and it was later transferred in error to this mineral. When impure, as it often is because of its somewhat variable content of water, chrysocolla becomes brown or black and has then been called pitchy copper ore.

RUTILE

KEYS: Nonmetallic luster. Leaves colored mark on streak plate. Red or orange mineral color.

Hardness: 6–6½. **Fracture:** Uneven.

Specific Gravity: 4.2–4.3 (heavy).

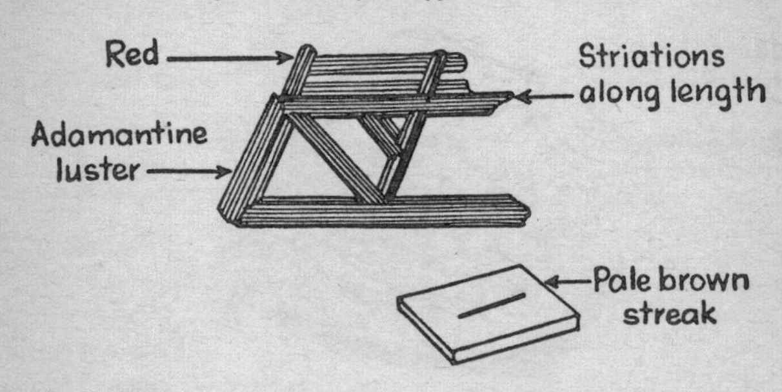

Rutile is the most familiar of the three minerals that are composed of titanium oxide and share the same formula (TiO_2), the others being anatase and brookite. The name rutile is derived from the Latin word for red, in reference to the color. The splendid specimens from Graves Mountain, Ga., are the finest in the United States. They consist of twinned crystals which repeat themselves until they make a complete ring. Magnet Cove, Ark., Stony Point, N.C., and Laws, Calif., are other outstanding American localities. Well-crystallized rutile comes from veins and rock crevices in a number of places in the Alps. Dark rutile crystals look a good deal like those of cassiterite, but they are not so heavy. Rolled pebbles are found in the diamond-bearing gravels in Brazil, and commercial deposits, where rutile is obtained as an ore of titanium, are found in the sand on Florida beaches. Needlelike red crystals of rutile are common as inclusions in quartz, which is then known as rutilated quartz; sagenite, a favorite of mineral collectors, is a related quartz material named from the network of crystals buried within it.

CINNABAR

KEYS: Nonmetallic luster. Leaves colored mark on streak plate. Red or orange mineral color.

Hardness: 2–2½. **Fracture:** Uneven.
Specific Gravity: 8.0–8.2 (very heavy).

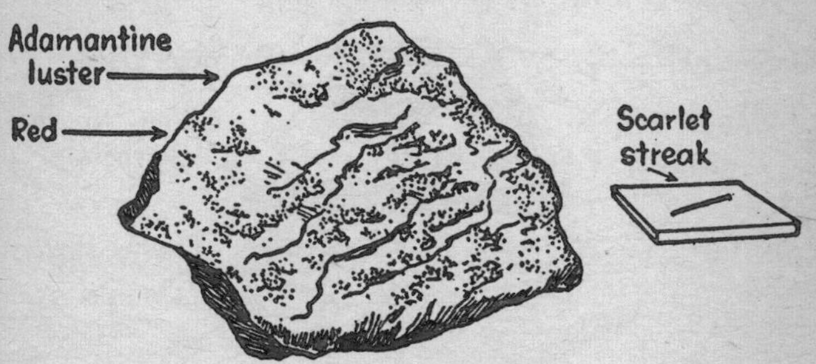

The chief ore of mercury (quicksilver) is cinnabar, mercury sulfide (HgS). Low-grade deposits are often deceiving because a thin crust of the bright red mineral gives a false appearance of richness. Impure cinnabar may be dark-red, almost black. Cinnabar forms near hot springs and is found near the earth's surface in areas of recent volcanic rocks. The most extensive occurrence in the world is at Almadén, Spain. Another large one is at Idria, Italy. Named after these ancient localities are the important California mines at New Almaden and New Idria. The mercury produced at New Almaden is credited with having made possible the tremendous gold production that took place during the California gold rush of the years immediately after 1848. At Terlingua, Tex., some of the cinnabar has altered to a group of rare mercury minerals. Pebbles of cinnabar, rolled round by stream action, are panned in gold placers in Dutch Guiana. Large crystals are obtained in China, and excellent ones also come from near Belgrade, Yugoslavia, and in Pike County, Ark. These show a pronounced cleavage not obvious in the usual finely granular material.

REALGAR

KEYS: Nonmetallic luster. Leaves colored mark on streak plate. Red or orange mineral color.

Hardness: $1\frac{1}{2}$–2. Cleavage: 1 direction.
Specific Gravity: 3.5 (medium weight).

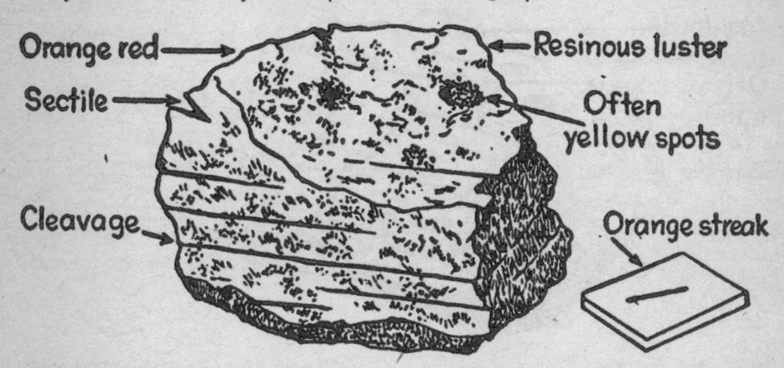

Realgar is arsenic sulfide (AsS) in its simplest form. It is not too stable a mineral, and exposure to light, which should be avoided, causes it to change rapidly from red to orange, eventually becoming yellow orpiment. The two minerals are almost always found together in nature. Besides ore veins, hot springs and volcanoes are the chief sources of realgar. Good crystals, otherwise rare, come from Mercur, Utah; the Binnental, Switzerland; and the island of Corsica in the Mediterranean. Fine specimens of this attractive mineral are also found at Manhattan, in Nevada. In Rumania it occurs with ores of silver and lead, occasionally in lovely translucent crystals. Nests of realgar are sometimes clustered in beds of clay. Thin coatings of realgar are deposited around Yellowstone geysers (in the Norris geyser basin) and Italian steam vents. The curious word realgar is derived from an Arabic term, *rahj al-ghār,* meaning "powder of the mine." The natural mineral was formerly used as a pigment and in fireworks, but is no longer. Realgar is softer and lighter in weight than cinnabar, which it may superficially appear to be.

ORPIMENT

KEYS: Nonmetallic luster. Leaves colored mark on streak plate. Yellow mineral color.

Hardness: $1\frac{1}{2}$–2. **Cleavage:** 1 direction.

Specific Gravity: 3.5 (medium weight).

Orpiment, like realgar, is arsenic sulfide but has a different formula (As_2S_3). Its tabular crystals are very uncommon and almost always small. Those from Mercur, Utah, however, are exceptionally large and fine; excellent ones also have come from Balin, Russia. Substantial amounts of orpiment occur at Acobambilla in Peru, and Julamerk in Turkey. The hot water at Steamboat Springs, Nev.; Yellowstone National Park, Wyo.; and Shimotsuke, Japan, deposits orpiment from springs and geysers onto the surrounding rocks, as do smoke vents in Italy. Lemon-yellow orpiment is often seen as an alteration product on pieces of realgar, and it is frequently scattered through certain layered rocks. At some places it has resulted from fires in a mine. Its name comes from the Latin name which means "golden paint," in reference to its color and because it was believed to contain gold—a compliment, indeed, to its vivid color. A little natural orpiment is used as a dye and in tanning skins, but the main use of the mineral is as specimens for collections. The handsome combinations of orpiment and realgar add life to any display.

CARNOTITE

KEYS: Nonmetallic luster. Leaves colored mark on streak plate. Yellow mineral color.

Hardness: 1–2. **Fracture:** Earthy.
Specific Gravity: 5.0 (heavy).

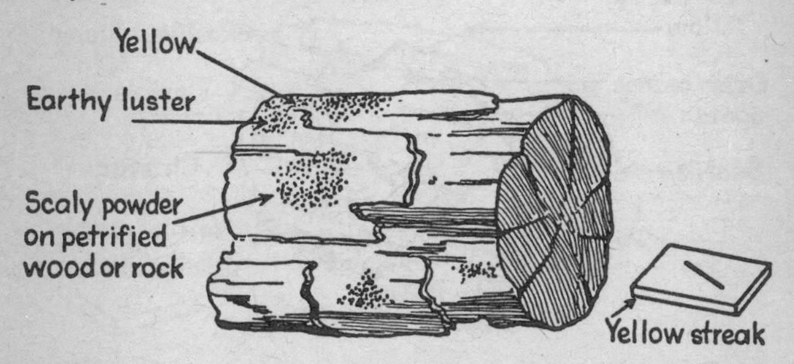

Carnotite is a complex mineral containing uranium, vanadium, and radium. Its chemical formula is close to $K_2(UO_2)_2(VO_4)_2 \cdot 3H_2O$. All three of the metals mentioned have in the past been extracted from it on a commercial scale. First discovered in Colorado, it was taken to France for analysis and was named there after a French mining engineer and chemist, Marie-Adolphe Carnot (1839-1920). It is at present the only significant ore of uranium in the United States, and this is now its sole use. In the remote plateau country of the Four Corners region—the only place in the nation where four states come together (Colorado, Utah, Arizona, New Mexico)—carnotite occurs uniquely in sandstone, associated with dinosaur bones, petrified wood, and vegetable matter. Two petrified logs from Calamity Gulch, Colo., and the rock between them yielded $350,000 in the three valuable metals. A little carnotite is known in other states, including Pennsylvania, and it forms a thin film on rock at Radium Hill, South Australia. Tiny micalike crystals can be expected at times, but a powdery or loosely granular form is the usual aspect.

SPHALERITE

KEYS: Nonmetallic luster. Leaves colored mark on streak plate. Brown mineral color.

Hardness: 3.5–4.0. Cleavage: 6 directions.

Specific Gravity: 3.9–4.2 (heavy).

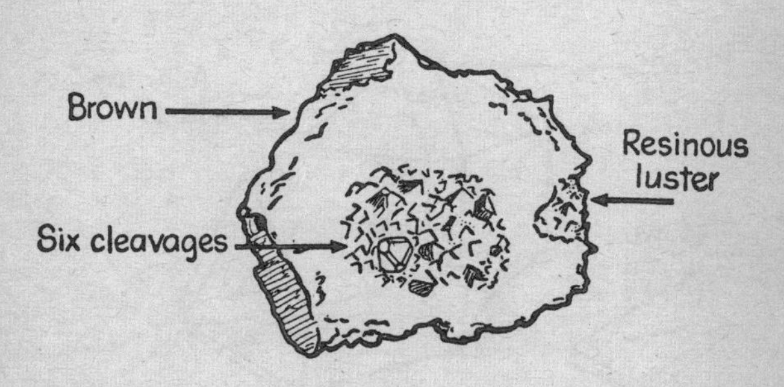

Zinc sulfide (ZnS), sphalerite, is the principal ore of zinc. Because it assumes various appearances, sphalerite is sometimes difficult to recognize and may be mistaken for minerals that bring a higher price; from this risk of disappointment it has obtained its name, which means treacherous. The name preferred in England is blende, which has a similar significance. Miners use additional terms, including zinc blende, blackjack, ruby zinc, and still others. Pure sphalerite is colorless, but iron is nearly always present, giving it a color that ranges from yellow to brown to black and may even be green. The world's greatest deposit of sphalerite is in the Tri-state area where Missouri, Kansas, and Oklahoma come together; the specimens from here are numerous and attractive. Some are as radiant as rubies. Butte, Mont., has also furnished remarkably good specimens. Fine groups occur at Alston Moor, England, and other localities in that country. Large masses of gorgeous golden color occur at Picos de Europa, Spain, and Cananea, Mexico. Unusually pure sphalerite has been analyzed from the Prince Frederick mine in Arkansas.

CASSITERITE

KEYS: Nonmetallic luster. Leaves colored mark on streak plate. Brown mineral color.

Hardness: 6–7. **Fracture:** Uneven.

Specific Gravity: 7.0 (very heavy).

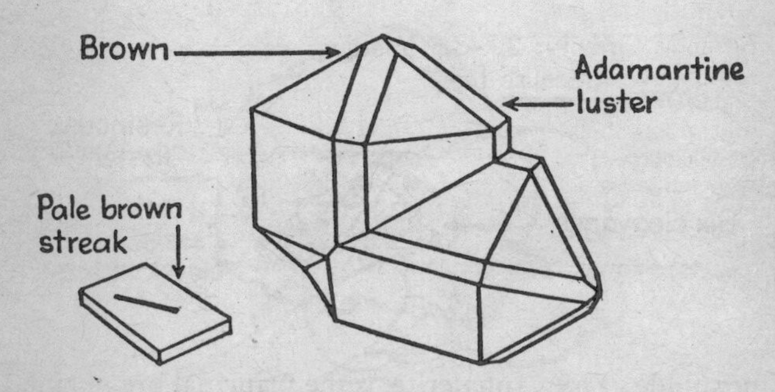

The oxide of tin, cassiterite (SnO_2), is the most important ore of tin. The vast deposits which stretch for 1,000 miles from Burma and China to the Netherlands East Indies yield cassiterite in large amounts, and it is also mined in Bolivia, Nigeria, the Belgian Congo, Australia, and a few other countries. Great Britain, known to ancient geographers as the Cassiterides or Tin Islands, was long a significant producer. Perhaps the most unusual occurrence of this mineral are the deerhorns found to have changed to cassiterite in the streams of Cornwall, England. Odd shapes exist, including sparable tin (like a cobbler's nail), wood tin (resembling a piece of dried wood), and toad's-eye tin. Because they are so often found in placer deposits, pebbles of cassiterite are popularly known as stream tin. Perfect crystals come from the tin mines of both the German and Czech sides of the mountain range called the Erzgebirge. Cassiterite is uncommon in the United States, marking a serious mineral deficiency, though it is found in a dozen scattered states, especially in the Black Hills of South Dakota.

MICA

KEYS: Nonmetallic luster. Leaves white mark or scratch on streak plate. Shows good cleavage. Can be scratched by fingernail.

Color: White, green = **muscovite.** Black, dark-brown = **biotite.** Yellowish-brown = **phlogopite.** Pink, purple = **lepidolite.**

Specific Gravity: 2.7–3.3 (medium weight, but may float on water because flaky).

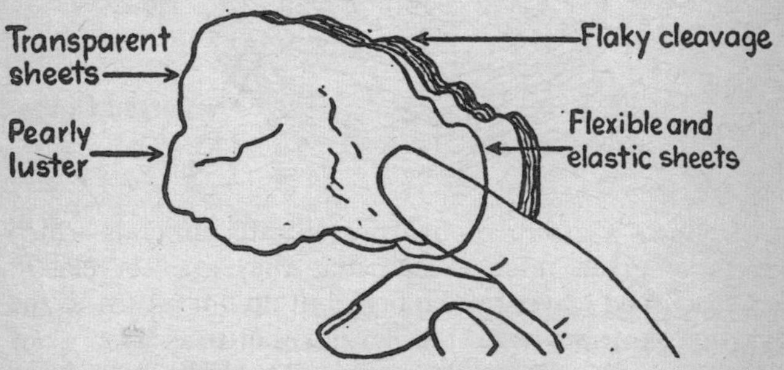

Mica is a group of minerals which are potassium-aluminum silicates and give off water when heated. They all have the remarkable property of peeling into thin sheets which not only can be bent but are also elastic, springing back to their original position when released, unless they have been carelessly broken. Thick crystals are called books, as they resemble a volume having many leaves or pages. The several kinds of mica have different colors because of variations in the chemical formula. Muscovite, also called white mica, has the simplest composition. Crystals of muscovite 33 feet long have been found in Ontario. The replacement of aluminum by magnesium produces phlogopite or brown mica; when both magnesium and iron are present, the mineral is biotite or black mica. Lepidolite or lithia mica has a lovely pink or purple color. White or light-brown mica, familiar as isinglass, is a strategic mineral for insulation.

CHLORITE

KEYS: Nonmetallic luster. Leaves white mark or scratch on streak plate. Shows good cleavage. Can be scratched by fingernail.

Color: Green. **Specific Gravity:** 2.6–3.0 (medium weight).

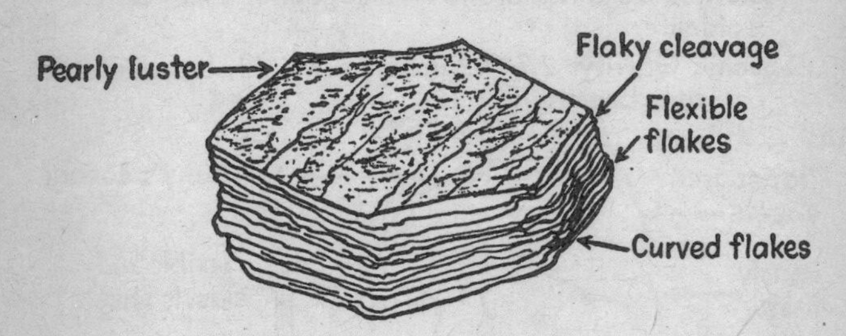

Chlorite is a group of hydrous silicate minerals which resemble green mica except that they are not elastic. Their curved leaves can be bent but do not return to the original position, as do the flat flakes of true mica. They seem to have a slightly soapy feel. The individual members of this group go under such names as clinochlore, penninite, and prochlorite; it is usually not necessary to try to distinguish among them. Their chemical formulas, as is the case with so many of the silicate minerals, are very complex. Chlorite makes up the mass of certain widespread green rocks and frequently dusts the surface of other minerals or occurs inside them. At Zermatt in the Swiss Alps are large green crystals of chlorite, which are especially noted among mineral collectors. Substantial plates are found at West Chester, Pa. Garnet is one of a number of minerals which occur in chlorite and alter to it; many of the big crystals from near Salida, Colo., have "rotted" to chlorite almost all the way through. The word chlorite means green, and this mineral is responsible for the color of many rocks, as a result of weathering and the action of hot water.

Minerals in Color

The following pages contain illustrations of forty-six minerals in full color. Arranged in alphabetical order for easy reference, they will be a further aid in identifying some of the minerals that are described in the text. All of these colored illustrations are reproduced by courtesy of Ward's Natural Science Establishment, Inc., Rochester, New York. They are from Ward's Color Slides for Mineralogy (photographs by Katherine H. Jensen), and from the Harvard Mineral Collection.

AMBER
Baltic.

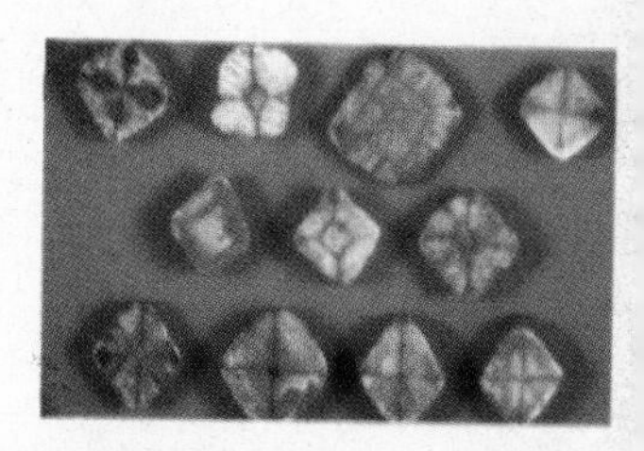

ANDALUSITE
Variety Chiastolite.
Madera County, California.

APATITE
Auburn, Maine.

AURICHALCITE
Kelly, New Mexico.

BERYL
Variety Aquamarine, Klein Spitzkopje, South-West Africa.

AZURITE
Bisbee, Arizona.

BARITE
Felsöbanya, Rumania.

CALCITE
Egremont, Cumberland, England.

CHALCOPYRITE
St. Agnes, Cornwall, England.

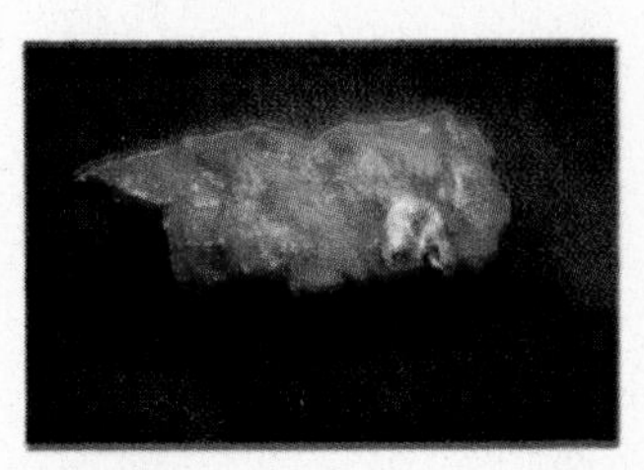

CINNABAR
Mercur, Utah.

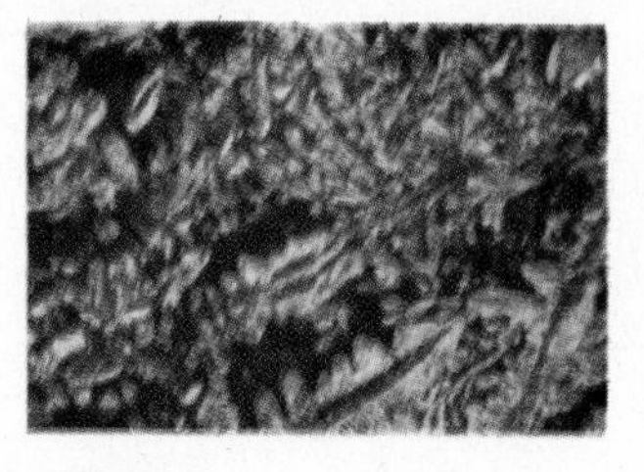

COPPER
Houghton County, Michigan.

CROCOITE
Near Dundas, Tasmania.

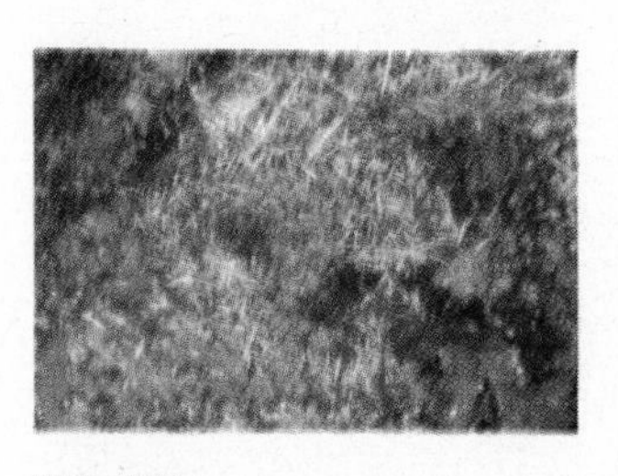

CUPRITE
Variety Chalcotrichite,
Bisbee, Arizona.

DATOLITE
Houghton County, Michigan.

DIAMOND
Kimberley, South Africa.

FLUORITE
Cave-in-Rock, Illinois.

FRANKLINITE
Franklin, New Jersey.

GOETHITE
Ishpeming, Michigan.

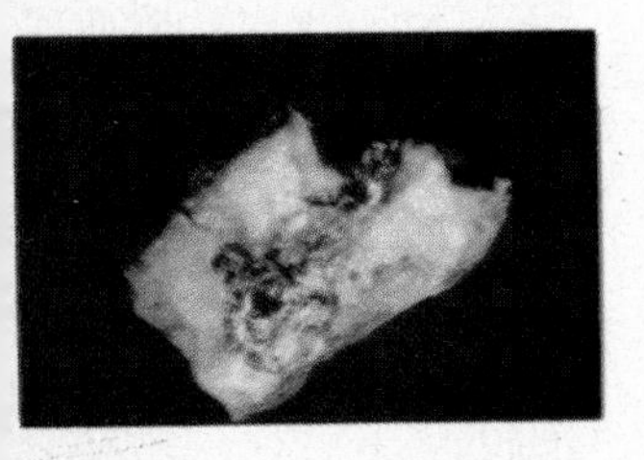

GOLD
Cederberg Mine,
El Dorado County, California.

GYPSUM
Variety Selenite,
Elsworth, Ohio.

GYPSUM
Variety Selenite,
England.

HALITE
Wieliczka, Galicia.

HEMATITE
Minas Gerais, Brazil.

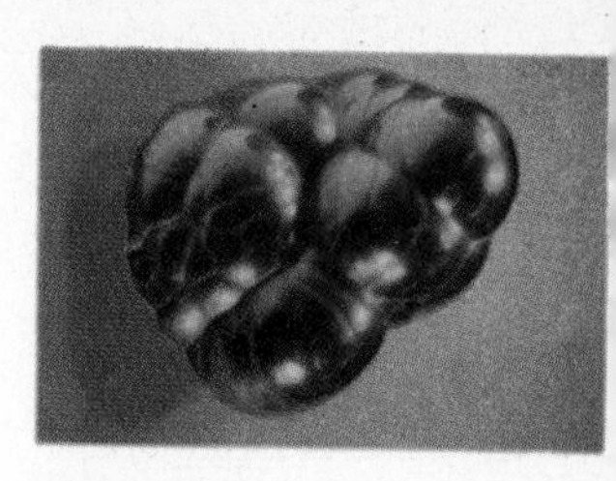

HEMATITE
Variety Kidney Ore, Cleator Moor, Cumberland, England.

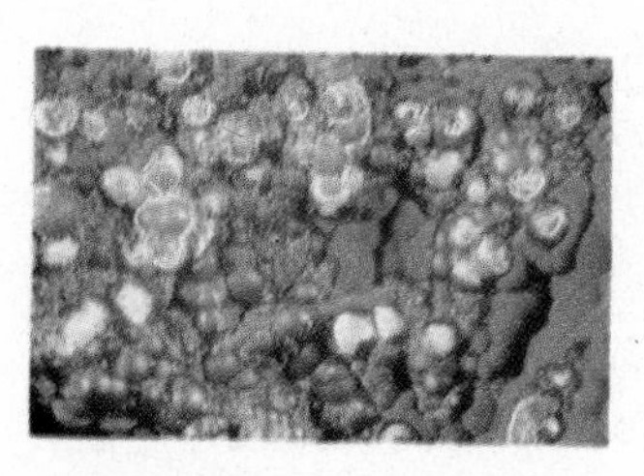

LIMONITE
Bisbee, Arizona.

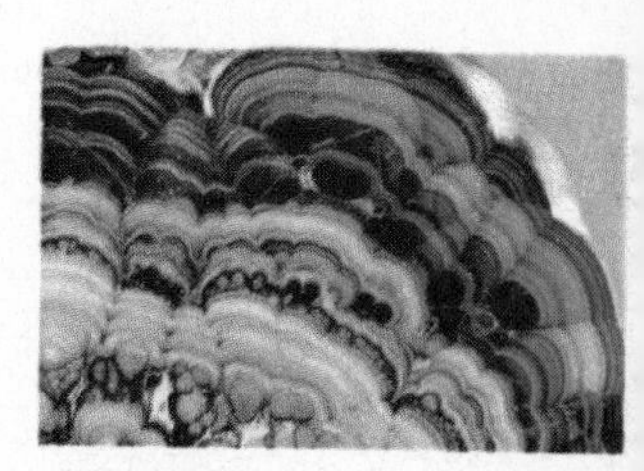

MALACHITE
Bisbee, Arizona.

MICROCLINE
Variety Amazonstone, near Florissant, Colorado.

MIMETITE
Variety Campylite, Dry Gill, Cumberland, England.

ORPIMENT
Mercur, Utah.

PYRITE
Bingham Canyon, Utah.

QUARTZ
Variety Jasper,
Oregon.

QUARTZ
Variety Rock Crystal,
Little Falls, New York.

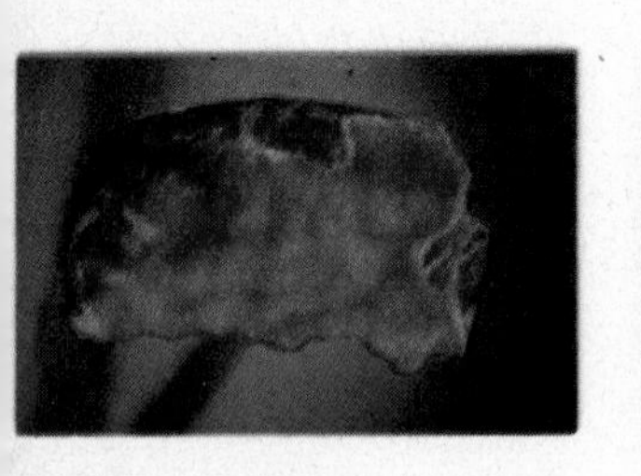

RHODOCHROSITE
Bockenrod, Odenwald,
Germany.

RHODONITE
Variety Fowlerite,
Franklin, New Jersey.

SILVER
Houghton County, Michigan.

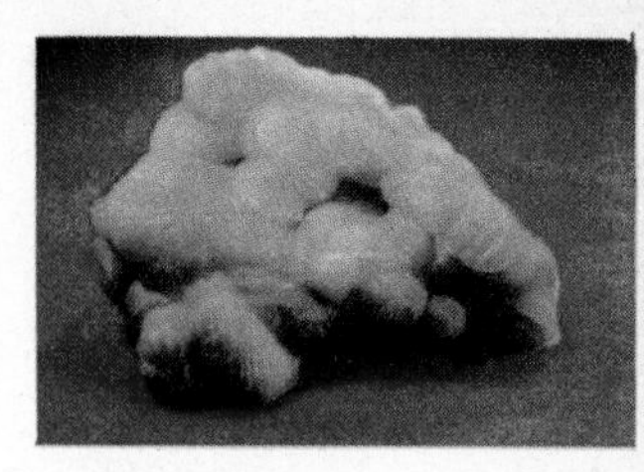

SMITHSONITE
Kelly, New Mexico.

STIBNITE
Ichinokawa, Iyo, Shikoku Japan.

SULFUR
Cianciana, Sicily.

TOPAZ
Devils Head, Colorado.

TOURMALINE
Madagascar.

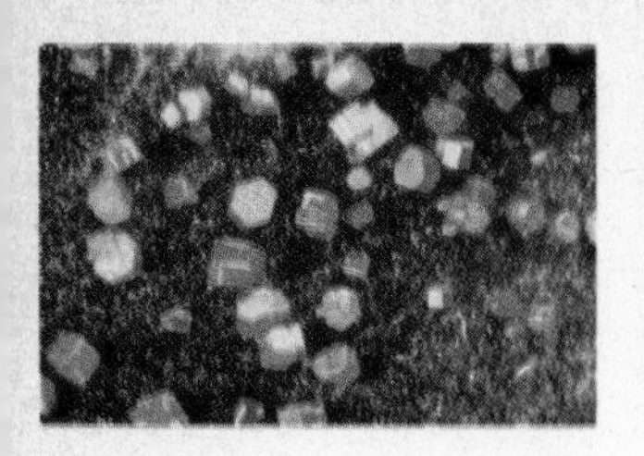

VANADINITE
Near Globe, Arizona.

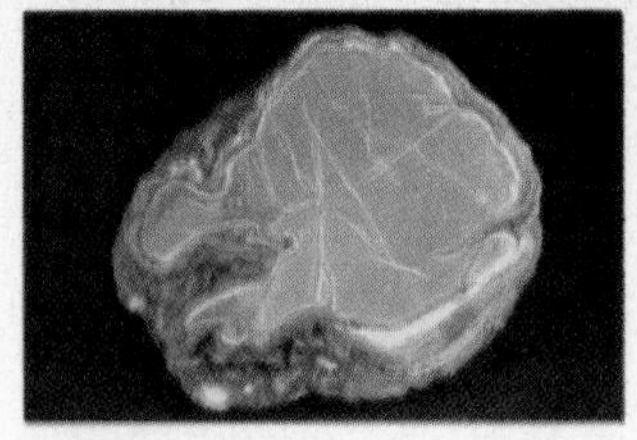

VARISCITE
Fairfield, Utah.

WAVELLITE
Near Hot Springs,
Arkansas.

WOLFRAMITE
Zinnwald, Bohemia.

WULFENITE
Sierra de los Lamentos,
Chihuahua, Mexico.

ZINCITE
Franklin, New Jersey.

GYPSUM

KEYS: Nonmetallic luster. Leaves white mark or scratch on streak plate. Shows good cleavage. Can be scratched by fingernail.

Color: White, gray. **Specific Gravity:** 2.2–2.4 (medium weight).

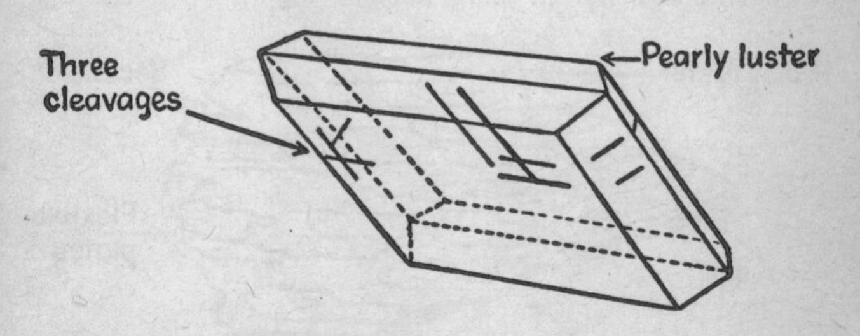

Calcium sulfate ($CaSO_4.2H_2O$) in composition, gypsum is the most common mineral of the sulfate class. Thick beds are known over large areas of the globe, supplying the basic raw material for making plaster of paris. This product gets its name from the gypsum deposits in the Paris basin in France. The crystals from Naica, Mexico, are of colossal size, and those from Wayne County, Utah, and Ellsworth, Ohio, are likewise exceptionally large. Among other clear and nicely formed crystals of gypsum are those from the salt mines at Bex, Switzerland, and Girgenti, Sicily. Transparent gypsum like this is called selenite. Compact material solid enough to be carved into ornaments and useful articles is familiar as alabaster, of which northern Italy and Colorado are the leading sources. Gypsum in veins composed of silky fibers is called satin spar, which has been cut into beads and sold for many years at Niagara Falls. The White Sands in New Mexico, near the rocket proving ground, consist of wind-blown dunes of gypsum sand. Earthy gypsum is called gypsite.

TALC

KEYS: Nonmetallic luster. Leaves white mark or scratch on streak plate. Shows good cleavage. Can be scratched by fingernail.

Color: Green, white.

Specific Gravity: 2.7–2.8 (medium weight).

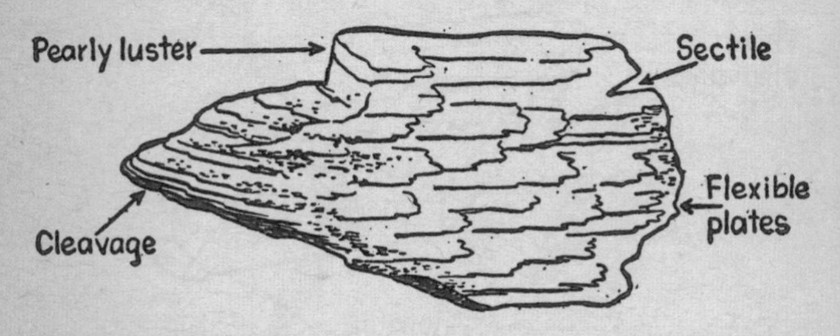

This hydrous magnesium silicate [$Mg_3(OH)_2Si_4O_{10}$] is closely related to serpentine. Although the origin of the word talc is lost in obscurity, everyone knows the most familiar product made from this mineral—talcum powder. Owing to its being the softest of all minerals, talc feels soapy. A somewhat more solid form, called soapstone or steatite, is used for chemical sinks and electrical switchboards. Small pieces, called French chalk, are used by tailors to mark cloth. Most of the low-priced objects of Chinese manufacture that are supposed to look like jade are really soapstone, and many of the rest are pyrophyllite, a related mineral grouped with talc when statistics of production are given. Beautiful sea-green specimens of talc come from various places in the Alps; talc from the French Pyrenees is the finest for the cosmetic industry. New York, California, and North Carolina are the leading American sources for talc, which is mined, at intervals, the length of the Appalachian Mountains. Talc combined with other minerals that have grown in it makes interesting specimens.

CALCITE

KEYS: Nonmetallic luster. Leaves white mark or scratch on streak plate. Shows good cleavage. Cannot be scratched by fingernail, but can be scratched by copper coin.

Color: White, colorless.

Specific Gravity: 2.7 (medium weight).

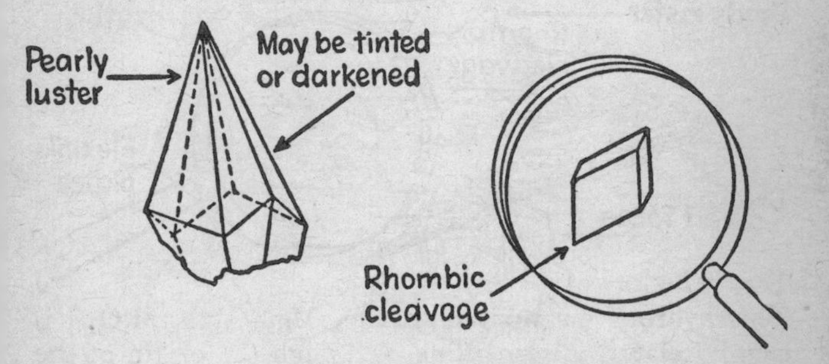

Calcite is calcium carbonate ($CaCO_3$), often very pure. Like all carbonates it fizzes in acid. Describing typical calcite would be difficult, for over 300 forms and more than 1,000 combinations have been recorded. Hence calcite may have almost any outward appearance, but it always breaks into fragments of one shape, the rhomb. Fortunately, some kinds of calcite crystals turn up frequently enough to become familiar. Absolutely clear pieces of calcite, first found in Iceland, are called Iceland spar; they have the interesting property of making a line seem double when viewed through them. One crystal of this variety from near Helgustadir, Iceland, measured 20 feet in length. Several crystals weighing more than 25 tons each have come from near Taos, in New Mexico. The golden calcite from Joplin, Mo., is little short of spectacular, as are the resplendent crystals from several localities in northern England. "Dogtooth spar" and "nailhead spar" owe their names to peculiar forms of calcite crystals.

DOLOMITE

KEYS: Nonmetallic luster. Leaves white mark or scratch on streak plate. Shows good cleavage. Cannot be scratched by fingernail, but can be scratched by copper coin.

Color: Pink, white.

Specific Gravity: 2.8–2.9 (medium weight).

The calcium-magnesium carbonate [$CaMg(CO_3)_2$] is called dolomite after Déodat de Dolomieu (1750–1801), a French engineer and mineralogist. Being a carbonate, it fizzes in acid, though less vigorously than calcite and though the acid may have to be warmed. Beds of dolomite of considerable thickness have been deposited in many parts of the world, where they may be used as building stone. Ordinary limestone turns to dolomite upon the addition of magnesium from any one of a number of underground sources. Large transparent dolomite crystals of choice quality occur near Djelfa, Algeria. Dolomite grows on the inside of the intriguing hollow rocks which are so abundant near Keokuk, Iowa; called geodes, they resemble rough, rocky balls until they are broken open, when they reveal a glitter of many tiny crystals. Large crystals of dolomite come from Roxbury, Vt. The mineral is found in cavities in rock at Niagara Falls, Lockport, and Rochester, N.Y. A good deal of translucent dolomite surrounds the lead and zinc minerals at Joplin, Mo.

BARITE

KEYS: Nonmetallic luster. Leaves white mark or scratch on streak plate. Shows good cleavage. Cannot be scratched by fingernail, but can be scratched by copper coin.

Color: White, colorless, blue.

Specific Gravity: 4.5 (heavy).

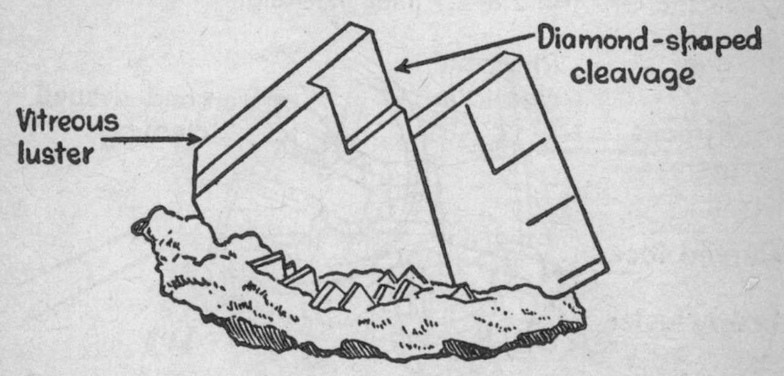

Barite is barium sulfate ($BaSO_4$), the most common mineral containing barium and one of the most common sulfate minerals. Its name appropriately means "heavy." Crystals of an enchanting blue color can be collected in abundance at two localities in Colorado, near Hartsel and Sterling. Reddish-brown flowerlike groups, such as those from Norman, Okla., are called barite roses. A single transparent crystal weighing 100 pounds was taken from a lead mine in Westmorland County, England. Large quantities of white barite, carrying brown stains in cracks and corners, are typical of the commercial deposits in Missouri. Stalactites of brown barite are found at Newhaven, England. In the Bad Lands of South Dakota crystals of barite have grown in distorted shapes inside the hollow bones of fossil animals buried there for millions of years. Barite localities are numerous in California. For its home this mineral favors limestone and metal-bearing veins. Barite is used in house paint and in many other ways.

CELESTITE

KEYS: Nonmetallic luster. Leaves white mark or scratch on streak plate. Shows good cleavage. Cannot be scratched by fingernail, but can be scratched by copper coin.

Color: Blue, colorless, white.

Specific Gravity: 3.9–4.0 (heavy).

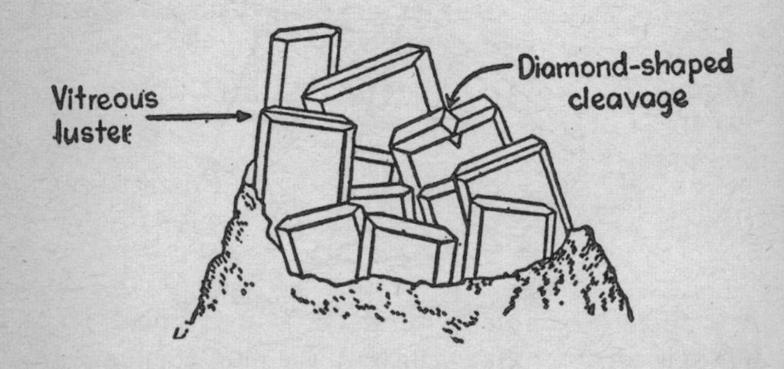

Celestite is strontium sulfate ($SrSO_4$) and was given its name because the first specimens, found near Bellwood, Pa., were a celestial blue. This color, though frequent enough in most places, is not an essential characteristic, however. In a cave at historic Put in Bay in Lake Erie excellent crystals over 18 inches long have been discovered. Daintily fashioned groups of crystals are collected at Clay Center, Ohio. The celestite in the sulfur beds at Girgenti, Sicily, is doubtless the best known. Complex blue crystals occur in cavities in copper mines at Herrengrund, Czechoslovakia. Large crystals are found at Lampasas, Tex. Some fossils are seen to have changed to celestite as a result of petrifaction under special geologic conditions. This mineral and barite often look exactly alike, especially when they have a tinge of blue. Then perhaps the best way to tell them apart is to hold a piece in a very hot flame, which will become green for barite or red for celestite when the mineral begins to decompose.

HALITE

KEYS: Nonmetallic luster. Leaves white mark or scratch on streak plate. Shows good cleavage. Cannot be scratched by fingernail, but can be scratched by copper coin.

Color: Colorless, white. **Specific Gravity:** 2.2 (light).

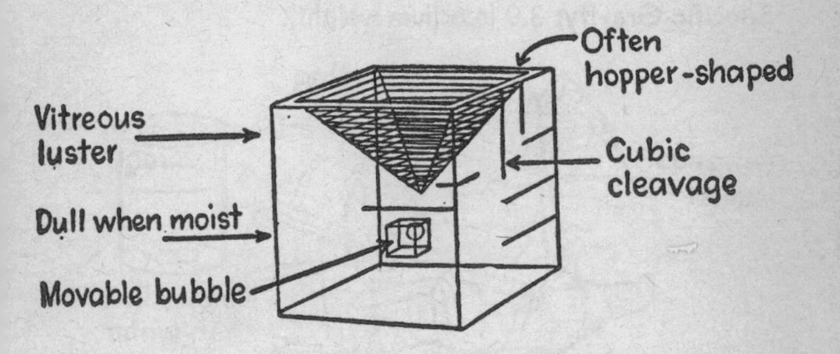

As a mineral, sodium chloride (NaCl) is called halite, but it is still the familiar table salt. Vast beds of such rock salt, and huge bodies called salt domes abound. Well-crystallized specimens have come from Stassfurt, Germany, and Bochnia, Poland, as well as several places on the island of Sicily. Peculiar distorted crystals are found in Humboldt County, Nev. Attractive masses of superior transparency are obtained in the Verde Valley, Ariz. A curious feature of many halite crystals is the hopper-shaped opening that penetrates the faces. Interesting, also, are the occasional hollow spots inside, containing a drop of water which moves back and forth like the bubble in a carpenter's spirit level. The salty taste of halite is a distinctive property of it, and of course it dissolves easily in water. Some halite is blue, possibly owing to the displacement of atoms in the structure. Contrary to general belief, most halite is used in the chemical industry rather than as food, but its use to sustain life cannot be dispensed with.

CRYOLITE

KEYS: Nonmetallic luster. Leaves white mark or scratch on streak plate. Shows good cleavage. Cannot be scratched by fingernail, but can be scratched by copper coin.

Color: Colorless, white.

Specific Gravity: 3.0 (medium weight).

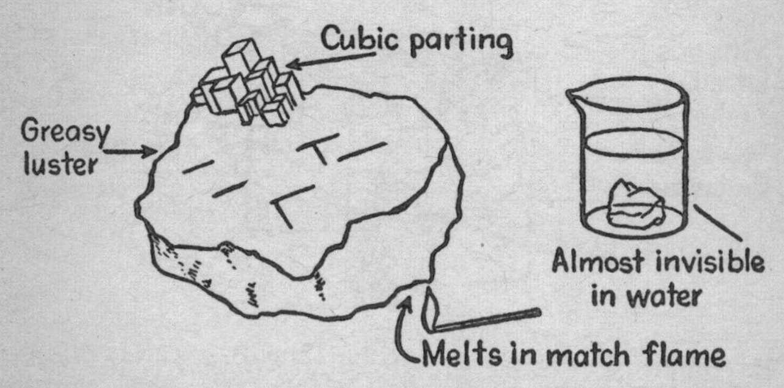

Natural sodium–aluminum fluoride (Na_3AlF_6) is cryolite. The early Norsemen who visited Greenland were astonished to find the Eskimos using as anchors a heavy stone which disappeared when lowered into the sea. Cryolite has the strange property of being almost invisible in water, because it has nearly the same light-bending power as water, and rays of light pass through it in a straight line. Its name means "frost stone," in allusion to its icy appearance. It can be melted in a candle flame. The occurrence of cryolite in Greenland is the more remarkable because the mineral is extremely rare except there; but at Ivigtut in Arksuk Fjord on the west coast it is found in an enormous deposit. Associated with the cryolite are a number of rare fluorine-bearing minerals derived from it, and some common ore minerals. The cryolite is taken to Denmark for processing, and it is used as an insecticide and in the aluminum industry. Very limited amounts have also been found near Miask, Siberia; Sallent, Spain; and Colorado Springs, Colo.

ANHYDRITE

KEYS: Nonmetallic luster. Leaves white mark or scratch on streak plate. Shows good cleavage. Cannot be scratched by fingernail, but can be scratched by copper coin.

Color: White. Specific Gravity: 2.9–3.0 (medium weight).

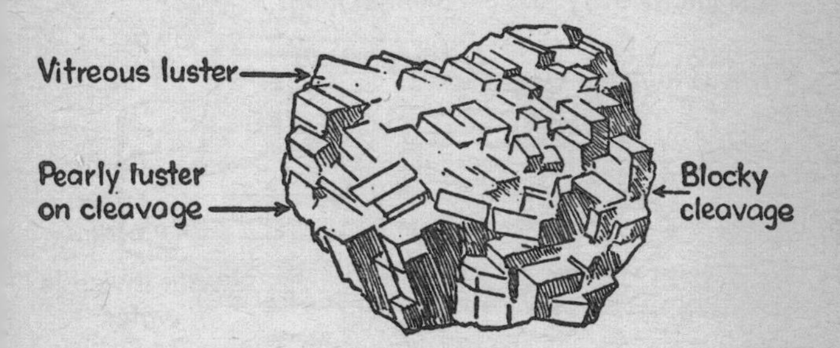

Its composition being calcium sulfate ($CaSO_4$), anhydrite in 1803 received its name because it does not contain water, as does gypsum, which otherwise has the same chemical formula. At Lockport, N.Y., fine blue anhydrite is found in cavities in limestone, and good crystals occur at Stassfurt, Germany. At times anhydrite appears in veins with metallic minerals and in the gas cavities of volcanic rocks. It occurs mostly, however, in large masses, together with rock salt and gypsum, which are likewise deposited by the evaporation of sea water in isolated arms of the ocean. Either anhydrite or gypsum will precipitate from the same solution, according to the temperature of the water, the salt content, and other factors; afterward anhydrite may change into gypsum by adding water, or gypsum may change into anhydrite by losing it. Thick beds of anhydrite are situated near Carlsbad National Park, N.M., and in the adjacent part of Texas. Nova Scotia also contains extensive beds. On Calumet Island, Que., anhydrite has replaced marble of very great geologic age.

KERNITE

KEYS: Nonmetallic luster. Leaves white mark or scratch on streak plate. Shows good cleavage. Cannot be scratched by fingernail, but can be scratched by copper coin.

Color: Colorless, white. **Specific Gravity:** 1.9 (light).

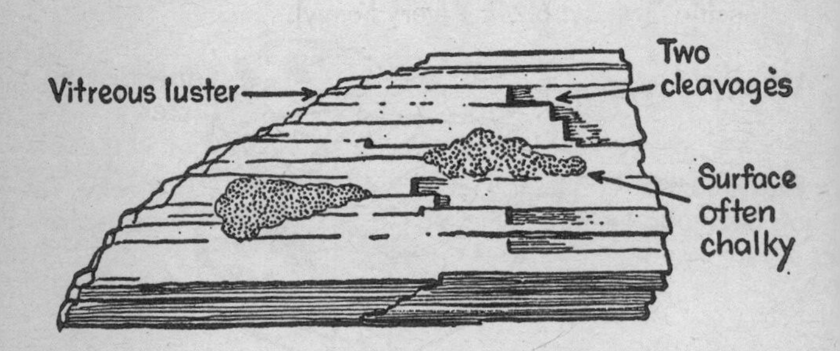

Kernite, a hydrous sodium borate ($Na_2B_4O_7.4H_2O$), is now the chief commercial source of borax. Found in 1926 and named after Kern County, Calif., kernite is not known anywhere else in the world. It occurs near Kramer in the Mojave Desert, in a deposit containing millions of tons. This is the unusual circumstance of a new mineral's being discovered in huge quantities at the start. Kernite is associated with the mineral borax, from which it is believed to have altered by contact with heated rocks that forced themselves up into a buried lake from beneath. The largest single crystal measured 8 feet long and 3 feet wide, and many others are several feet thick. When in contact with other borate minerals, the surface of kernite turns chalky white, but isolated specimens do not behave this way. This coating is tincalconite, named from the ancient Oriental word for borax powder. When placed in water, kernite becomes white and opaque, and then dissolves—slowly in cold water, more rapidly in hot water.

ANGLESITE

KEYS: Nonmetallic luster. Leaves white mark or scratch on streak plate. Shows good cleavage. Cannot be scratched by fingernail, but can be scratched by copper coin.

Color: Colorless, white, gray.

Specific Gravity: 6.2–6.4 (very heavy).

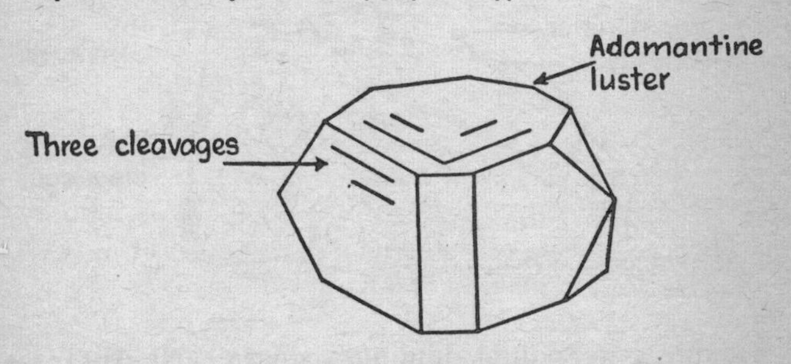

Anglesite, which is lead sulfate ($PbSO_4$), results from the oxidation of galena and is often recognized as a gray band enclosing a core of still-shiny galena, which has been preserved from change. Another lead mineral which forms at the same time is cerussite, which may in turn alter from the anglesite. Interesting to find are cavities in galena lined with crystals of anglesite and sulfur. Though much less important than galena, anglesite is also used as an ore of lead. Large amounts are mined in Mexico and Australia. Crystals are embedded in sulfur at Los Lamentos, Mexico. Superlative crystals have come from Sidi-Amor-ben-Salem, Tunis. The crystals from Monte Poni, Sardinia, are also of exciting quality. The original locality after which the mineral was named is the island of Anglesey in the Irish Sea; but the specimens there were small, although good ones have been obtained from Pary's mine. In the United States the largest are those labeled Wheatley mine, Phoenixville, Pa.

SODALITE

KEYS: Nonmetallic luster. Leaves white mark or scratch on streak plate. Shows good cleavage. Cannot be scratched by copper coin, but can be scratched by knife blade.

Color: Blue. **Specific Gravity:** 2.2–2.4 (medium weight).

Sodalite is a sodium-aluminum silicate ($Na_4Al_3Si_3O_{12}$-Cl). A test for the chlorine it contains is often needed for an accurate identification of this mineral, particularly if it happens not to be blue. The name, adopted in 1811, refers to the sodium that is present. The rich blue color of sodalite makes it a satisfying ornamental stone. Masses of this select quality occur in Canada on Ice River near Kicking Horse Pass, B.C.; Dungannon, Ont.; and several places in Quebec. Litchfield, Me., and Salem, Mass., are American sources. Unusual transparent white crystals are found in the lavas of Mount Vesuvius. Sodalite is a member of the feldspathoid group of minerals, so called because they take the place of feldspar in certain rocks that are deficient in silica. Other feldspathoid minerals that also have a deep-blue color, but are less abundant, are lazurite, noselite, and hauynite—this last one constituting most of the gemmy rock known as lapis lazuli, which is marked by white streaks of calcite and golden flecks of pyrite and was known to antiquity as sapphire.

PYROXENE

KEYS: Nonmetallic luster. Leaves white mark or scratch on streak plate. Shows good cleavage. Cannot be scratched by copper coin, but can be scratched by knife blade.

Color: Black, green, white.

Specific Gravity: 3.2–3.4 (medium weight).

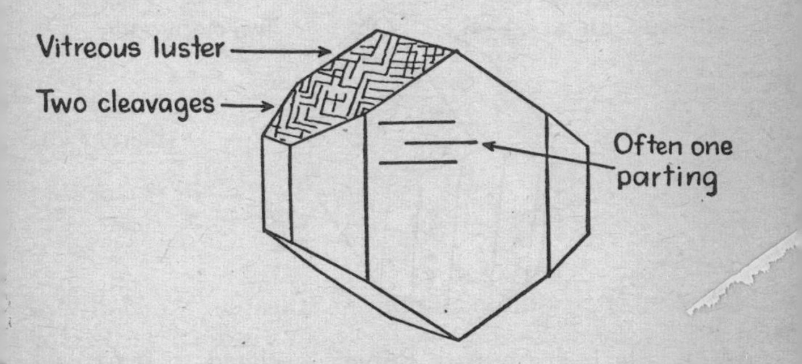

Pyroxene is one of the most important groups of minerals, the essential constituent of many rocks formed at high temperatures. The members of the group are all silicates but vary in composition considerably among themselves. Jadeite, the preferred of the two kinds of true jade, is a pyroxene found mainly in Upper Burma. Spodumene is remarkable because of its enormous crystals, some individuals from near Keystone, S.D., measuring 40 feet or more in length and weighing up to 90 tons. A delicate variety of spodumene, cut into lovely pinkish-violet gems, is kunzite, found mostly at Pala, Calif., and in Madagascar. Diopside, another pyroxene, occurs largely in marble, as do the clear crystals at Ala, Italy. Enstatite is common in meteorites, and grades into hypersthene as the percentage of iron increases. Of all the pyroxenes, however, the one by far the likeliest to turn up is augite; hence this is the one illustrated above. Crystals of it are common in the volcanic cinders of the Hawaiian Islands and elsewhere.

AMPHIBOLE

KEYS: Nonmetallic luster. Leaves white mark or scratch on streak plate. Shows good cleavage. Cannot be scratched by copper coin, but can be scratched by knife blade.

Color: Black, green, white.

Specific Gravity: 2.9–3.4 (medium weight).

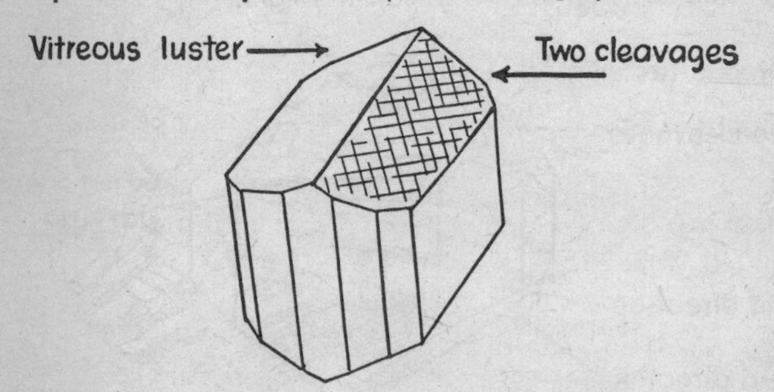

Amphibole is a group of minerals related to pyroxene and of great importance as constituents of rocks. Unlike the pyroxenes they yield some water when sufficiently heated, and their crystals tend toward being six-sided rather than squarish. In composition they are complex silicates, hornblende, the most common of them, having a chemical formula nearly as long as a line of type in this book. Hornblende is taken as the typical amphibole and is illustrated here, but the other minerals of the group have the same oblique cleavage and are thereby distinguished from pyroxene. Arfvedsonite is a sodium-rich amphibole found in large crystals near Julianehaab, Greenland. Glaucophane, occurring in the Coast Ranges of California, has also a high content of sodium but a distinctive blue color. Anthophyllite, named from the Latin word for clove because of its clove-brown color, is one of the simpler amphiboles. White tremolite grades into green actinolite; when either of them is compact and tough, it is called nephrite, which is a true jade.

KYANITE

KEYS: Nonmetallic luster. Leaves white mark or scratch on streak plate. Shows good cleavage. Cannot be scratched by copper coin, but can be scratched by knife blade.

Color: Blue, white.

Specific Gravity: 3.5–3.7 (medium weight).

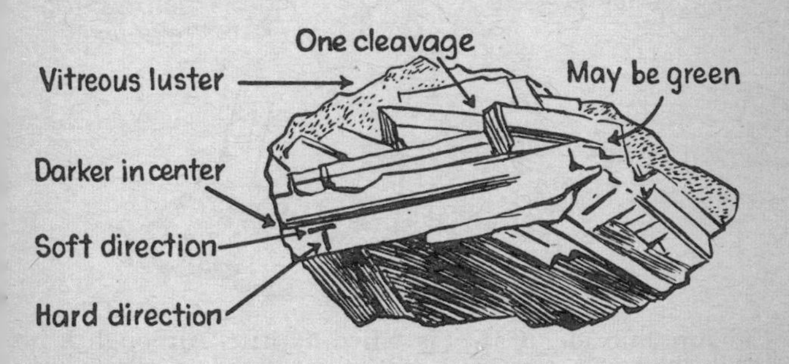

An aluminum silicate (Al_2SiO_5), kyanite has a chemical composition identical with those of andalusite and sillimanite. When heated to the neighborhood of 1000°C., it becomes a substance called mullite, which furnishes a heat-defying and shock-resisting porcelain used for spark plugs and chemical ware. The variable hardness of kyanite, whereby it can be scratched by a knife along the "grain" but resists being scratched in the perpendicular direction, is a unique characteristic. Its attractive bicolored, blade-shaped crystals are the principal reason, however, for its strong appeal to the mineral collector. The name kyanite refers to its blue color, which is often in spots or streaks. Beautiful combinations of kyanite and staurolite occur at Monte Campione, Switzerland. The clear green crystals from Yancey County, N. C., are different but none the less lovely. The chief commercial deposits are at Lapsa Bura, India, and in Kenya, the British colony in East Africa.

FLUORITE

KEYS: **Nonmetallic luster. Leaves white mark or scratch on streak plate. Shows good cleavage. Cannot be scratched by copper coin, but can be scratched by knife blade.**

Color: Purple, light-green, yellow.

Specific Gravity: 3.2 (medium weight).

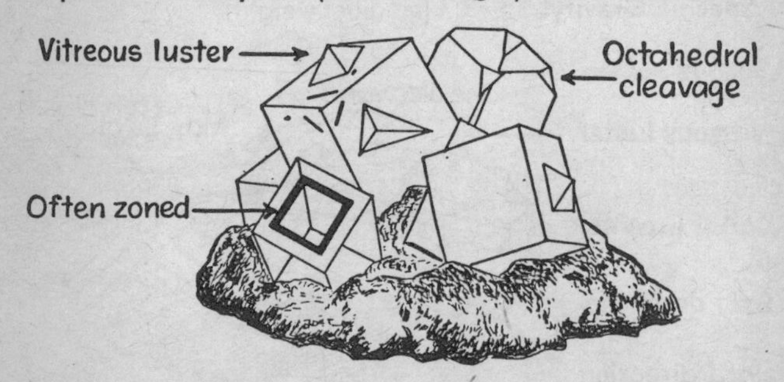

Calcium fluoride (CaF_2) is called fluorite. Although it is the mineral that gave its name to fluorescence, this interesting effect is weakly shown. Superb crystal groups come from noted English localities, including Castleton in Derbyshire and Cleator Moor in Cumberland. From Derbyshire, also, came the prized blue john, a banded blue variety which was carved into vases. Large sea-green cubes are found at Muscalonge Lake, N.Y. Pretty brown crystals come from Clay Center, Ohio. The gorgeous purple specimens from near Rosiclare, Ill., are indeed outstanding; some of the large, clear crystals look almost like stained-glass church windows when the sun gleams through. Clear, colorless crystals come from Modoc, Ont. Scarcely any lovely hue—plum, rose, any you prefer—is missing from the colors that fluorite may possess. This mineral received its name from the Latin word meaning "to flow" because it melts at a low temperature; today its main use is as a flux to help melt iron ore when making steel.

RHODONITE

KEYS: Nonmetallic luster. Leaves white mark or scratch on streak plate. Shows good cleavage. Cannot be scratched by copper coin, but can be scratched by knife blade.

Color: Rose-red, pink, brown.

Specific Gravity: 3.4–3.7 (medium weight).

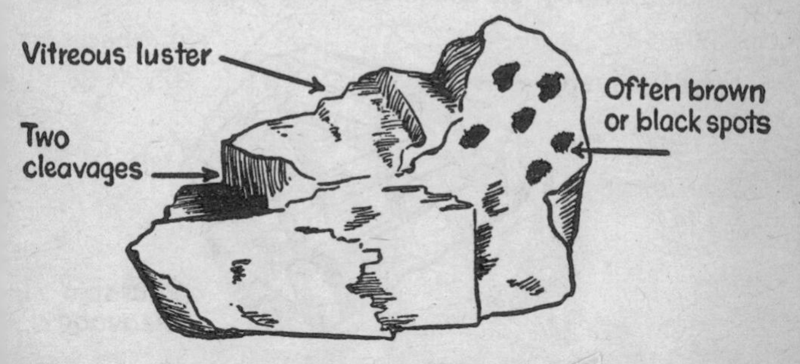

Given its name from the Greek word for a rose, on account of its rose-pink color, rhodonite is manganese silicate ($MnSiO_3$). Large quantities of it have been mined near Sverdlovsk (formerly Ekaterinburg) in the Ural Mountains and were extensively used in old Russia as an ornamental stone. Among the best-known sources of rhodonite crystals are Franklin, N.J.; Långban, Sweden; and Broken Hill, New South Wales. The New Jersey variety contains zinc and is also called fowlerite. The black coating on the surface of typical specimens is the result of an external alteration to manganese oxide, which may extend along cracks within the mineral. Rhodonite is a minor ore of manganese, generally when it is associated with other minerals of greater economic importance. Rhodonite looks like pink feldspar, which is lighter in weight; and somewhat like rhodochrosite, which is a carbonate and has a different cleavage. It also resembles the pyroxene minerals in crystallization but is no longer regarded as belonging to the same group.

RHODOCHROSITE

KEYS: Nonmetallic luster. Leaves white mark or scratch on streak plate. Shows good cleavage. Cannot be scratched by copper coin, but can be scratched by knife blade.

Color: Rose-red, pink.

Specific Gravity: 3.3–3.6 (medium weight).

Manganese carbonate ($MgCO_3$) is rhodochrosite, so named because of its lovely rose-red color. Like other carbonate minerals it fizzes when a drop of acid is applied, and finally dissolves completely in warm acid. Rhodochrosite is an important ore of manganese at Butte, Mont., but has only a little use elsewhere. Unrivaled crystals, almost ruby-red in color and clarity, have come from old silver mines in central Colorado. Rhodochrosite is a common mineral in the silver mines at Austin, Nev. It is also found elsewhere in the United States, especially at Branchville, Conn., and Franklin, N.J. In Europe the leading localities include Kapnik, Rumania, and Freiberg, Germany, where it occurs in silver veins. Rhodochrosite is softer than rhodonite, which likewise has a pink color. A black or brown surface covering indicates chemical alteration. Apart from its color, it has the appearance of calcite, dolomite, siderite, and smithsonite, which are all carbonate minerals belonging to the same group and having the same rhombohedral cleavage.

SIDERITE

KEYS: Nonmetallic luster. Leaves white mark or scratch on streak plate. Shows good cleavage. Cannot be scratched by copper coin, but can be scratched by knife blade.

Color: Brown. **Specific Gravity:** 3.8–3.9 (heavy).

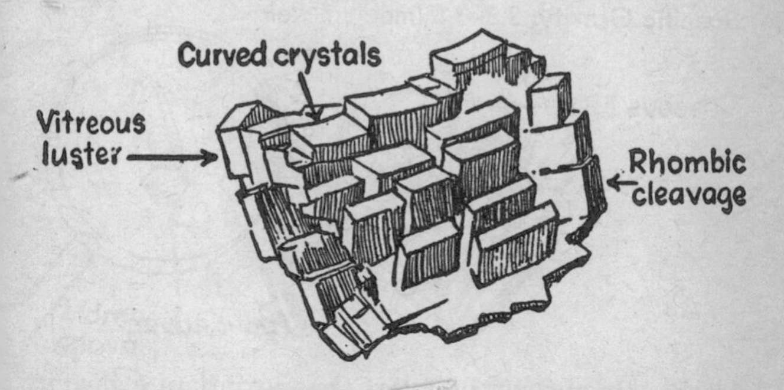

Iron carbonate ($FeCO_3$) is known as siderite from the Greek word meaning iron. Spathic iron and chalybite are miners' names for this mineral. The tendency of siderite crystals to seem curved is worth noting, for this property is restricted to only a few minerals, including dolomite. The specimens from many of the mines in Cornwall, England, are exceptionally good; the six-sided plates from Wheal Maudlin are evenly developed and highly attractive. Good crystals also occur at Brosso, Italy, and Allevard, France. A deposit of economic value is situated at Styria, Austria, and siderite is also mined in Great Britain, but the proportion of iron is too low for it to be used very much in most countries, where better ores are available. Veins of lead and silver ores in Idaho contain much siderite. Impure siderite, mixed with clay and known as clay ironstone, is distributed through the coal beds that extend from Pennsylvania to Ohio. Siderite alters readily to other minerals, especially goethite, which retain the original siderite shape.

STRONTIANITE

KEYS: Nonmetallic luster. Leaves white mark or scratch on streak plate. Shows good cleavage. Cannot be scratched by copper coin, but can be scratched by knife blade.

Color: White. **Specific Gravity:** 3.7 (medium weight).

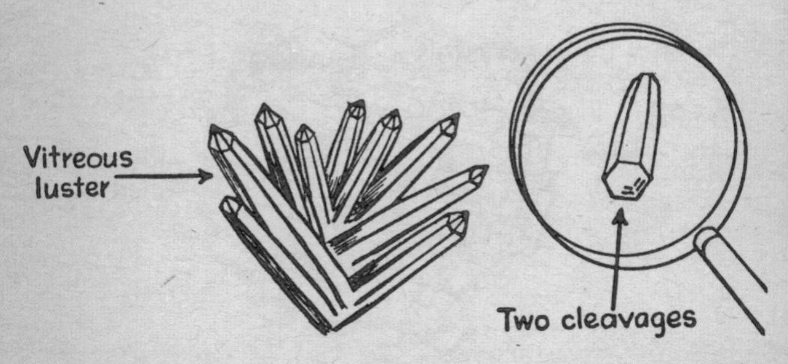

As carbonate of strontium ($SrCO_3$), strontianite gave its name in 1790 to the chemical element of which it is one source of supply. Like other carbonate minerals it fizzes in acid. The original locality was Strontian, Scotland, the town after which it received its name. The biggest deposits are situated in Germany at Drensteinfurt, Ascheberg, and Ahlen, and these have yielded fine crystals. Well-proportioned crystals occur in the lead mines at Pateley Bridge, England; strontianite is sometimes associated in this way with metals in veins, more especially in Germany and also in Mexico. Nests and spheres of crystals are found at Schoharie, N.Y. Good-sized deposits occur in the Strontium Hills, north of Barstow, Calif., and the mineral comes from other places in that state. In Texas strontianite occurs on Mount Bonnell (near Austin) and in the cap rock that overlies the salt domes along the Gulf of Mexico. In Washington it is collected near La Conner. Strontianite resembles aragonite in its over-all nature, except that it is much less likely to form in distinct crystals.

SMITHSONITE

KEYS: Nonmetallic luster. Leaves white mark or scratch on streak plate. Shows good cleavage. Cannot be scratched by copper coin, but can be scratched by knife blade.

Color: White, brown, green. **Specific Gravity:** 4.4 (heavy).

Smithsonite, zinc carbonate ($ZnCO_3$), is one of the most variable of all minerals in appearance. Some of its varieties are so disguised that they do not look a bit like smithsonite. Take, for example, the so-called dry-bone ore, which, of course, resembles a dried bone; it is mined in the zinc district of Wisconsin-Illinois-Iowa. Another curious variety is turkey-fat ore, yellow in color because it contains cadmium; stalactites of it, with concentric banding, come from Sardinia. White spheres of smithsonite are found in the mines in the province of Santander, Spain. Probably the most appealing smithsonite is a rich green, solid enough for gem cutting, and coming from Kelly, N.M. Several of the smithsonite colors are associated together at Laurium, Greece. Matchless crystals have come from Rhodesia. Large deposits of smithsonite occur in Germany. This mineral was named in 1832 in honor of the Englishman James Smithson (1765–1829), who founded the Smithsonian Institution in Washington; in England it used to be called calamine.

STILBITE

KEYS: Nonmetallic luster. Leaves white mark or scratch on streak plate. Shows good cleavage. Cannot be scratched by copper coin, but can be scratched by knife blade.

Color: White. **Specific Gravity:** 2.1–2.2 (light).

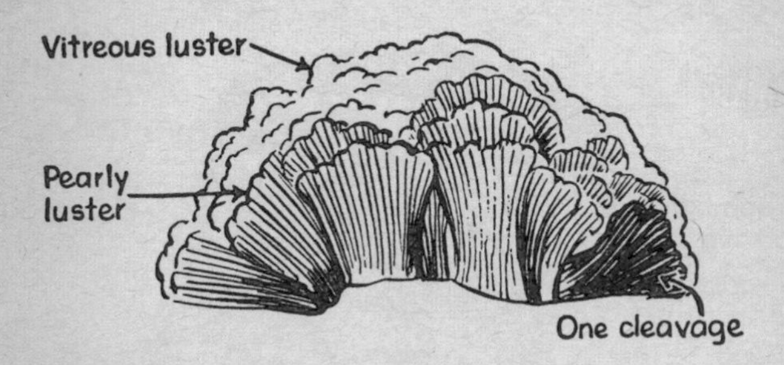

An aluminum silicate with a complex formula, stilbite is one of the numerous attractive members of the zeolite family, all of which are characterized by the fact that they give off water in copious amounts at a steady rate when they are heated. Its distinctive form is that of sheaflike groups of crystals, which spread out at both ends. Single, untwinned crystals are not known, but twins of stilbite often resemble a tabular crystal—a common type of occurrence. The name stilbite comes from the Greek word for luster, in reference to the pearly luster on the faces that correspond to the cleavage surfaces. Stilbite occurs with other zeolites in cavities in lava rocks which have cooled upon or near the surface of the earth. Fine-quality specimens of stilbite are numerous in northern New Jersey, in Nova Scotia, and at Guanajuato, Mexico. Large salmon-colored tabular crystals are found at Poona, India. Peerless white crystals of the same shape line cavities in the basalt of the Faeroe Islands, in the North Atlantic Ocean. The desirable crystals from Kilpatrick, Scotland, are red.

HEMIMORPHITE

KEYS: Nonmetallic luster. Leaves white mark or scratch on streak plate. Shows good cleavage. Cannot be scratched by copper coin, but can be scratched by knife blade.

Color: Colorless, white.

Specific Gravity: 3.4–3.5 (medium weight).

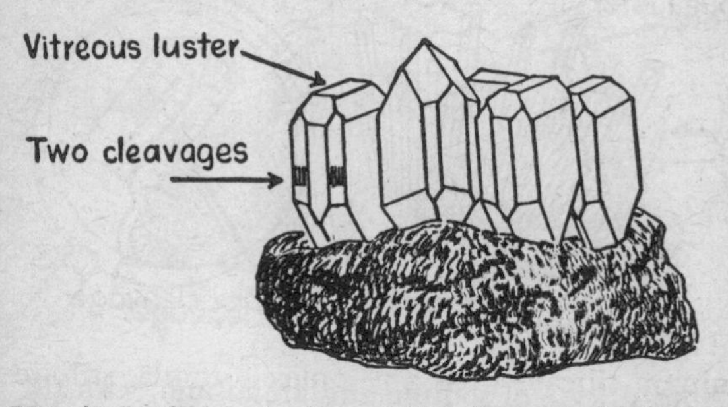

Hemimorphite, a hydrous silicate of zinc [$Zn_4Si_2O_7(OH)_2 \cdot H_2O$], has been the innocent victim of a confusion in names which has also involved other zinc minerals. Most mining people still call it calamine, but the scientific name of hemimorphite was suggested to apply solely to this one mineral. It refers to the fact that the crystals are developed in halves, the opposite ends being different from each other. This sometimes produces a peculiar effect of unbalance and lack of symmetry as the sheaflike groups are examined closely, and the pointed ends of the individual crystals are seen to be attached to the rock. The glossy crystals from the old zinc mines at Aachen, Germany, are well known. Truly splendid crystals have come from Djebel Guergour, Algeria. Elkhorn, Mont., and Granby, Mo., are American localities for fine specimens. Hemimorphite serves as a significant ore of zinc. It is a secondary mineral, originating from the action of silica-bearing water upon other zinc minerals. Its closest companion is smithsonite.

NATROLITE

KEYS: Nonmetallic luster. Leaves white mark or scratch on streak plate. Shows good cleavage. Cannot be scratched by copper coin, but can be scratched by knife blade.

Color: Colorless, white. **Specific Gravity:** 2.2–2.3 (light).

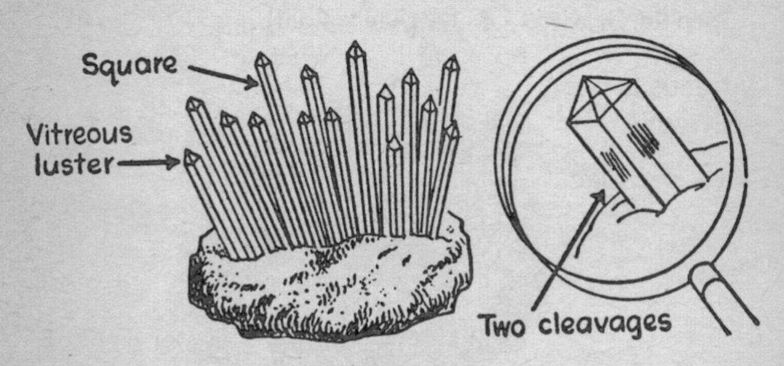

This hydrous silicate of sodium and aluminum, with the formula $Na_2Al_2Si_3O_{10} \cdot 2H_2O$, is one of the zeolite minerals, with their property of becoming dehydrated at a constant rate upon being heated. Its name alludes to its sodium content. As one of the last minerals to solidify, natrolite incrusts the surface of cracks and cavities in volcanic rocks, along with other zeolites and calcite. The radiating groups of slender crystals are so typical that natrolite has been called needle zeolite. It fuses more easily than aragonite, for which it might be taken. Among the largest of all known specimens are the dazzling white crystals that used to come from Puy de Marman, France. Large crystals come from British Columbia's Ice Valley, and needles several inches long are known at Bishopton, Scotland. Fine specimens occur in the trap quarries at Weehawken and other towns in New Jersey, and in the renowned zeolite-bearing rocks of Nova Scotia. Aussig, Czechoslovakia, is another important locality for natrolite.

COLEMANITE

KEYS: Nonmetallic luster. Leaves white mark or scratch on streak plate. Shows good cleavage. Cannot be scratched by copper coin, but can be scratched by knife blade.

Color: Colorless, white.

Specific Gravity: 2.4 (medium weight).

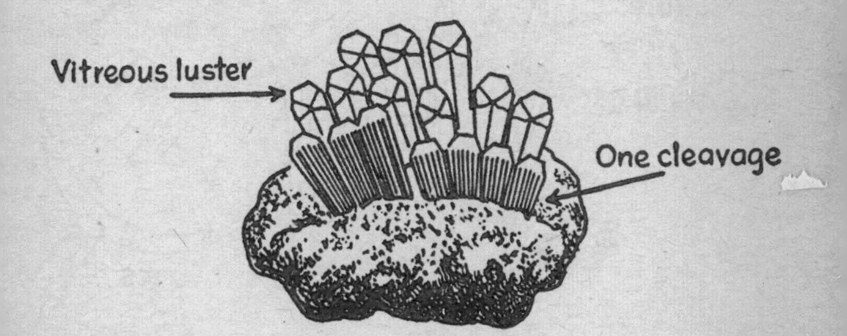

The handsomest of the borate minerals is colemanite, a hydrous calcium borate ($Ca_2B_6O_{11} \cdot 5H_2O$). The brilliant clear crystals, up to several inches in length, often occur as a lining inside porcelainlike chunks of the same mineral. The crystals look rather like calcite but have a brighter luster. Rounded masses, however, are the usual mode of occurrence. First noticed in Death Valley in 1883 and furnishing the main supply of the world's borax at the time of the discovery of kernite in 1926, colemanite is found as a buried lake deposit in a number of counties in southern California and western Nevada. It is believed to be an alteration of ulexite, a mineral sometimes known as cotton-ball borax because it forms in soft, rounded, white masses of loose texture. A little colemanite is found in Siberia and Argentina. A most interesting occurrence is in a fossil egg picked up along the Gila River in Arizona. Colemanite bears the name of a founder of the California borax industry, William T. Coleman, of San Francisco.

APOPHYLLITE

KEYS: Nonmetallic luster. Leaves white mark or scratch on streak plate. Shows good cleavage. Cannot be scratched by copper coin, but can be scratched by knife blade.

Color: Colorless, white.

Specific Gravity: 2.3–2.4 (medium weight).

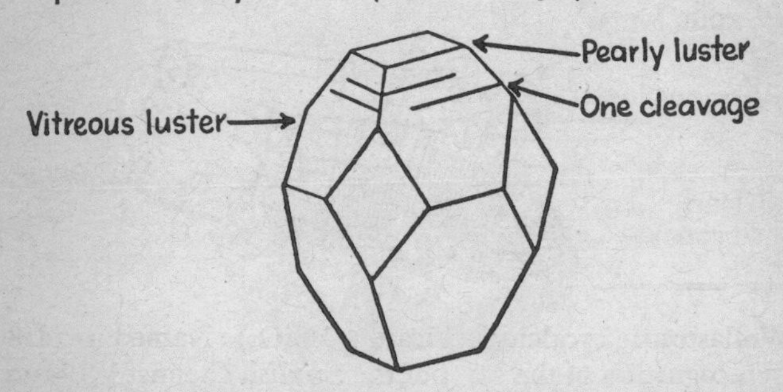

A silicate mineral containing a large amount of water [$Ca_4K(Si_4O_{10})_2F.8H_2O$], apophyllite was named from the fact that it unfolds like a leaf when it is heated. Its whitish-pearly look has been described as like the eye of a boiled fish, and it once bore a much weirder name which meant "fish eye." The natural home of apophyllite is in cavities in basalt and other lava rocks, in many localities throughout the world. It is thus associated with the zeolite minerals, which it resembles in many ways. The largest and most beautiful crystals of this mineral were uncovered during the construction of a railroad at Poona, India. Good-sized crystals stained with bitumin occur in the New Almaden mercury mines in California. Delicate pink specimens are found in the silver veins at Andreasberg in the Harz Mountains, Germany, and appealing crystals of the same tint rest firmly upon amethyst at Guanajuato, Mexico. The volcanic rocks near Paterson, N.J., near Philadelphia, Pa., and in northern Michigan yield apophyllite.

WOLLASTONITE

KEYS: Nonmetallic luster. Leaves white mark or scratch on streak plate. Shows good cleavage. Cannot be scratched by copper coin, but can be scratched by knife blade.

Color: White. **Specific Gravity:** 2.8–2.9 (medium weight).

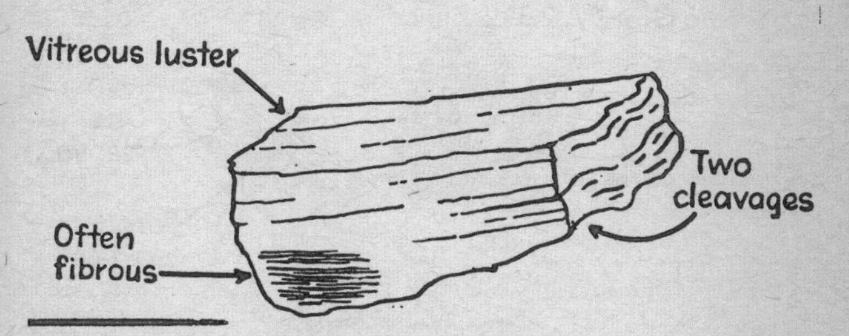

Wollastonite is calcium silicate ($CaSiO_3$). Named in 1818 in recognition of the work of the English chemist William Hyde Wollaston (1766-1828), its name is easy to remember when you know that it is pronounced to rhyme with "wool" and that this mineral is used industrially as raw material in the making of rock wool for insulation. Wollastonite is one of the interesting minerals referred to as geologic thermometers because they indicate the temperature at which they must have originated within the rocky crust of the earth. Wherever wollastonite is found, the temperature there is known to have been below about 1125°C., because above that point a different kind of calcium silicate is formed instead. Large white crystals of wollastonite are common at Diana, N.Y. Showy crystals line some of the cavities in blocks thrown out by the volcanic explosions of Mount Vesuvius. Crestmore, Calif., is a noted locality for large amounts of wollastonite, as well as for a diversity of unusual minerals scarcely equaled anywhere else. A compact variety of wollastonite is found in Isle Royale National Park, Mich.

EPIDOTE

KEYS: Nonmetallic luster. Leaves white mark or scratch on streak plate. Shows good cleavage. Can scratch glass and be scratched by quartz.

Color: Yellowish-green, blackish-green.

Specific Gravity: 3.3–3.5 (medium weight).

Epidote, a hydrous silicate mineral [$Ca_2 (Al,Fe)_3 (SiO_4)_3$-OH], occurs in many localities. When found in good crystals, it is a most attractive mineral, in spite of its typical, rather monotonous yellowish-green color, which is often described as pistachio-green and is a fairly distinctive property for identifying epidote. This color grades into brownish-green, gray, and black, though it may be red or even disappear entirely in the very rare colorless specimens from remote Tierra del Fuego at the tip of South America. Magnificent dark-green crystals, transparent and lustrous, are present in rock cavities near Salzburg, Austria. On Prince of Wales Island, Alaska, are found dark crystals of extraordinary size and beauty, which have dominated the market in recent years. Other excellent crystals carry labels reading Haddam, Conn., and Bourg d'Oisans, France. Those from the Zillerthal, Austria, are sometimes rose-red in color. Epidote is associated with native copper in northern Michigan, as a product of alteration from other minerals. Clear epidote, when cut into gems, is dark-green in one direction and brown in another.

FELDSPAR

KEYS: Nonmetallic luster. Leaves white mark or scratch on streak plate. Shows good cleavage. Can scratch glass and be scratched by quartz.

Color: White, pink.

Specific Gravity: 2.6–2.8 (medium weight).

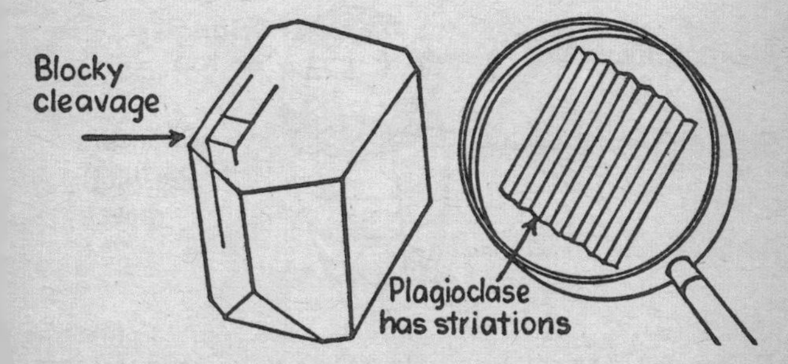

Feldspar is a group of minerals of the greatest scientific importance. All members of the group are aluminum silicates and have varying amounts of other chemical elements, especially potassium, sodium, and calcium. The feldspars resemble one another so closely that they usually have to be identified with a microscope. It is customary to divide them into two main types—plagioclase and potash feldspar. Plagioclase is recognized by the presence of a series of closely spaced straight lines on the cleavage surface. This type has been arbitrarily divided into six members, of which albite and labradorite are the best known, but only labradorite can be named at sight, owing to its dark color and radiant blue sheen which spreads across the surface as the specimen is turned. Of the other type, called potash feldspar, the chief members are orthoclase and microcline. If the specimen is a clear crystal, it is orthoclase; if green, it is sure to be microcline—the attractive variety called amazonstone, most abundant in the Pikes Peak region of Colorado. The feldspars are the most common of all minerals.

CORUNDUM

KEYS: Nonmetallic luster. Leaves white mark or scratch on streak plate. Shows good cleavage. Cannot be scratched by quartz.

Color: Bluish-gray, brown, pink, blue.

Specific Gravity: 4.0 (heavy).

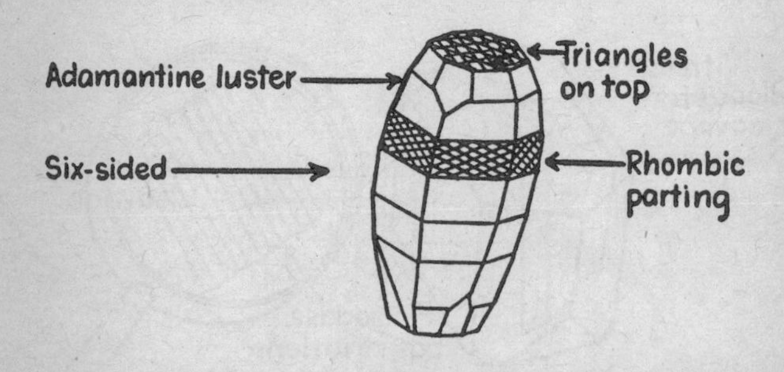

Corundum is aluminum oxide (Al_2O_3). Its hardness, surpassing that of all other minerals except diamond, enables it to serve as an abrasive, but its real value lies in the beauty of its colors. Few of us would think that the fiery red of ruby and the serene blue of sapphire belong to the same mineral, unless we were to see the original crystals. Sapphires of yellow, green, purple, and other colors are also corundum. The Orient—Ceylon, Kashmir, Burma—is the favored home of all these gems, but they are found in Siam, in Australia, and elsewhere as well. A prized variation of corundum is a star ruby or star sapphire. Large rough crystals of ordinary corundum come from Steinkopf, South Africa, and from the districts of Zoutpansberg and Pietersburg, Transvaal—a jumbo-sized specimen from Pietersburg weighed 335 pounds. Corundum is abundant in parts of North Carolina, South Carolina, and Georgia, and in Ontario, Canada. When it is intimately mixed with magnetite, the natural product is called emery, a useful grinding material coming chiefly from Turkey and islands off the coast of Greece.

TOPAZ

KEYS: Nonmetallic luster. Leaves white mark or scratch on streak plate. Shows good cleavage. Cannot be scratched by quartz.

Color: Colorless, yellow, blue.

Specific Gravity: 3.4–3.6 (medium weight).

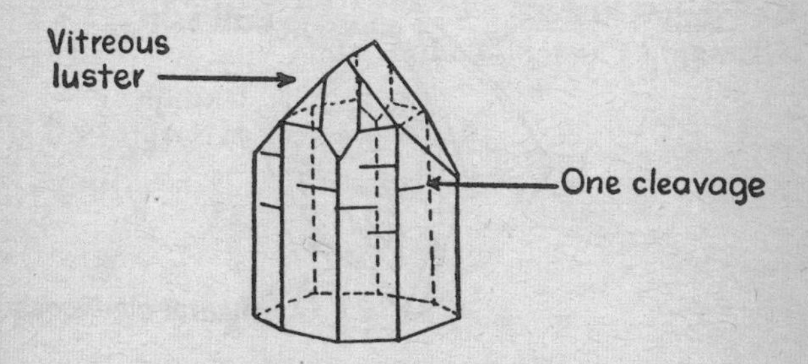

Topaz, an aluminum silicate with fluorine [Al_2SiO_4 (F,-OH)$_2$], constitutes one of the major gem minerals. Although usually thought of as a yellow stone, topaz is more apt to occur in some other color, of which blue and pink are certainly the loveliest. Many crystals fade upon exposure to much sunlight, and others can be altered by heat to produce hues that are more salable. Enormous crystals, colorless and blue, and weighing hundreds of pounds each, have come from the state of Minas Gerais, Brazil, in late years. Charming peach-colored crystals, which soon lose all traces of color in the bright desert sun, can be obtained in almost unlimited numbers in the Thomas Range of western Utah. Large blue crystals come from cavities on the steep slopes of Pikes Peak, Colo. Those from Mason County, Tex., are similarly fine. The deep-wine crystals from south of Nerchinsk, Siberia, make outstanding specimens. The word Topazion, from which topaz is derived, is the name of an island in the Red Sea between Egypt and Arabia, but previously was applied to a different mineral.

DIAMOND

KEYS: Nonmetallic luster. Leaves white mark or scratch on streak plate. Shows good cleavage. Cannot be scratched by quartz.

Color: Colorless, white, gray.

Specific Gravity: 3.4 (medium weight).

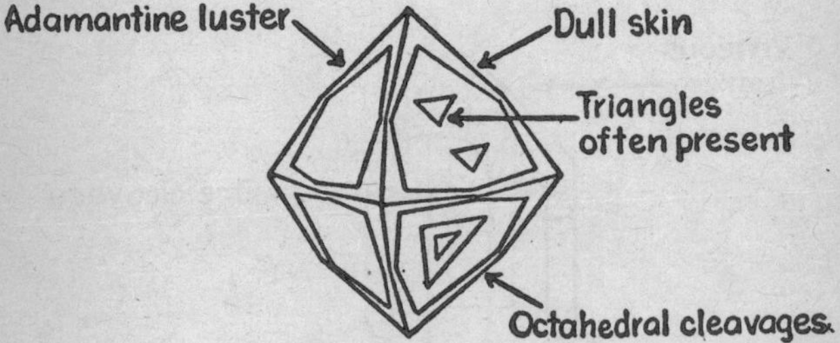

Adamantine luster
Dull skin
Triangles often present
Octahedral cleavages

Pure carbon in composition (C), diamond is the hardest of all known substances, the most popular of all gems, and scientifically the most remarkable of all minerals. Industrial diamonds are unexcelled for their ability to cut anything from granite rock to other diamonds. The word diamond comes from the Greek language and means invincible, in reference to this extraordinary power. With their sensitive cleavage, however, gem diamonds cannot be subjected to sudden blows, in spite of their resistance to scratching—this fact is the basis for the convenient method used to cleave diamond crystals in order to remove flaws and prepare the stones for faceting. India was long the principal source of diamond and furnished most of the famous stones of history. In the eighteenth century it was replaced by Brazil as the leading producer, a position assumed by South Africa in about 1870. The Belgian Congo is today the chief supplier of industrial diamond. A considerable yield of diamond has come from Pike County, Ark., in currently unproductive fields.

SULFUR

KEYS: Nonmetallic luster. Leaves white mark or scratch on streak plate. Does not show good cleavage. Can be scratched by fingernail.

Color: Yellow. **Fracture:** Even.

Specific Gravity: 2.1 (light).

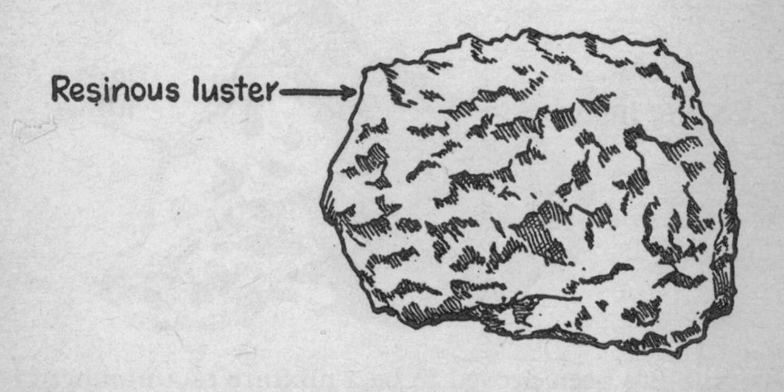

Known to the ancients as brimstone, native sulfur (S) is a mineral of widespread occurrence. To the mineral collector, any of the bright yellow masses are worth having, but the crystals themselves are indeed intriguing. When they are held close to the ear, they can be heard to crackle, on account of the warmth of your hand, because the outer layers expand away from the still-cool interior. Obviously a crystal of sulfur should be handled carefully. The large crystals from Girgenti, Sicily, and nearby are the most beautiful known. Good crystals are found with asphalt at Perticara, Italy. Attractive porous specimens come from Sulphur, Nev. The vast deposits of Louisiana and Texas, which lie above the so-called salt domes and are "mined" by melting the sulfur with superheated steam, furnish most of the world's needs. Rocks in the vicinity of practically every active volcano are coated with sulfur. Orpiment may resemble sulfur, but it has a pronounced cleavage. Sulfur burns easily with a bluish flame, giving off the pungent odor of sulfur dioxide.

BAUXITE

KEYS: Nonmetallic luster. Leaves white mark or scratch on streak plate. Does not show good cleavage. Can be scratched by fingernail.

Color: White, gray, brown. **Fracture:** Uneven.

Specific Gravity: 2.0–2.6 (medium weight).

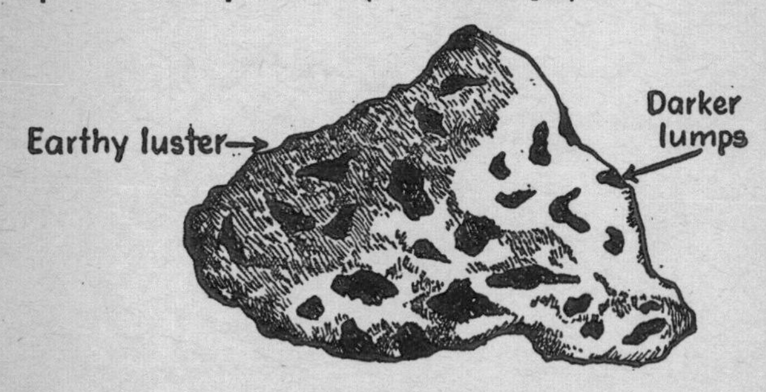

Bauxite has been proved to be a mixture of a number of water-containing aluminum oxide minerals, and not a single mineral as was formerly believed. The constituents are shown by X rays to be mostly gibbsite, boehmite, and diaspore. Still, the name has come into such general use for a highly important commercial substance, and bauxite is usually so uniformly easy to recognize, that we are accustomed to regard it as a mineral instead of a rocklike mixture. The nobby structure is almost always present, the rounded grains varying in size and color; iron is the staining matter. Bauxite originates from the weathering of aluminum-bearing rocks in a warm climate. First discovered at Les Baux, France, it is produced in enormous quantities in Dutch Guiana, British Guiana, and Arkansas and in the Mediterranean countries of Southern Europe. Whether you prefer to think of bauxite as a mineral or a rock, its significance cannot be denied. From it comes most of our supply of the light, strong, conductive, and resistant wonder metal of the twentieth century—aluminum.

KAOLINITE

KEYS: Nonmetallic luster. Leaves white mark or scratch on streak plate. Does not show good cleavage. Can be scratched by fingernail.

Color: White. **Fracture:** Earthy.

Specific Gravity: 2.6 (medium weight).

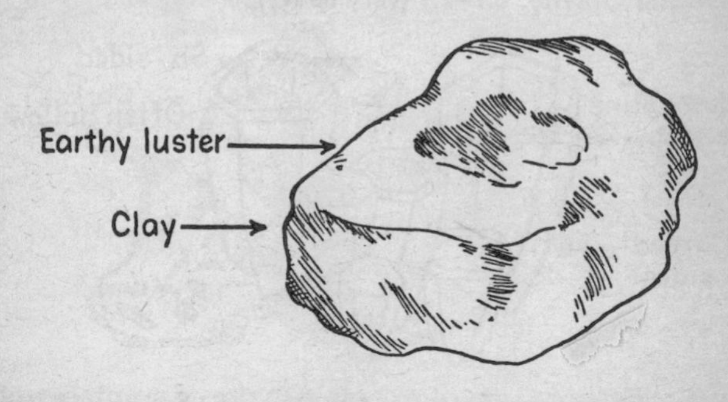

The best known of the many clay minerals, kaolinite , like the rest of them, a hydrous aluminum silicate [$Al_2Si_2O_5(OH)_4$]. Other species of clay minerals related to kaolinite include dickite, nacrite, beidellite, montmorillonite, and halloysite. An impure mixture of various of these minerals—often called simply kaolin—is common clay, which is the basis of the porcelain, pottery, and china industries. Both names are a corruption of the Chinese name for a hill near Juachu Fa, where the fine-quality clay was produced from which china was made. Kaolinite is formed by the weathering of rocks that contain a large proportion of feldspar; until the alteration is complete, particles of feldspar are found mixed in the soil as it is being created. The thin crystal plates of kaolinite are seldom large enough to be seen without a microscope; they tend to curl up like dry mud. Masses of kaolinite can often be recognized by a peculiar earthy odor when they are breathed upon, and they become plastic when moistened, adhering slightly to the tongue.

VANADINITE

KEYS: Nonmetallic luster. Leaves white mark or scratch on streak plate. Does not show good cleavage. Cannot be scratched by fingernail, but can be scratched by copper coin.

Color: Orange. **Fracture:** Uneven.

Specific Gravity: 6.7–7.1 (very heavy).

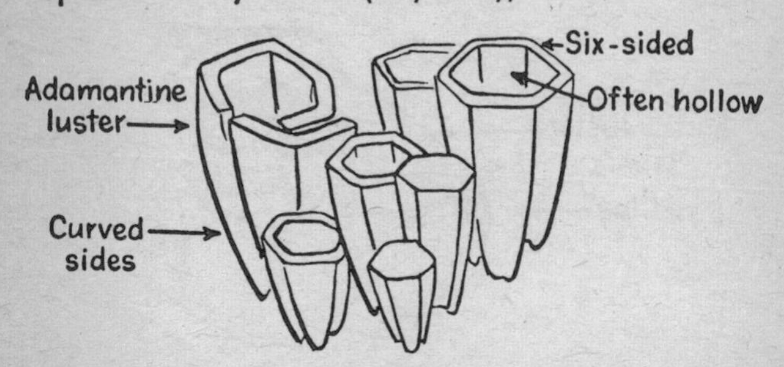

In composition a vanadate of lead and chlorine ($Pb_5Cl(VO_4)_3$], vanadinite is an ore of both vanadium and lead. It occurs with other lead minerals, though never in quantity. The most interesting feature of this mineral is its curious crystals. Often they grow in barrel-shaped forms, hollow inside. When straight, they have smooth faces and sharp edges and resemble battlements of a six-sided castle. They look a good deal like crystals of pyromorphite and mimetite, unless their color happens to be quite reddish. Arsenic is a frequent impurity; as it increases, vanadinite becomes the light-yellow variety formerly called endlichite. Lustrous yellow and red crystals of vanadinite have been found in Arizona and New Mexico. Those from the Old Yuma mine in Pima County and the Red Cloud mine in Yuma County, both in Arizona, are truly thrilling to see. Zimapán, Mexico, was the first known locality. Large crystals have come from Djebel Mahseur, Morocco, and fine ones also from Grootfontein, South-West Africa.

SERPENTINE

KEYS: Nonmetallic luster. Leaves white mark or scratch on streak plate. Does not show good cleavage. Cannot be scratched by fingernail, but can be scratched by copper coin.

Color: Green. **Fracture:** Uneven.

Specific Gravity: 2.5–2.8 (medium weight).

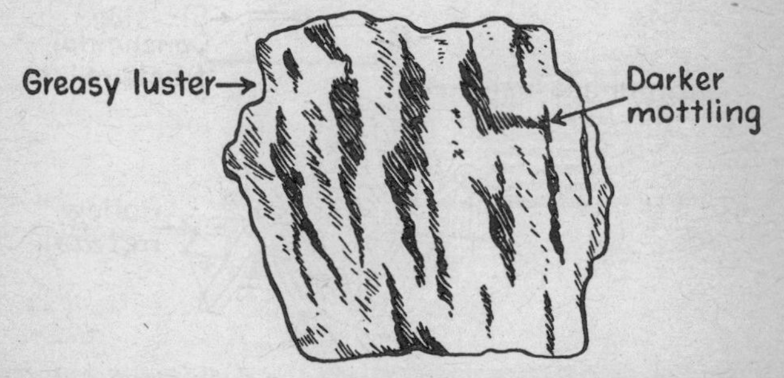

Serpentine, hydrous magnesium silicate [$Mg_3Si_2O_5(OH)_4$], owes its name to the snakelike pattern of the variegated patches of darker and lighter color that are so typical of it. This mineral may be either platy or fibrous. The platy type is termed antigorite. When fibrous, the variety is called chrysotile, which may have the fibers so well developed as to become true asbestos, although this is not the only asbestos mineral. Thetford, Que., is the asbestos-mining capital of the world. The Canadian deposits extend across the border into New York and Vermont. Among other places, some is even found in the Grand Canyon. Crystals of serpentine are completely unknown, except when they have resulted from the alteration of some older mineral, as, for instance, at the Tilly Foster mine, near Brewster, N.Y. Masses of serpentine have long been used for decorative purposes and as a building stone; a mixture with white carbonate minerals is called verd antique. Serpentine looks like green marble, which, in fact, is often almost solid serpentine.

CERUSSITE

KEYS: Nonmetallic luster. Leaves white mark or scratch on streak plate. Does not show good cleavage. Cannot be scratched by fingernail, but can be scratched by copper coin.

Color: White, gray. **Fracture:** Conchoidal.

Specific Gravity: 6.4–6.6 (very heavy).

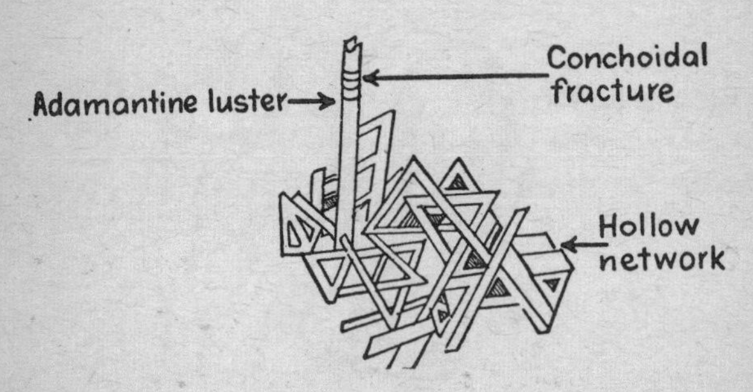

A lead carbonate ($PbCO_3$), cerussite is an important ore of lead, and sometimes it contains silver which was present in the original mineral, galena, from which it alters. Anglesite, the lead sulfate, sometimes represents an intermediate stage. The Friedrichssegen mine near Ems, Germany, gave us the first known specimens of cerussite. Large crystals of several colors, even including green, have been found at Nerchinsk, Siberia. Groups of crystals shaped like arrowheads come from Broken Hill, New South Wales. Incomparable specimens occur at Tsumeb, South-West Africa. Heart-shaped twins of large size have been collected in Doña Ana County, N.M. Cerussite is abundant at Leadville, Colo., and in the Coeur d'Alene district, Idaho. Its name is derived from the Latin word meaning white lead, an artificial product known by 400 B.C. or earlier; natural cerussite is sometimes called white lead ore. As can be said of all carbonate minerals, cerussite fizzes in acid, but satisfactory results can be had only with nitric acid, which is required to dissolve it.

BORAX

KEYS: Nonmetallic luster. Leaves white mark or scratch on streak plate. Does not show good cleavage. Cannot be scratched by fingernail, but can be scratched by copper coin.

Color: White, colorless. **Fracture:** Even.

Specific Gravity: 1.7 (light).

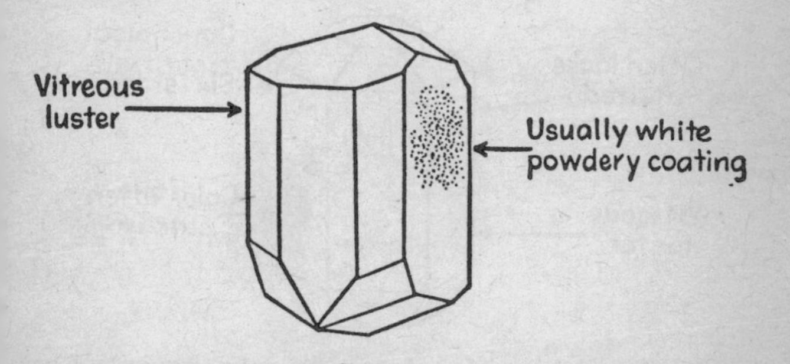

A hydrous sodium borate ($Na_2B_4O_7.10H_2O$), borax is a mineral having an old Arabic name. In 1856 it had been discovered at Borax Lake, Calif., and large crystals were removed from the mud at the bottom of the lake. Later, borax supplied the famous Death Valley twenty-mule teams with the useful product also called borax, which is employed in a hundred industries. From Furnace Creek and Resting Springs they hauled it to the railroad at Mojave. Searles Lake is now the world's largest deposit, one of astonishing volume. Around the borax lakes in California, and similarly in Tibet, the mineral is found to have crystallized on the shore. Some of the American deposits are situated in Nevada. Borax is also obtained from hot springs and brines in northern Italy. The dyed-in-the-wool mineral enthusiast who enjoys licking samples to see them shine would find that borax has a slightly sweetish yet alkaline taste. It is soluble in water and turns to chalky white tincalconite in a dry atmosphere.

APATITE

KEYS: Nonmetallic luster. Leaves white mark or scratch on streak plate. Does not show good cleavage. Cannot be scratched by copper coin, but can be scratched by knife blade.

Color: Green, brown. **Fracture:** Even.

Specific Gravity: 3.1–3.2 (medium weight).

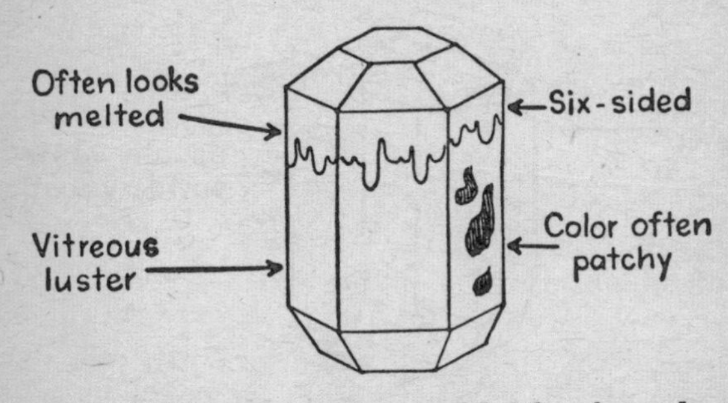

Apatite is calcium phosphate with the formula $Ca_5(PO_4)_3(F,Cl,OH)$. This intriguing name has nothing to do with food but comes from a Greek word meaning "to deceive," because of the resemblance to other minerals. Still, apatite does relate to food, in that it is a constituent of tooth enamel. No other crystals of apatite have ever exceeded in quality those found at Knappenwand in Austria, where they are complexly formed and wonderfully limpid. The largest apatite deposit is situated on the Kola Peninsula in the Soviet Union, where it is mined for fertilizer on account of its phosphate content. Substantial amounts occur along the southern coast of Norway. The clear greenish-yellow crystals from Mexico are appropriately called asparagus stone. The many excellent specimens from New England include purple crystals from Maine and dark-greenish and blue ones from Connecticut. A single crystal weighing over 550 pounds was found in Buckingham Township, Que. The luster of apatite has almost a resinous look.

PYROMORPHITE

KEYS: Nonmetallic luster. Leaves white mark or scratch on streak plate. Does not show good cleavage. Cannot be scratched by copper coin, but can be scratched by knife blade.

Color: Green. **Fracture:** Even.

Specific Gravity: 6.5–7.1 (very heavy).

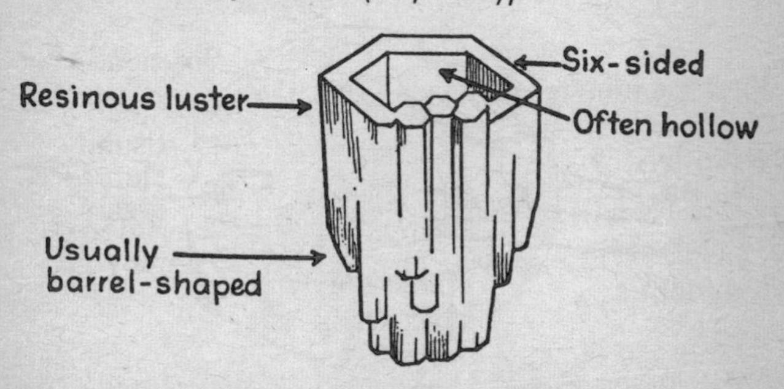

Phosphate of lead and chlorine [$Pb_5Cl(PO_4)_3$], pyromorphite is the most prominent member of a series of minerals which closely resemble one another in composition. With a substitution of arsenic for phosphorus, pyromorphite grades into mimetite; the crystals of both are similar to those of vanadinite, and all these minerals have a fairly wide range of shades besides the most typical colors stated here as their properties. Not only do the crystals of pyromorphite occur in hollow barrel-shaped forms, but they also grow in parallel six-sided tubes which expand upward from a slender point. Some of the finest crystals are the violet and brown ones from Poullaouen and Huelgoat, France. Good specimens have come from Phoenixville, Pa.; Friedrichssegen, Germany; and Horcajo, Spain. Pyromorphite is a lesser ore of lead, and it occurs with other lead minerals in the upper levels of mines. The name is derived from Greek words meaning "fire" and "form," because a melted drop acquires a crystalline shape when it cools.

WILLEMITE

KEYS: Nonmetallic luster. Leaves white mark or scratch on streak plate. Does not show good cleavage. Cannot be scratched by copper coin, but can be scratched by knife blade.

Color: Yellowish-green, brown. **Fracture:** Uneven.

Specific Gravity: 3.9–4.2 (heavy).

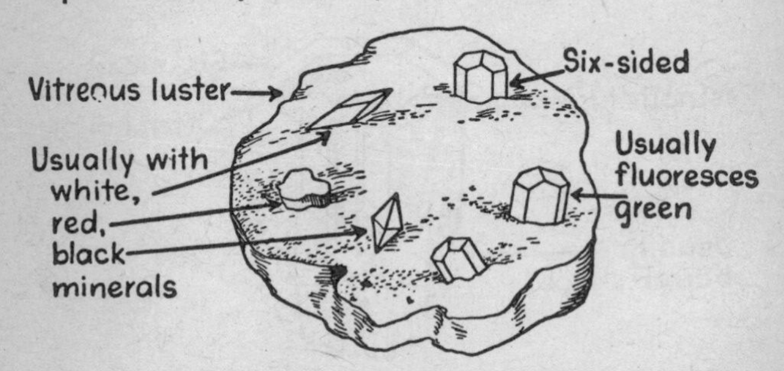

Willemite, zinc silicate (Zn_2SiO_4), is a valuable ore of zinc at Franklin, N.J., where its intimate association with black franklinite, red zincite, and white calcite makes one of the most distinctive combinations of minerals known anywhere. Willemite is white when pure, but its normal colors are yellowish-green and reddish-brown. Slender crystals of a delicate apple-green color, and larger flesh-red crystals containing manganese and known as troostite also occur in New Jersey. The glowing fluorescence of two of the minerals from this extraordinary locality—willemite appearing green and calcite rose-red—constitutes a striking feature of the mineral assemblage. Because of it the willemite can be hand-picked from conveyer belts moving under an ultraviolet light. Willemite has also been found in a few isolated localities in the western part of the United States; at Altenberg, Belgium; Musartut, Greenland; and several places in Africa. It was named after King William I of the Netherlands (Willem Frederik, who reigned from 1815 to 1840).

WULFENITE

KEYS: Nonmetallic luster. Leaves white mark or scratch on streak plate. Does not show good cleavage. Cannot be scratched by copper coin, but can be scratched by knife blade.

Color: Yellow. **Fracture:** Even.

Specific Gravity: 6.3–7.0 (very heavy).

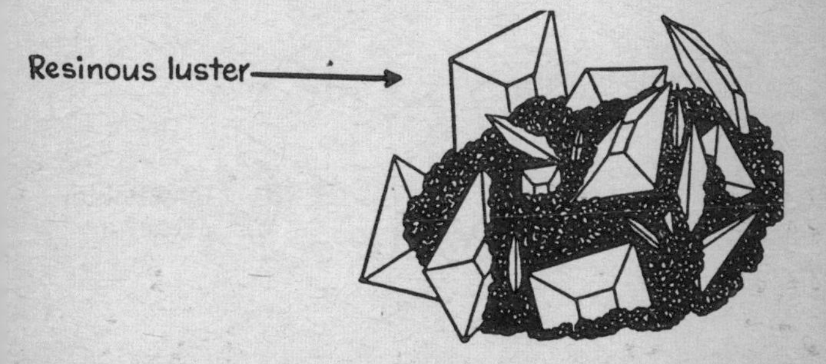

Wulfenite, which is a lead molybdate ($PbMoO_4$), is only to a small extent an ore of molybdenum, but its crystals are some of the loveliest in the mineral kingdom. Some of them, resembling wafers of butterscotch candy, look tasty enough to be eaten. The orange-red tabular crystals from the Hamburg and Red Cloud mines in Yuma County, Ariz., are as much as 2 inches long. Paper-thin crystals of good size come from Box Elder County, Utah; and a dozen other localities in the Western states of Nevada, New Mexico, Arizona, and Utah have produced superior crystals grouped at various angles like the disarranged compartment of a candy box. The color runs from a brilliant red to orange, yellow, and brown and at times may be green or gray. Specimens from the Sierra de los Lamentos, Mexico, grace many a collector's cabinet. This mineral was named in 1845 for Franz Xaver von Wulfen (1728–1805), an Austrian Jesuit priest and mineralogist. It usually results from the decomposition of other minerals. Its associates are vanadinite and pyromorphite.

SPHENE

KEYS: Nonmetallic luster. Leaves white mark or scratch on streak plate. Does not show good cleavage. Cannot be scratched by copper coin, but can be scratched by knife blade.

Color: Greenish-yellow, brown. **Fracture:** Conchoidal.

Specific Gravity: 3.4–3.5 (medium weight).

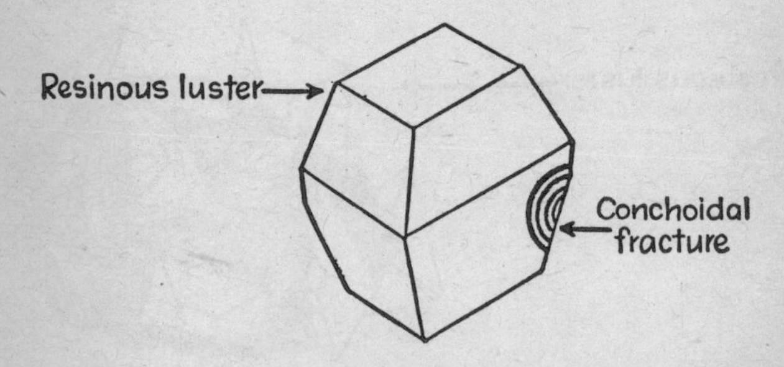

A silicate of calcium and titanium ($CaTiSiO_5$), sphene owes its name to the wedge-shaped crystals in which it often grows. An equally familiar name is titanite, indicating its chemical composition. Large crystals, darker in color than average, are found in a number of places in New York, Ontario, and Quebec. Those from Diana, N.Y., and Eganville, Ont., are dark-brown; those from Litchfield, Que., are shiny-black. Some of the broad reddish crystals from the Ala Valley in Italy are exceptionally attractive. Numerous places in Switzerland yield good crystals of sphene, including the large pale-green twins occurring at Saint Gotthard. The Kola Peninsula of Russia, between the Arctic Ocean and the White Sea, contains the largest deposit, used there as an ore of titanium. Transparent sphene, though not overly abundant, makes spectacular gems because of its superior luster and light-refracting power, but its softness hinders its use in jewelry. Sphene is common in granite but as an accessory to the more essential minerals.

SCHEELITE

KEYS: Nonmetallic luster. Leaves white mark or scratch on streak plate. Does not show good cleavage. Cannot be scratched by copper coin, but can be scratched by knife blade.

Color: White, gray. **Fracture:** Even.

Specific Gravity: 5.9–6.1 (heavy).

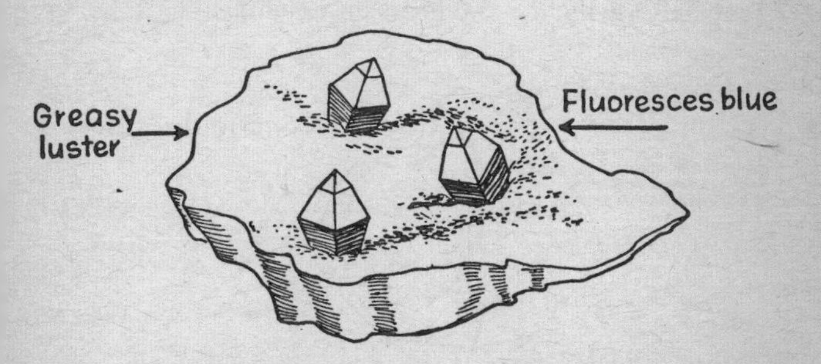

Calcium tungstate ($CaWO_4$) is scheelite. Although other ores yield more of the world's supply of tungsten, scheelite is the most important American source. It is one of the few minerals that can almost always be relied upon to fluoresce in ultraviolet light, the ensuing color being a bright bluish-white. As molybdenum replaces some of the atoms of tungsten, scheelite grades toward another mineral, powellite, and the fluorescence becomes white and then yellowish. Mineral collectors using short-wave ultraviolet lamps have come across numerous small occurrences of both minerals during the past decade. Scheelite was named in honor of Karl Wilhelm Scheele (1742–1786), the Swedish chemist who discovered in it the element tungsten, now called wolfram. Crystals of scheelite are not common; Traversella, Italy, and Framont, France, are noteworthy localities for them, and some of considerable size have been found in the tin mines of Germany, Czechoslovakia, and England. Large deposits of scheelite occur near Mill City, Nev., and Bishop and Atolia, Calif.

DATOLITE

KEYS: Nonmetallic luster. Leaves white mark or scratch on streak plate. Does not show good cleavage. Cannot be scratched by copper coin, but can be scratched by knife blade.

Color: Colorless, white, light-green.

Fracture: Conchoidal.

Specific Gravity: 2.9–3.0 (medium weight).

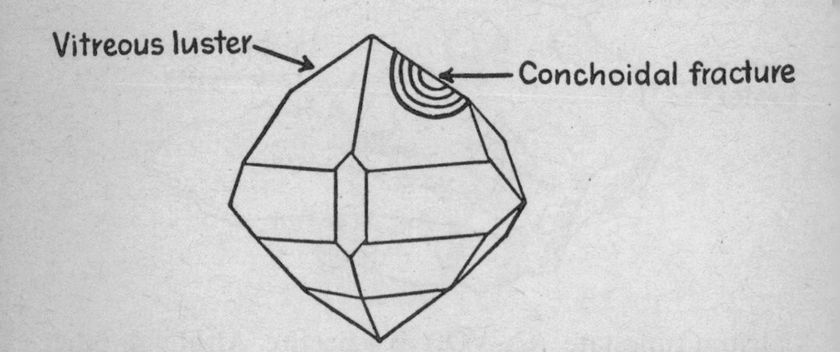

A basic silicate of calcium and boron [$CaBSiO_4(OH)$], datolite is a mineral of secondary origin, forming in cavities in lava rock, such as basalt. It is associated with the zeolite minerals. Its occurrences are in regions where volcanic rock is abundant; for instance, in New Jersey and the Connecticut River Valley in the United States, and in the Harz Mountains of Germany. Datolite is one of the characteristic minerals in the Michigan copper deposits around Lake Superior, where, in addition to fine crystals having a greenish tinge, cream-colored and pinkish porcelainlike masses are found which contain inclusions of native copper and are sometimes polished as gem material. Italy and Norway are other leading countries for specimens of datolite. The complex crystals, usually of pale-green tint, have many faces distributed at odd angles over the surface. Otherwise this mineral is difficult to recognize without chemical tests.

ARAGONITE

KEYS: **Nonmetallic luster. Leaves white mark or scratch on streak plate. Does not show good cleavage. Cannot be scratched by copper coin, but can be scratched by knife blade.**

Color: Colorless, white, gray. **Fracture:** Conchoidal.

Specific Gravity: 2.9 (medium weight).

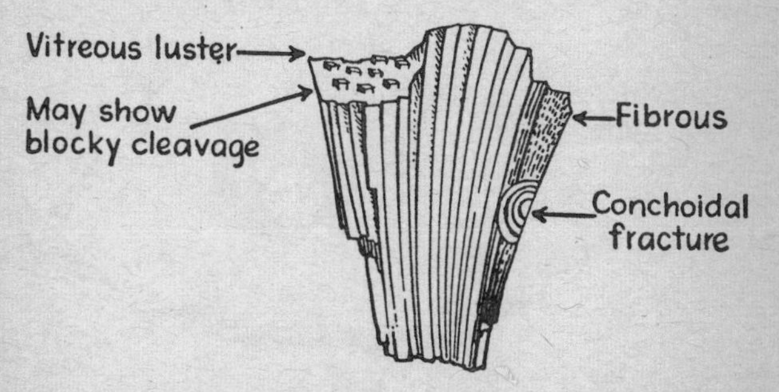

Aragonite is calcium carbonate ($CaCO_3$). It thus has the same chemical composition as calcite, and, like all carbonates, it fizzes in acid. Although less common than calcite, aragonite is formed under various conditions ranging from the hot water of geysers to the cold water of the ocean. It also forms as a crust inside of teakettles and water tanks. Named in 1796 from its original locality in the former kingdom of Aragón, Spain, this interesting mineral has been found in almost every country. Some collectors like best the six-sided disks known in Wyoming and Colorado as "Indian dollars" and in New Mexico as "Aztec money." Some of these are twin crystals which have changed over to calcite. Other collectors prefer the twisting branches that resemble snow-white coral and are known as "flos ferri." Large, well-formed crystals of aragonite occur in the sulfur deposits on the island of Sicily. The upper part of many coral reefs in the Pacific Ocean consists of aragonite, as does the mother-of-pearl of oyster and abalone shells.

ANALCIME

KEYS: Nonmetallic luster. Leaves white mark or scratch on streak plate. Does not show good cleavage. Cannot be scratched by copper coin, but can be scratched by knife blade.

Color: Colorless, white. **Fracture:** Even.

Specific Gravity: 2.2–2.4 (medium weight).

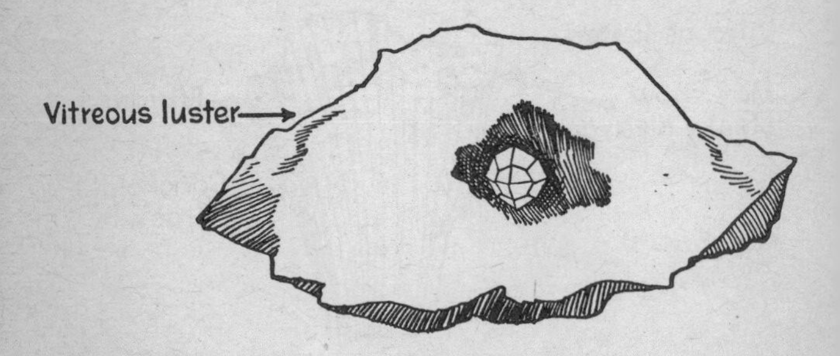

Analcime is a hydrous silicate of sodium and aluminum ($NaAlSi_2O_6.H_2O$). It is one of the most important members of the zeolite family, all of which boil up, giving off water evenly when heated. The word zeolite, in fact, comes from the Greek word meaning "to boil." The beautiful glassy crystals of analcime in the Cyclopean Islands in the Mediterranean Sea are typical of how this mineral occurs in cavities in volcanic rock. Large white crystals are found on the Seiser Alp, Italy. Some giant crystals of analcime measure a foot in diameter. Among many other localities are those on isolated Kerguelen Island in the Indian Ocean; at Cape Blomidon, Nova Scotia; North Table Mountain, overlooking Golden, Colo.; Bergen Hill, N.J.; and in the Lake Superior copper district. Analcime, also written analcite, has the same appearance as leucite and white garnet; unlike leucite, it grows in rock cavities, and it is softer than garnet. Analcime was named in 1797 from the Greek word for "weak" because of its feeble electrical nature.

MAGNESITE

KEYS: Nonmetallic luster. Leaves white mark or scratch on streak plate. Does not show good cleavage. Cannot be scratched by copper coin, but can be scratched by knife blade.

Color: Green. **Fracture:** Conchoidal.

Specific Gravity: 2.9–3.1 (medium weight).

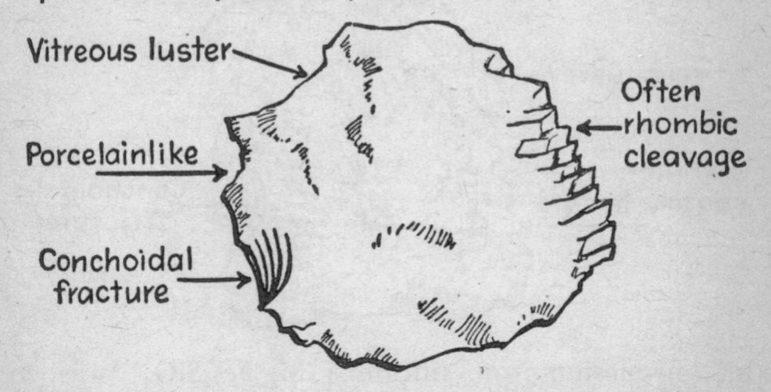

As its name suggests, magnesite is magnesium carbonate ($MgCO_3$). It, like the rest of the carbonates, fizzes in acid, which should be warmed for best results. Magnesite is used to make bricks for lining metallurgical furnaces, and it has served as an ore of magnesium metal, now extracted mostly from sea water. Large clear crystals occur at Bom Jesús dos Meiras, Brazil. Some of the rare prismatic crystals are found at Orangedale, Nova Scotia. Sizable deposits of commercial magnesite are situated at Chewelah, Wash.; bordering both the Coast Ranges and the Sierra Nevada in California; and in the Paradise Range in Nevada. Abroad they are especially large in Manchuria, the Ural Mountains, and Austria. A classic locality is the island of Euboea, Greece. Magnesite is slightly harder than calcite, and when occurring in cleavable masses it may require a chemical test for magnesium to distinguish it from calcite. At times the usual porcelainlike compact varieties give the impression of being harder and tougher than they are.

OLIVINE

KEYS: Nonmetallic luster. Leaves white mark or scratch on streak plate. Does not show good cleavage. Can scratch glass and be scratched by quartz.

Color: Green. **Fracture:** Conchoidal.

Specific Gravity: 3.3–3.4 (medium weight).

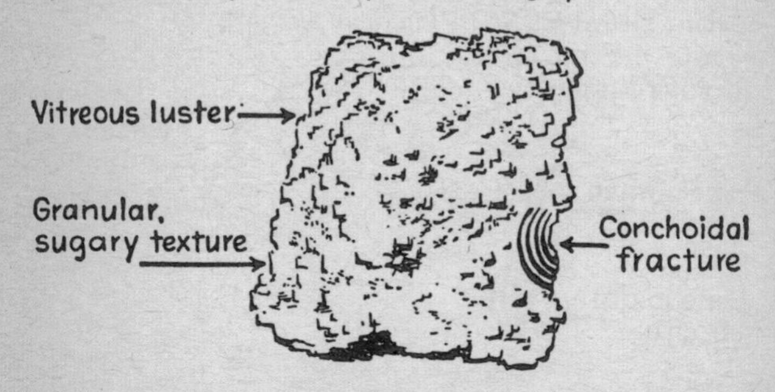

This magnesium-iron silicate [$(Mg,Fe)_2SiO_4$] was so named because of its olive-green color. With its tendency to form separate grains, a specimen may resemble somewhat a bowl of nearly round pale olives much shrunken in size. Olivine is a member of a mineral series grading from forsterite to fayalite. When transparent and having a distinctive bottle-green shade, olivine is fashioned into gems called peridot. St. John's Island in the Red Sea is the most celebrated locality for peridot, and rounded grains may be secured on some of the Indian reservations in the American Southwest. Common olivine is abundant in many dark and heavy rocks, those formed deep in the earth's crust. The rocks called dunite and peridotite are composed entirely or mostly of olivine. Volcanic bombs are often solid masses of olivine, and crystals of olivine are found in the lava which has flowed from Mount Vesuvius. Olivine is the most typical mineral in nonmetallic meteorites. The largest known crystals, from Snarum, Norway, have almost completely altered to serpentine.

IDOCRASE

KEYS: Nonmetallic luster. Leaves white mark or scratch on streak plate. Does not show good cleavage. Can scratch glass and be scratched by quartz.

Color: Green, brown. **Fracture:** Uneven.

Specific Gravity: 3.4 (medium weight).

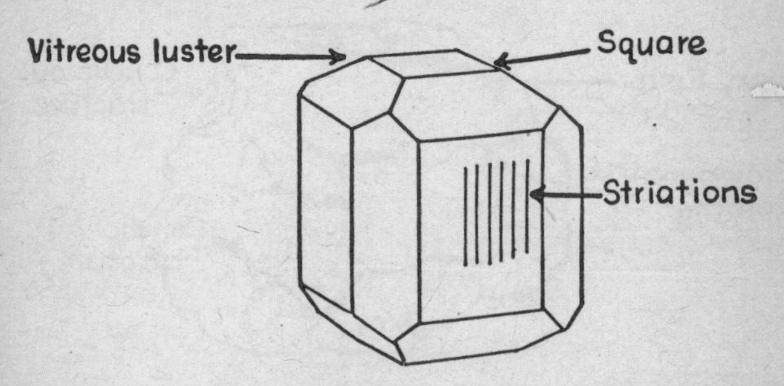

A complex silicate of aluminum, idocrase is also known by its older name, vesuvianite, which indicates one of its first known localities, Mount Vesuvius, where sparkling brown crystals occur. A compact green variety with whitish streaks, resembling jade, is called californite; it is found in Siskiyou, Fresno, and Tulare Counties, Calif. Other localities in the United States include those situated in Arkansas, Maine, Vermont, New Jersey, and New York. In Quebec large brownish-yellow crystals of idocrase occur at Calumet Falls, while at Templeton the crystals are brownish-red. The clearest and best-formed crystals are the transparent green and brown ones from Ala, Italy. Large brown crystals come from Egg, near Kristiansand, Norway. Idocrase originates as a result of the action of heated rocks on beds of limestone, which may be changed to marble with segregations of idocrase and other minerals, such as garnet and diopside. Besides the californite variety, clear specimens of idocrase have been used as gem stones; a superior locality for them is Eden, Vt.

TURQUOISE

KEYS: Nonmetallic luster. Leaves white mark or scratch on streak plate. Does not show good cleavage. Can scratch glass and be scratched by quartz.

Color: Blue, green. **Fracture:** Conchoidal.

Specific Gravity: 2.6–2.8 (medium weight).

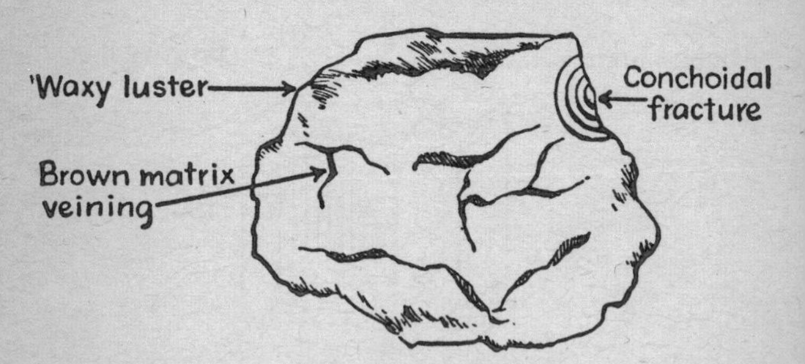

Turquoise, a hydrous aluminum phosphate [$CuAl_6(PO_4)_4(OH)_8 \cdot 4H_2O$], is one of the minerals most favored as a gem since prehistoric times. Ancient mines in Egypt and Persia produced it many centuries ago, and the Persian deposits near Nishapur are still productive. The material they yield is accepted as the standard of quality for clear blue stones containing a minimum of iron-colored matrix. When the matrix, or adjoining rock, is present as a delicate veining, it creates the delightful spider-web pattern, desired by many buyers as a sign of genuineness. Turquoise reaches its peak of popularity with the American Indian, to whom it holds a good deal of symbolism as well as beauty. The once extensive deposits in New Mexico are largely depleted, the leading states now being Nevada and California. The mineral occurs in stringers and small nodules. The largest nugget of turquoise on record, weighing almost 9 pounds, was mined in the King mine near Manassa, Colo., in 1945. The word turquoise is French for "Turkish," the Persian stones having reached Europe by way of Turkey.

PREHNITE

KEYS: Nonmetallic luster. Leaves white mark or scratch on streak plate. Does not show good cleavage. Can scratch glass and be scratched by quartz.

Color: Light-green. **Fracture:** Uneven.
Specific Gravity: 2.8–3.0 (medium weight).

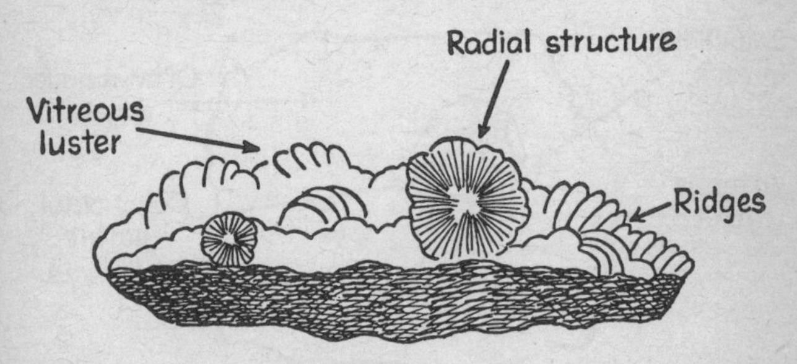

A hydrous aluminum silicate [$Ca_2Al_2Si_3O_{10}(OH)_2$], prehnite was named in 1790 in recognition of Col. van Prehn, who brought the first specimen to Europe from South Africa. It resembles the zeolite minerals in some respects and occurs with them in cavities in volcanic rocks. First-rate crystals are found at Coopersburg, Pa., but elsewhere prehnite grows mostly in jug-shaped or rounded aggregates, in which the individual rectangular plates of the cockscomb structure are scarcely noticeable except upon close examination. Prehnite looks like hemimorphite, which is, however, far more resistant to heat; although prehnite fuses easily, it does not give off water quite so readily. Interesting barrel-shaped groups, enclosed in white asbestos, have been found near Bourg d'Oisans, France. Leading localities in America for prehnite are Farmington, Conn.; Somerville, Mass.; the New Jersey trap quarries; and the Michigan copper region. Localities in other countries include the Kilpatrick Hills in Scotland, and Cradock, Union of South Africa, from where the original material came.

LEUCITE

KEYS: **Nonmetallic luster. Leaves white mark or scratch on streak plate. Does not show good cleavage. Can scratch glass and be scratched by quartz.**

Color: White, gray. **Fracture:** Conchoidal.

Specific Gravity: 2.5 (medium weight).

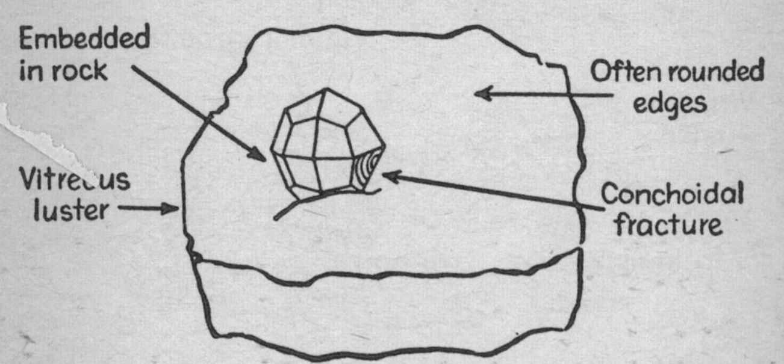

Leucite is a potassium–aluminum silicate ($KAlSi_2O_6$) and was named because of its color; it is often called white garnet, which it resembles. Like sodalite, leucite belongs to the feldspathoid group of minerals. It originates at high temperatures in lava rocks. The best crystals are from Mount Vesuvius, where small clear crystals fall like hailstones during eruptions and large perfect crystals are found in the big blocks of rock thrown out by the violence of the explosion. Magnificent groups of leucite crystals have been picked up as drift boulders on the shore of Vancouver Island, B.C. The Leucite Hills in Wyoming contain this mineral in abundance, and so do some of the mountains in Montana—the Bear Paw and Highwood Mountains, for example—but otherwise leucite is rare in the United States. It can be distinguished from garnet by its being softer and from analcime, another similar-looking mineral, by its favoring solid rock in which to grow, rather than cavities. Leucite is not too stable a mineral, converting to white or gray alteration products from its naturally colorless state.

OPAL

KEYS: Nonmetallic luster. Leaves white mark or scratch on streak plate. Does not show good cleavage. Can scratch glass and be scratched by quartz.

Color: White. **Fracture:** Conchoidal.
Specific Gravity: 1.9–2.3 (light).

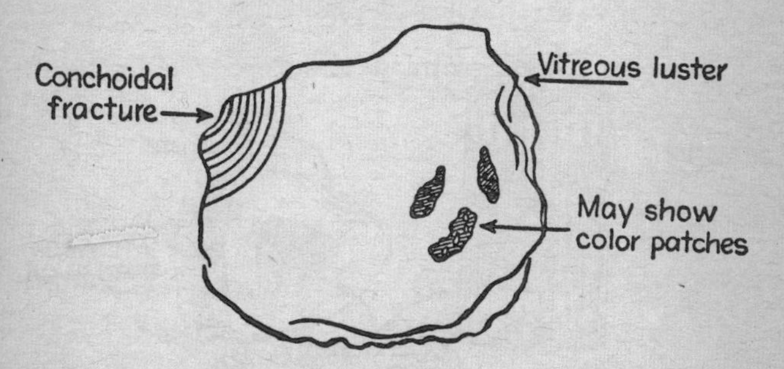

When water is present in a chalcedony-like substance, the material is hydrous silica ($SiO_2.nH_2O$), called opal. This is one of the few minerals not having a definite atomic structure and never occurring in crystal form. Its varying appearance seems to reflect this inconstancy. Many lovers of fine gems regard opal as their favorite. Lacking any color of its own except as a background, it reveals all the hues of the rainbow in ever-changing, purest aspect. White opal, also called Hungarian opal, has a pale or white background. Black opal has a background which is usually dark-blue or gray, against which the colors flash. Australia is the true home of black opal, first discovered in 1905 at Lightning Ridge, New South Wales. Some of it is also produced from time to time in Humboldt County, Nev., but is apt to crack after exposure. The reddish fire opal from Querétaro, Mexico, is occasionally quite attractive. Mineral collectors, however, are likely to find only the so-called common opal, which does not show the distinctive play of colors. Opalized wood is abundant in western United States.

TOURMALINE

KEYS: Nonmetallic luster. Leaves white mark or scratch on streak plate. Does not show good cleavage. Cannot be scratched by quartz.

Color: Black, pink, green. **Fracture:** Conchoidal.

Specific Gravity: 2.9–3.2 (medium weight).

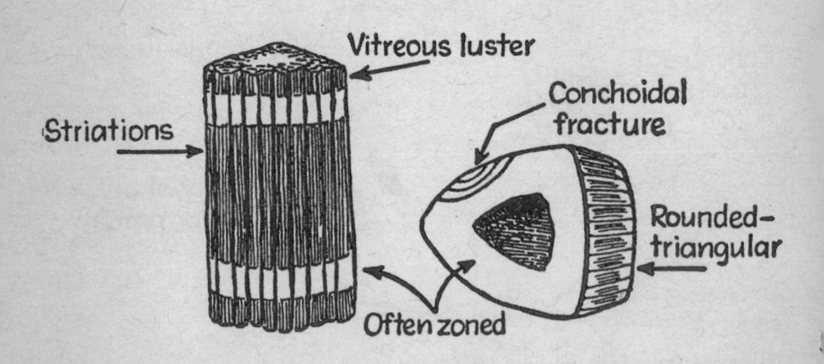

Tourmaline is an aluminum silicate with a formula so complex that John Ruskin said, "The chemistry of it is more like a medieval doctor's prescription than the making of a respectable mineral." It occurs in a tremendously wide range of colors. More than that, the colors are often zones either along the length or across the width of the unique rounded-triangular crystals. Watermelon tourmaline, for example, has a green exterior, surrounding first a white zone and then a red core. Each of the colors of tourmaline has a different name—rubellite, indicolite, achroite, dravite are some of them—but they are still tourmaline and eminently suited for use as gems. The jet-black specimens, which resemble hornblende, tend to fracture like coal. Pierrepont Manor, N.Y., is a renowned locality for black tourmaline. The more colorful varieties are especially noteworthy in the United States at Pala, Calif., and at Auburn and Paris, Me. The most prominent localities abroad are situated in Brazil, the Ural Mountains, and the islands of Ceylon, Madagascar, and Elba.

STAURÓLITE

KEYS: Nonmetallic luster. Leaves white mark or scratch on streak plate. Does not show good cleavage. Cannot be scratched by quartz.

Color: Brown. **Fracture.** Conchoidal.

Specific Gravity: 3.7 (medium weight).

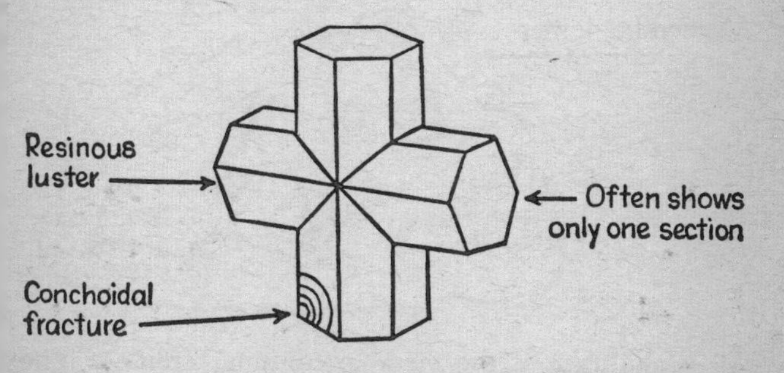

Staurolite is an iron-aluminum silicate [Fe (OH)Al_4-($AlSi_2$) O_{12}]. Although twin crystals have already been described for a number of minerals, staurolite is the one mineral above all others whose twins are of outstanding interest. Penetrating each other to form a Greek cross, to which staurolite owes its name, they are widely collected and kept as amulets. Called fairy crosses and figuring in local legends, those from Georgia and Virginia are eagerly sought, some being almost as smooth as though they had been polished. Rougher ones come from Cherokee County, N.C., and near Taos, N.M. The original localities for these crosses are in western France; large ones come from there and from Scotland. When the twin crystals of staurolite do not make a cross, they are shaped like the letter X instead. Single brown crystals of staurolite—lustrous and translucent—are found on Monte Campione, Switzerland. Fine crystals occur at Chesterfield, Mass. The untwinned crystals bear a resemblance to andalusite, which, however, is nearly square in outline.

ZIRCON

KEYS: Nonmetallic luster. Leaves white mark or scratch on streak plate. Does not show good cleavage. Cannot be scratched by quartz.

Color: Brown. **Fracture:** Uneven.

Specific Gravity: 4.7 (heavy).

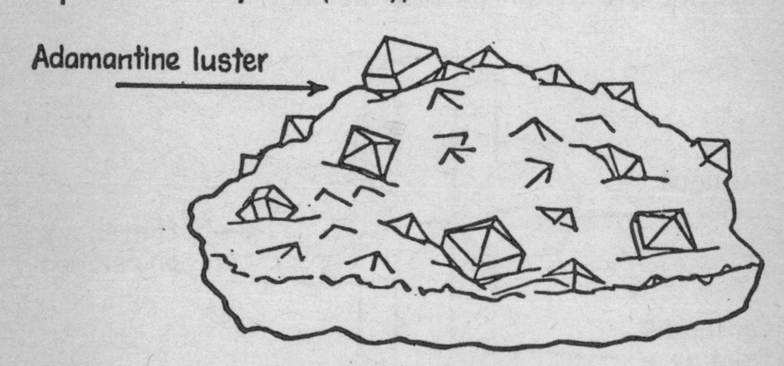

This is a silicate of the metal zirconium ($ZrSiO_4$). The name zircon has an obscure origin dating back many centuries. The metal was named from the mineral, which has been known since ancient times as one of the more remarkable of the gem stones. Three structural types have been proved to exist; these are termed high, intermediate, and low zircon. Several beautiful colors are available, including blue and golden yellow, as well as colorless stones which resemble diamonds. Those that are some shade of orange are called hyacinth and jacinth. These have almost all been heat-treated to produce the desired hue. Deep-red and mysterious green zircons are entirely natural. The gemmy crystals are found mostly in Ceylon and Indo-China. In Canada large crystals of ordinary zircon come from Sebastopol, Ont., and Templeton Township, Que. In Madagascar they are numerous on Mount Ampanobe. Exquisite tiny zircon crystals accumulate in beach sands in North Carolina, Florida, and elsewhere, for they have washed out of granite and similar rocks, in which they are a frequent constituent.

ANDALUSITE

KEYS: Nonmetallic luster. Leaves white mark or scratch on streak plate. Does not show good cleavage. Cannot be scratched by quartz.

Color: Gray, brown. **Fracture:** Uneven.

Specific Gravity: 3.1–3.2 (medium weight).

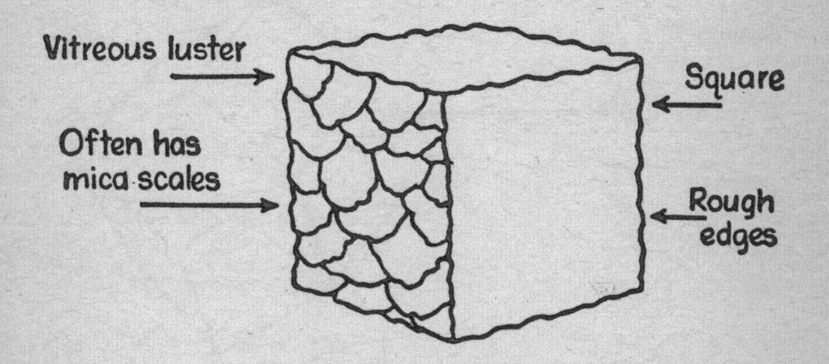

Andalusite (named after the province of Andalusia in Spain) is an aluminum silicate with the same chemical formula as kyanite and sillimanite (Al_2SiO_5). When heated, it becomes mullite, which is the porcelain used in making spark plugs. The variety known as chiastolite has inside a dark cross of organic matter, which assumes different shapes as the crystal is sliced—sometimes appearing as a wedge, sometimes as an hourglass. The large specimens of chiastolite from Rohan, France, are outstanding, as are those from the Lisenser Alp in the Austrian Tirol. Superior crystals are also found at Bimbourie, South Australia. Gem-quality andalusite is not common and is remarkable for the fact that the cut stones appear either olive-green or blood-red, according to how they are held. Stream-worn pebbles of this quality come from Brazil. The mineral is mined in commercial quantities near Laws, Calif. Good specimens come from Maine, Pennsylvania, and several places in Massachusetts; the stout crystals often project as knots from the rock. Andalusite-rich sand occurs in South Africa.

GARNET

KEYS: Nonmetallic luster. Leaves white mark or scratch on streak plate. Does not show good cleavage. Cannot be scratched by quartz.

Color: Red, brown, yellow, green, black, white.

Fracture: Even. **Specific Gravity:** 3.5–4.3 (heavy).

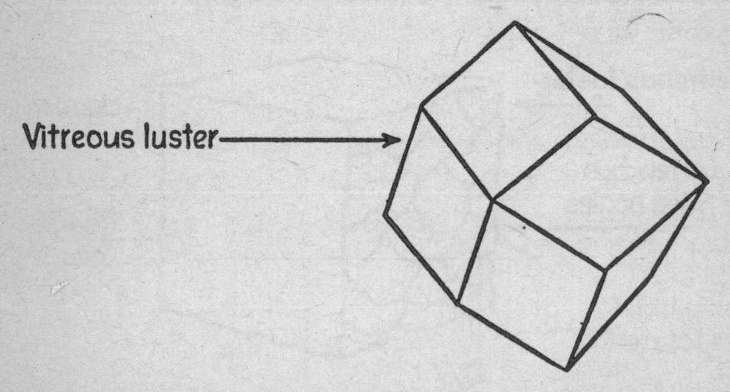

Garnet is a group of minerals which are silicates of aluminum, calcium, and other elements. The various garnets closely resemble one another, and even their colors usually give no assurance as to their individual identity. They are often recognized most readily by the other minerals associated with them, because each of the different garnets has its own type of geologic occurrence. Almandite, as mined in heavy crystals in eastern New York, is an important abrasive. When transparent and deep-red, this kind of garnet is known as precious garnet. Pyrope, the familiar dark-red Bohemian garnet in grandmother's jewelry, is also called precious garnet. Rhodolite is a lovely rose-colored garnet from North Carolina, corresponding to two parts of pyrope and one of almandite. Spessartite is brown or red and occurs in light-colored igneous rock. Grossularite includes white crystals, as well as those of more usual colors. Uvarovite is always green. Unsurpassed among all the gem garnets, however, is demantoid, a brilliant green variety of andradite from the Ural Mountains, used as a substitute for emerald.

BERYL

KEYS: Nonmetallic luster. Leaves white mark or scratch on streak plate. Does not show good cleavage. Cannot be scratched by quartz.

Color: Bluish-green, light-yellow, white.

Fracture: Conchoidal.

Specific Gravity: 2.6–2.8 (medium weight).

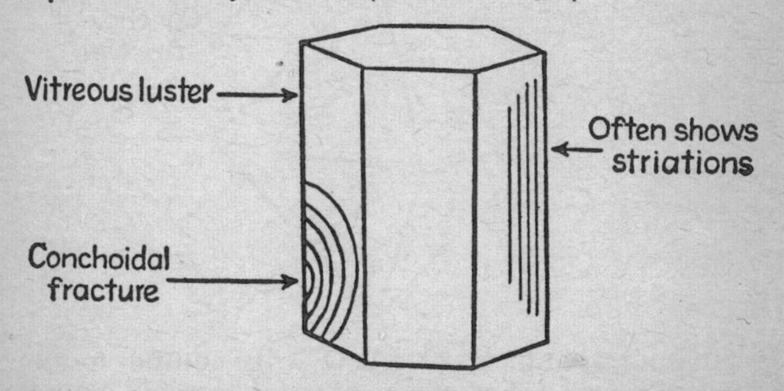

Beryl is a silicate of two light metals, beryllium and aluminum [$Be_3Al_2(SiO_3)_6$]. From it is extracted the strategic metal beryllium, which was named after it. Beryl, furthermore, is one of the major gem stones. When green, it is emerald; when blue or bluish-green, it is aquamarine; when pink, it is morganite—all gems of exceptional loveliness. The emeralds from Muzo, Colombia, have been the model of quality since the middle of the sixteenth century. The other beryl gems are obtained most abundantly in Brazil, Madagascar, Siberia, Ceylon, and California. Pretty aquamarine crystals are found at the very summit of 14,245-foot Mount Antero, Colo., the highest mineral locality in North America. Common beryl, used industrially, may occur in huge rough crystals, such as the two weighing 25 and 18 tons which were uncovered at Albany, Me., and the 40-ton monster reported from Madagascar. Another, with a weight of 3,000 pounds, came from Grafton, N.H. Aquamarine crystals often weigh several hundred pounds.

SPINEL

KEYS: Nonmetallic luster. Leaves white mark or scratch on streak plate. Does not show good cleavage. Cannot be scratched by quartz.

Color: Black, brown, green, pink. **Fracture:** Conchoidal.
Specific Gravity: 3.6 (medium weight).

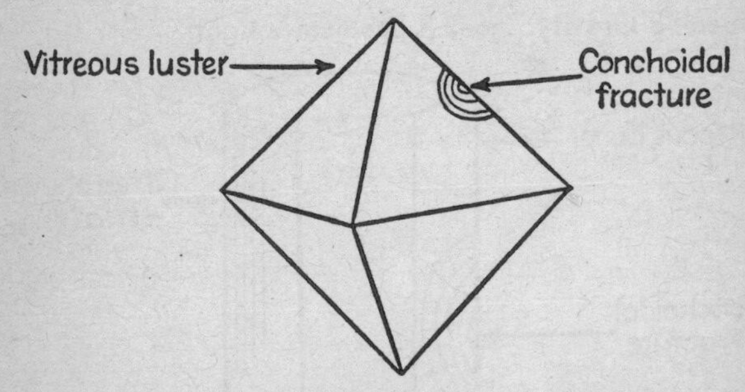

Magnesium aluminate ($MgAl_2O_4$) in natural form is spinel. An anciently known mineral, carrying a name whose origin was lost in the distant past, spinel furnishes gems in a considerable range of colors which resemble those of other gems, especially ruby and sapphire. The Black Prince's ruby, one of the most historic stones among the British crown jewels, has been proved to be actually spinel. Owing to its hardness, spinel is found as rolled pebbles in placer sand in the gem fields of Ceylon and Burma, together with the corundum which looks so much like it. Crystals of ordinary spinel, colored green, brown, and black, are distributed in a belt of rock extending from Andover, N.J., to Amity, N.Y.; and including a number of established collecting localities. Large crystals are found at Ambatomainty, Madagascar. Spinel crystals are like those of diamond and magnetite but are not so hard as diamond and are not magnetic like magnetite. Gahnite, often called zinc spinel, is a similar mineral found in many places; crystals 5 inches across have been acquired at Franklin, N.J.

CHAPTER 5

Four Keys to Recognizing Rocks

ROCK KEY NO. 1 TEXTURE AND STRUCTURE

The size, shape, and pattern of the mineral grains in a rock are included in the term *texture*. The larger features of rocks, as seen in the field, are called *structures*, but in specimens of the size that can be conveniently held in one's hand there is scarcely any difference between texture and structure.

Nothing indicates better than its texture the conditions under which a rock has been formed. If the rock is igneous, the texture tells whether it is intrusive or extrusive; if sedimentary, it tells whether it is an accumulation or a precipitate; if metamorphic, it tells what changes the original rock has undergone.

One of the most significant aspects of rock texture depends upon whether the individual particles can be seen by the unaided eye. Since even the smallest grain becomes visible when you examine it closely, this statement really refers to whether the separate minerals are large enough to be recognized by name, as in typical granite, without having to be magnified with a lens.

Some igneous rocks contain holes left by the escape of gas from the lava while it cooled. Pumice is an ideal example. This sort of porous texture or structure can be useful in recognizing certain extrusive rocks.

The structure of many rocks is layered or banded. This may mean successive deposits of sediment, each laid on top of the older ones, as in sandstone. Or it may show repeated flows of lava, or the streaked effect that cooling magma sometimes gives. Or it may be proof of metamorphism, which squeezes and stretches the minerals until they take on a ribboned appearance, as in gneiss.

Until you are able to recognize the origin of an unknown rock—this skill will come with practice in collecting rocks and reading about them—you can at least determine whether it can be split into layers with a prospector's pick. This experiment classifies the rock as either cleavable or not cleavable.

ROCK KEY NO. 2 COLOR

Color is even less reliable a guide to the identity of rocks than it is for minerals, for the obvious reason that most rocks are composed of several different minerals, each of which may have a quite different color. When the size of the individual mineral grains is small, however, a rock may present an over-all color easy to describe and compare.

Just as marble ranges from snow-white to jet-black, so many other rocks also occur in a variety of colors. Those colors, however, which are fairly characteristic of certain rocks are used in the outline and descriptive section for the purpose of helping you to name them as readily as possible.

Light-colored igneous rocks such as granite tend to be lighter in weight, that is, have a lower specific gravity, than dark-colored ones. This is because the iron that so often makes rocks dark also makes them heavy. In the outline and descriptive section, therefore, color and weight are given together. The relationship is not always dependable, though, because some lightweight specimens are dark as a result of structural peculiarities; obsidian, for example, has the chemical composition of granite and weighs even less, but it is often black because of tiny dust-like specks which absorb the light.

ROCK KEY NO. 3 ACID TEST

The carbonate rocks, such as limestone and marble, will fizz, or effervesce, when touched with acid, owing to the evolution of carbon dioxide gas. A good idea is to gouge the rock with a knife blade, producing a powder which dissolves more rapidly than the solid rock. Any acid may be used, but ordinary household vinegar will do.

Many igneous rocks, especially those from ore deposits, have veins of calcite or some other carbonate mineral in them and appear to effervesce vigorously. The action is confined to certain places and soon ceases, however, whereas a true carbonate rock will continue to fizz all over for a long time if enough acid is applied.

Pieces of carbonate minerals and rocks may similarly be present in a sedimentary rock, such as conglomerate or sandstone. These should not be confused with the bulk of the rock, which may scarcely react at all. Even more deceptive is the fizzing, often violent, of carbonate cement in a sedimentary rock, particularly sandstone. With such a rock it is necessary to wait and see whether the grains themselves are also dissolving or only the cementing material is being affected.

ROCK KEY NO. 4 MINERAL CONTENT

Rocks can best be named by recognizing their individual minerals where visible. This method requires a knowledge of the physical properties of minerals, as described in the previous section of this book. Because the mineral grains in rocks are generally so much smaller than when found as separate mineral specimens, a sample collection of good-sized pieces is worth buying for a few cents each from an established mineral dealer, so that you will become familiar with them and be able to recognize them when you meet them again in smaller grains in ordinary rocks.

Most rocks are named scientifically according to their mineral content. A simplified classification of this sort is used in this book as a secondary means of identifying the coarse-grained igneous rocks, in which the minerals are large enough to be recognized by anyone familiar with their appearance.

Identifying the Rocks. Outline of Keys

PORPHYRY

KEYS: Minerals easily seen with unaided eye. One kind of mineral set in finer-grained background.

Color: Variable. **Acid Test:** Does not fizz in acid.

Mineral Content: Variable.

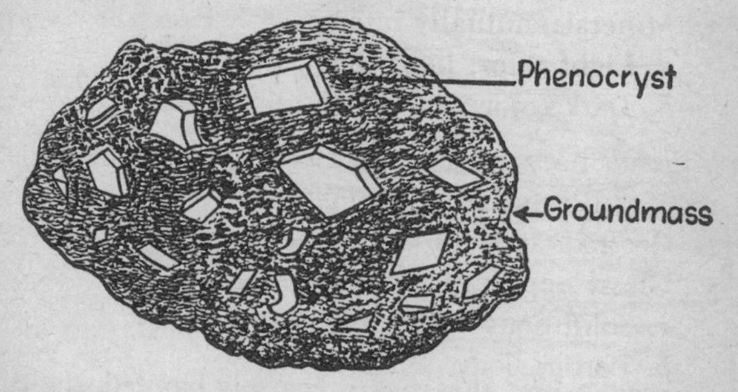

The term porphyry is used for igneous rocks that exhibit individual grains or crystals of a mineral set "like plums in a pudding" against a general background of finer texture. The background is called the groundmass, and the larger grains—the "plums"—are called phenocrysts. As long as there is a distinct difference in size between the two parts of the pattern, either can be of any degree of coarseness. For instance, the groundmass may consist of grains so tiny that it appears to have a uniform surface, and then the phenocrysts need only be large enough to be separately visible. Or the groundmass may be as coarse as granite, in which case the phenocrysts will have to be of substantial size, each perhaps several inches or more across. Porphyry is thus a descriptive term, including rocks of quite different composition. Thus, there are granite porphyry, syenite porphyry, monzonite porphyry, gabbro porphyry, felsite porphyry, and basalt porphyry. Miners and prospectors in the American West, however, commonly use the term for almost any fine-grained rock found in dikes associated with ore deposits.

GNEISS

KEYS: Minerals easily seen with unaided eye. Minerals in layers.

Color: Variable. **Acid Test:** Does not fizz in acid.

Mineral Content: Feldspar, quartz, biotite, hornblende.

Pronounced "nice," this rock is coarsely banded, the different layers of minerals being roughly parallel in a wide curving pattern. Dark and light bands occur in succession across the specimen, and each band may consist of several different layers. The minerals are predominantly feldspar and quartz, but biotite mica and hornblende are fairly abundant as well. Gneiss is a metamorphic rock created when either an igneous or a sedimentary rock is subjected to heat and enormous pressure. This causes it to be squeezed and stretched, pulling the minerals into stringers which occasionally narrow and widen along their length. An interesting variety is augen-gneiss, in which oval fragments of feldspar look like eyes peering out of the rock. As the bands become thinner, gneiss grades into another rock, called schist. Although it can be almost any age, gneiss is especially frequent in the older rocks, which have had full occasion to be buried deeply under thick layers of sediments and to be involved in the mountain-making processes. Fine examples of gneiss occur in the Highlands of Scotland, in Scandinavia, and in eastern Canada.

CONGLOMERATE

KEYS: Minerals easily seen with unaided eye. Minerals in layers.

Color: Variable. **Acid Test:** Does not fizz in acid.

Mineral Content: Quartz, feldspar, variable.

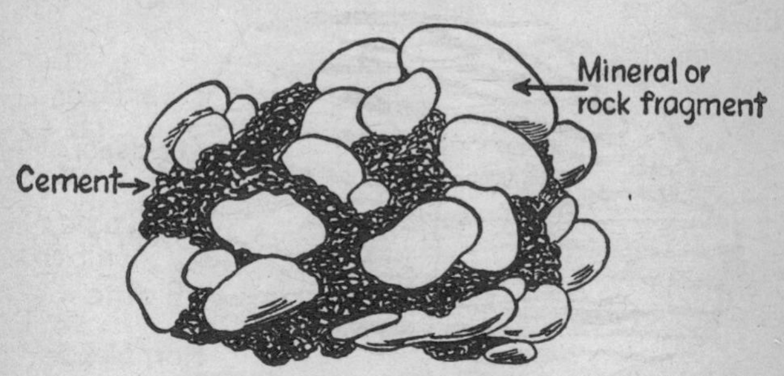

The individual fragments in the sedimentary rock called conglomerate may be the size of gravel, or as large as boulders, or a mixture of various coarse sizes larger than sand. A filling of sand generally occupies the spaces between them. The particles may consist of a single mineral, usually quartz or feldspar, or they may be a mixture of many minerals or pieces of rock. The cementing material between the grains, though mostly hardened sand, may also be clay, calcite, iron, or pure silica. Puddingstone is a conglomerate which shows a distinct contrast between its large pebbles and the dense matrix in which they are enclosed. When the fragments have sharp corners, not well rounded by stream action, the rock is known as a breccia. Conglomerates otherwise are deposited mostly by water, though some are the result of glacial action. The most extensive example of this rock in the United States, formerly called the Great Conglomerate, lies underneath the coal beds in Pennsylvania and adjacent states. Another Great Conglomerate, in northern Michigan and Wisconsin, is 2,200 feet thick. Ancient conglomerates are widespread in Canada.

GRANITE

KEYS: Minerals easily seen with unaided eye. Minerals mutually intergrown. Light color; light weight.

Acid Test: Does not fizz in acid.

Mineral Content: Feldspar, quartz, biotite, hornblende.

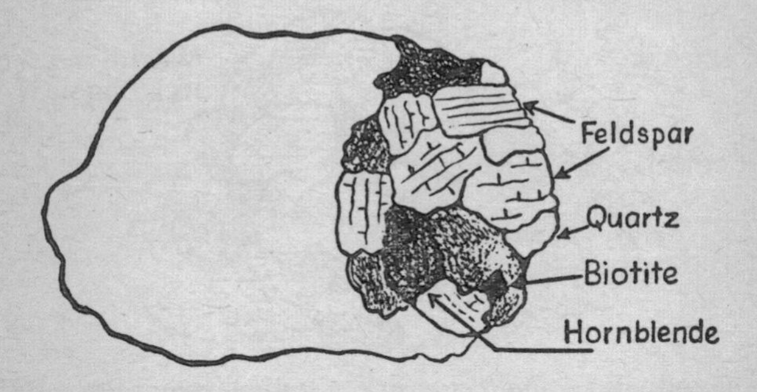

The igneous rock that consists of potash feldspar and quartz in readily visible grains of about equal size is called granite. Other minerals, especially plagioclase feldspar, biotite mica, and hornblende, may be present; but potash feldspar and quartz are essential, and they predominate. Granite should typically be a light-colored rock. It is true that the color is normally white or light gray, but when the feldspar is darker because of its structure, the rock is correspondingly dark. The well-known Quincy granite from Massachusetts is dark-gray, and even red granite, as it occurs so extensively in Minnesota and Scotland, is not uncommon. Though it may appear dark, granite is less heavy than the true dark rocks—the so-called "basic" rocks, such as gabbro—which are dark because of their prominent iron content. The cores of many of the world's great mountain ranges are composed of granite, and elsewhere it is deeply hidden. Granite is one of the major building and monument stones. A strikingly curious variety, called orbicular granite, is pock-marked with large knobs of foreign minerals.

PEGMATITE

KEYS: Minerals easily seen with unaided eye. Minerals mutually intergrown. Light color; light weight.

Acid Test: Does not fizz in acid.

Mineral Content: Feldspar, quartz, muscovite.

Extremely coarse igneous rock is called pegmatite, and the bodies themselves are spoken of as pegmatites. The minerals in the majority of specimens are perhaps twice as large as those in granite, but frequently they grow to gigantic sizes; the 47-foot spodumene in the Black Hills is the largest on record. Superlative crystals, unexcelled for perfection and beauty, as well as for size, are a feature of this kind of rock. The usual minerals in pegmatite are the same as those in granite–quartz and potash feldspar, mostly microcline. The mica is chiefly muscovite. A distinctive variety of pegmatite is graphic granite, so named because the grains of quartz and feldspar are intergrown in an angular fashion, so as to resemble ancient writing. Noted for their rare minerals as much as for their coarse texture, pegmatites are the home of fine gems and other minerals that are not found anywhere else. Rose quartz, smoky quartz, and moonstone are gems for which pegmatite is the only original source. Although the known masses of pegmatite may be of almost any shape, they are so commonly tabular that they are often referred to as pegmatite dikes.

SYENITE

KEYS: Minerals easily seen with unaided eye. Minerals mutually intergrown. Light color; light weight.

Acid Test: Does not fizz in acid.

Mineral Content: Feldspar, biotite, hornblende.

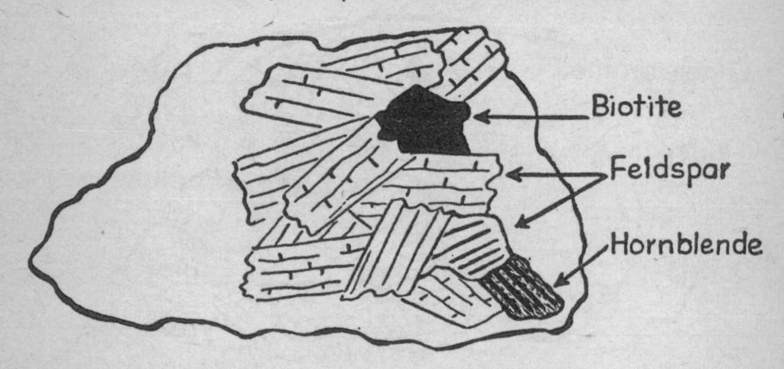

A rock very similar to granite in appearance but having little or no quartz is called syenite. The chief mineral is potash feldspar; in addition there is usually some plagioclase feldspar and a small amount of the dark minerals such as hornblende and biotite mica. The feldspar in syenite has a tendency to assume a rectangular shape. The name came from the old locality of Syene (now Aswân) in Egypt, which furnished a stone extensively used for obelisks in the times of the Pharaohs. The largest amount of syenite in the United States appears in the Adirondack Mountains, while other bodies are found in the White Mountains and the Rockies, and at the edge of the Ozark Mountains near Little Rock, Ark. In comparison with granite, however, syenite is relatively uncommon. Syenite serves the same commercial uses as granite, though it is more resistant to fire because of the absence of quartz. Laurvikite is an exceptionally handsome syenite from Laurvig, Norway, the feldspar of which shows a beautiful blue opalescence; this stone decorates the front of office buildings in New York and other cities in America and Europe.

MONZONITE

KEYS: Minerals easily seen with unaided eye. Minerals mutually intergrown. Light color; light weight.

Acid Test: Does not fizz in acid.

Mineral Content: Feldspar, biotite, hornblende, pyroxene.

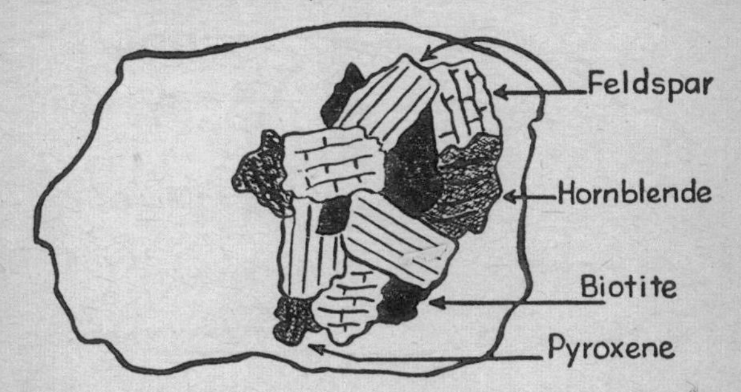

Closely resembling granite and syenite in the size and pattern of the minerals of which it is composed, monzonite is regarded as an intermediate igneous rock. When molten, it had less silica than molten granite; whatever amount was present has been taken up by the various silicate minerals, leaving little or none for the forming of quartz, which is pure silica. Having more iron than granite has, it contains more of the dark minerals, but not so many as gabbro, which has a still-higher content of iron. Hence monzonite stands between granite and gabbro in classification. Its essential minerals are about equal proportions of both kinds of feldspar—plagioclase and potash feldspar; the dark minerals present are biotite mica, hornblende, and augite. Since the two kinds of feldspar—usually so alike in appearance—are somewhat different in color when they occur together, monzonite is rather easily recognized by this fact of one being gray and the other white, or one white and the other pink. This is an important rock in connection with the metal-bearing mineral deposits in Colorado and elsewhere in western North America.

GABBRO

KEYS: Minerals easily seen with unaided eye. Minerals mutually intergrown. Dark color; heavy weight.

Acid Test: Does not fizz in acid.

Mineral Content: Feldspar, pyroxene, hornblende, olivine.

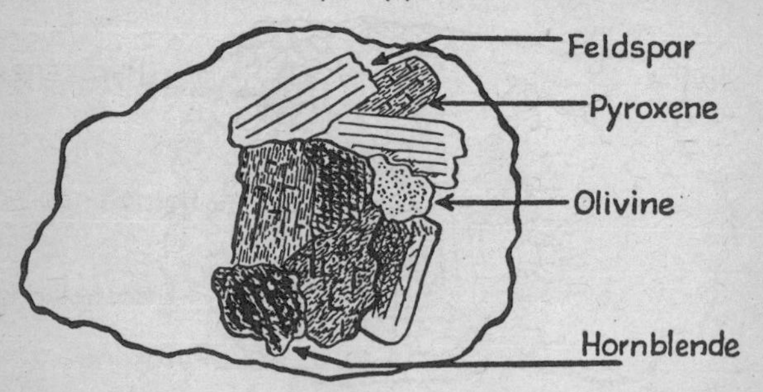

An igneous rock which is dark and heavy and which consists of plagioclase feldspar and other mineral grains large enough to be visible and recognized is called gabbro. The minerals are typically black, dark-gray, or dark-green in color, being chiefly plagioclase feldspar (mainly labradorite) and pyroxene (commonly augite), with some hornblende and olivine. When gabbro is composed almost exclusively of labradorite, the rock is called anorthosite, of which large amounts occur in Wyoming, eastern Canada, and Scandinavia. Another kind of gabbro, called norite, encloses huge deposits of nickel ore, especially at Sudbury, Ont., and chromium and platinum ore, as in South Africa. Gabbro is a deep-seated rock, formed at high temperatures. It is a familiar sight in the vicinity of Baltimore, Md.; at Duluth, Minn.; and elsewhere around Lake Superior; and in the Adirondack Mountains. Less popular than granite on account of its somber appearance, gabbro is easier to work; in Sweden it is favored for monuments and sculpture. When it decomposes, it yields a reddish soil because of the high content of iron in the dark minerals.

PERIDOTITE

KEYS: Minerals easily seen with unaided eye. Minerals mutually intergrown. Dark color; heavy weight.

Acid Test: Does not fizz in acid.

Mineral Content: Olivine, pyroxene, hornblende.

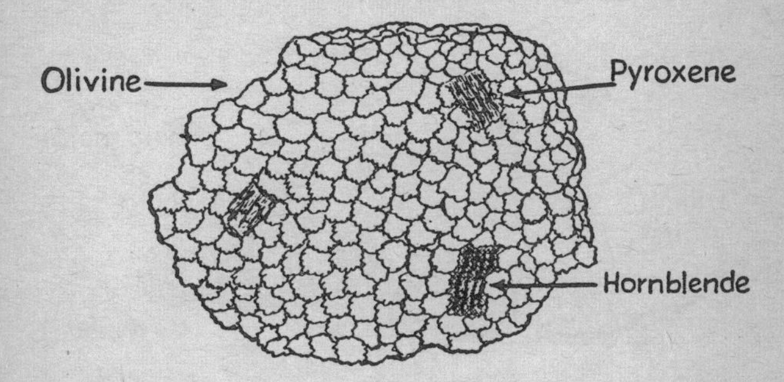

A dark rock resembling gabbro but heavier and containing little or no plagioclase feldspar is called peridotite. It has a comparatively high content of iron, and the color is dark green or black. The dominant mineral is olivine, and it is the French word (peridot) for this mineral that has given us this name. Pyroxene (mostly augite) and hornblende are less in quantity. Peridotite has formed under conditions of maximum temperatures and often considerable pressure. It sometimes is a valuable source of metals, notably nickel, chromium, and platinum, and in Rhode Island it contains a good deal of magnetite. The most significant mineral of any to be found in it is diamond. The diamond-bearing variety—the only proved mother rock of this gem—was named kimberlite after the South African city which is the center of the industry. The same occurrence of diamond in peridotite is known in Pike County, Ark., and in India. Other bodies of peridotite, but without diamonds, are distributed throughout the world. Tremendous volumes are present in New Caledonia and Cuba. Peridotite weathers readily to serpentine, with which asbestos may be associated.

METEORITE

KEYS: Minerals not easily seen with unaided eye. Metallic appearance.

Color: Dark. **Acid Test:** Does not fizz in acid.

Mineral Content: Iron, olivine.

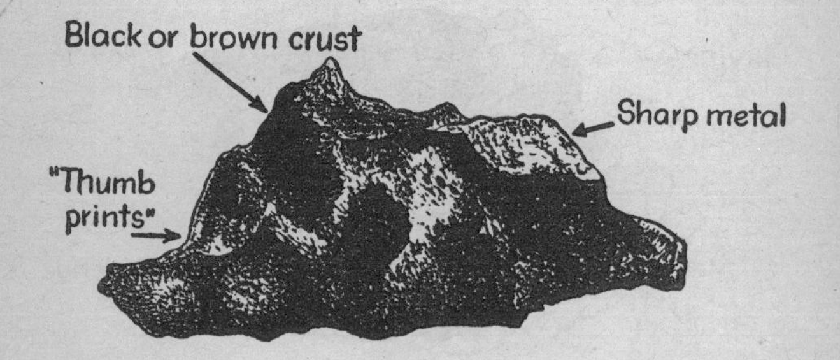

Although so rare that the average mineral collector is unlikely ever to find one, meteorites are of such vital scientific importance that the chance of your coming across a specimen and failing to recognize it should be reduced as much as possible. Only about 1,400 different meteorite "falls" have been recorded to date, though some falls are represented by many separate fragments. Each fall is different from the rest, and an expert can tell from which locality any given specimen has come. The classification of meteorites embraces three major kinds. Siderites (not to be confused with the mineral siderite), or so-called iron meteorites, are metallic, consisting of an alloy of iron, nickel, and cobalt. Aerolites, or so-called stony meteorites, resemble many ordinary heavy rocks; consisting mainly of olivine and pyroxene, they always reveal at least traces of metal. Those of an intermediate type are siderolites or ironstones, an example of which are the pallasites, showing nuggets of olivine set in a handsome meshwork of metal. The brown or black iron oxide coatings and the depressions or "thumbprints" are characteristics of meteorites.

COAL

KEYS: Minerals not easily seen with unaided eye. Coal-like appearance.

Color: Black. **Acid Test:** Does not fizz in acid.

Mineral Content: None.

Coal is regarded as a sedimentary rock because it is found in layers or beds. All coal once existed as growing plants which died, became partly decayed, and then were preserved by burial. The original plant life was of an amazing variety, over 3,000 different species having been identified from the age of greatest coal making. Appropriately called the Carboniferous Period, this was a time of lush vegetation, when ferns grew the size of today's trees and rushes were 90 feet tall. The first stage in the forming of coal is called peat. As further burial continues, the gases and water are forced out and the material left behind is thereby enriched in carbon. Peat thus turns to lignite or brown coal, which gives way to bituminous or soft coal, and eventually to anthracite or hard coal. As these changes proceed, the coal becomes brighter and harder, and it breaks more regularly. If coal is squeezed by pressure from the sides during the building of a mountain range, the ultimate product may be the mineral graphite. The thickest seams of coal are situated in Victoria, Australia, and the most valuable are in northeastern Pennsylvania.

OBSIDIAN

KEYS: Minerals not easily seen with unaided eye. Glassy appearance. Solid body.

Color: Black. **Acid Test:** Does not fizz in acid.

Mineral Content: Glass.

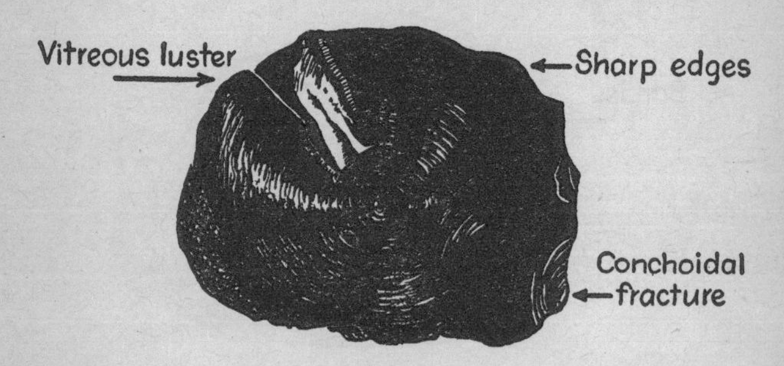

When lava flows onto the surface of the ground and cools so quickly that separate minerals do not have time to form, the resulting natural glass is known as obsidian. Its chemical composition is such that it would have become a normal granite if it had solidified very slowly at depth. The usual jet-black color is due to the presence of tiny specks of magnetite scattered like dust so that they absorb the light. Inside, also, may be seen the beginnings of crystals which failed to grow further, and often appear in flowerlike spots. Owing to its tendency to break with sharp edges, this natural glass was a boon to the people of primitive races who used it for all sorts of implements and weapons. Obsidian Cliff in Yellowstone National Park is a noted occurrence, and Mono Lake, Calif., is another. Distinctive obsidian from certain islands in the Mediterranean is mottled in red and black and appears somewhat pitchy. True pitchstone, however, is natural glass with a higher water content than obsidian and a pitchy luster. Ultimately obsidian seems to crystallize, so that all natural glass dates from relatively modern geologic time.

PUMICE

KEYS: Minerals not easily seen with unaided eye. Glassy appearance. Porous body.

Color: Gray. **Acid Test:** Does not fizz in acid.

Mineral Content: Glass.

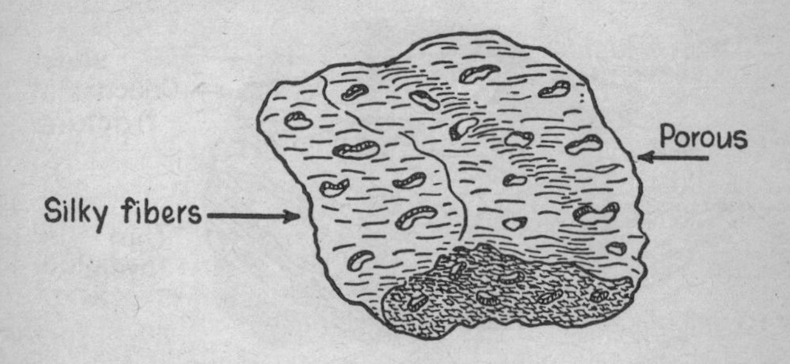

Perforated by the explosion of steam as it escapes from a volcano and puffed up into a froth of glass, pumice is a foamy mass of silky glass fibers. These fibers may be intertwined or else drawn out in parallel strands. Its porous nature and the many isolated cells of air enable pumice to float on water for a long while, pieces of it drifting ashore on almost every seacoast before they become waterlogged. The chemical composition of pumice is like that of obsidian or granite, except as the peculiar conditions under which it was formed make a difference. Although most pumice is light-colored, some of it is brownish or occasionally red. The sharp cutting edges of the bits of glass make pumice a serviceable abrasive, used in scouring-soap and as a dental polish. The Lipari Islands, between Sicily and the mainland of Italy, have long been the leading source of commercial pumice. New Mexico, California, and Oregon produce the most American pumice. A thick bed of California pumice is mined and sliced for use as an insulating material in refrigerators. Smaller pieces are mixed with cement and plaster to give these construction materials a lighter weight.

SHALE

KEYS: Minerals not easily seen with unaided eye. Stony appearance. Can be split into layers.

Color: Gray, black. **Acid Test:** Does not fizz in acid.

Mineral Content: Clay.

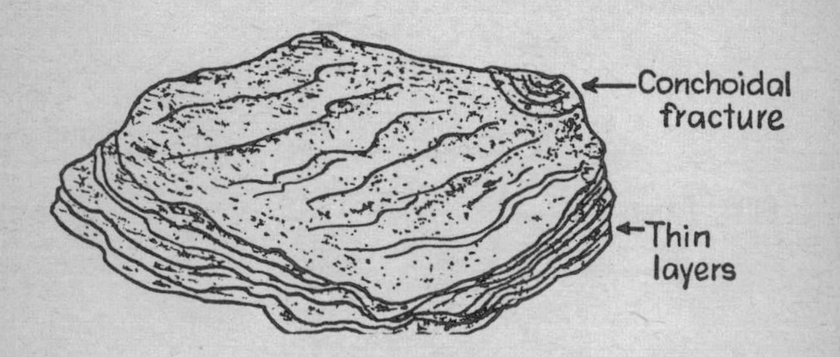

The sedimentary rock called shale consists of various clay minerals, which have ceased to be plastic and have accumulated into thin beds. The flaky grains are too tiny to be recognized at sight, but tests show them to be kaolinite and the related aluminum silicate minerals collectively known as clay. Small flakes of white mica, bits of quartz sand, and cementing limestone are commonly present, and almost any mineral can be incorporated into a shale. Lumpy inclusions called concretions are sometimes large. Shale is a soft and easily eroded rock, and it can be split with little effort. Some black shale is rich in carbon; other shale is gray or almost any color. Fuel has been produced from oil shale in Scotland for a century; the colossal reserves in western Colorado and eastern Utah are said to be the largest mineral deposit in the world except the ocean. Its weakness prevents the use of shale as a building stone, but this rock, abundant throughout the globe, has value as a mixing substance in the manufacture of cement. As shale increases in coarseness by the addition of sand, it grades into siltstone.

SCHIST

KEYS: Minerals not easily seen with unaided eye. Stony appearance. Can be split into layers.

Color: Variable. **Acid Test:** Does not fizz in acid.

Mineral Content: Variable.

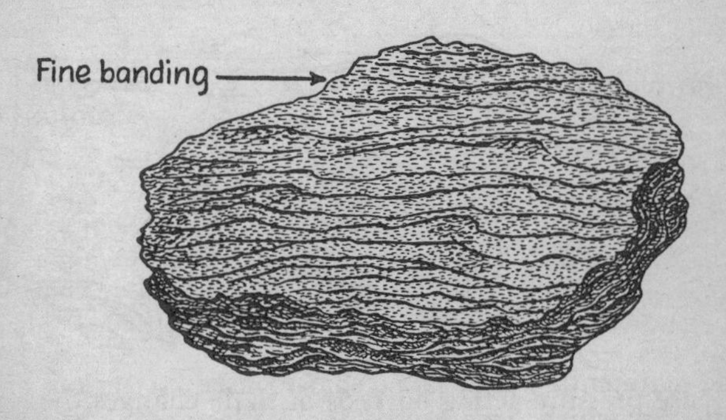

Schist is a closely layered metamorphic rock. Its name comes from the Greek word meaning "to divide," because of the ease with which it can be split between the layers. These layers are narrower than those of gneiss, but the two kinds of rock grade into each other, and no definite line can be drawn between them. As a rule, adjacent layers in a schist consist of the same minerals, and so schist is much more uniform in appearance and composition than gneiss. To this fact it owes much of its ability to separate by splitting. Unlike gneiss, schist is not so likely to contain feldspar as a significant mineral. Mica, instead, is extremely common; mica schist, composed of quartz associated with abundant flakes of black biotite or silvery muscovite, is the most widespread variety of schist and separates the most readily. Hornblende schist is another important rock, and there are other kinds of schist marked by red garnet, green chlorite, shiny-gray graphite, or white talc. These often make colorful specimens. As the layers of schist become still narrower, the rock grades into phyllite and then into slate.

SLATE

KEYS: Minerals not easily seen with unaided eye. Stony appearance. Can be split into layers.

Color: Gray. **Acid Test:** Does not fizz in acid.

Mineral Content: Clay.

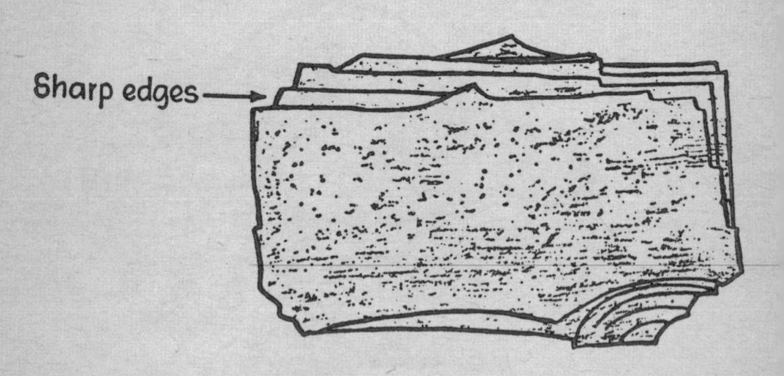

Intense pressure acting on beds of shale changes them to slate, a metamorphic rock. As a result, a smooth cleavage is developed at an angle to the original bedding and straight across the direction of pressure. The individual grains, like those in shale, are too small to be visibly recognized without magnification. Although the normal color of slate is dark gray, inclining toward black, varieties are known which are red, green, purple, or brown. Some slate contains conspicuous crystals of pyrite, well-shaped and attractive against their dark background. Another kind of slate with inclusions is knotted slate, having coarse crystals of silicate minerals scattered through it; this slate indicates the nearness of an igneous rock and a possible ore deposit. As might be expected, slate occurs in mountainous regions where the required pressure was developed in past ages. Commercial production in the United States, for blackboards and roofing purposes, is carried on mostly in Pennsylvania and Vermont. Broad, thin sheets of extraordinary size are quarried at Pen Argyl, Pa. Otherwise useful deposits may be too far from adequate markets.

LIMESTONE

KEYS: Minerals not easily seen with unaided eye. Stony appearance. Cannot be split into layers. Fizzes in acid.

Color: White, gray. **Mineral Content:** Calcite.

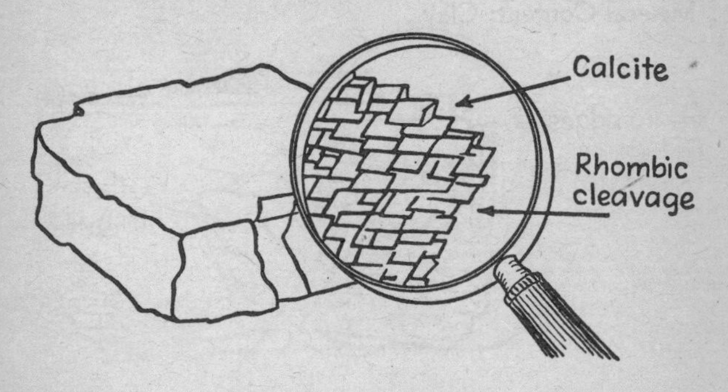

Limestone is a sedimentary rock composed solely of one mineral, calcite. It is generally white or gray, except when impurities cause a darkening. Limestone can be formed through the life processes of a wide range of organisms, from one-celled plants, such as algae, to specialized animals, such as corals. These extract calcium carbonate from the water and use it to build their skeletons and shells. Limestone also can be deposited inorganically, by strictly chemical means. There are many different kinds of limestone. A well-known one is chalk, which seems to be a fine powder until seen under a microscope, when it proves to be made up of the tiny plates of algae and the minute shells of lowly forms of animals. Coquina is limestone composed of an accumulation of loosely packed shells, cemented together firmly enough so that it is used in Florida as a building stone. Travertine is porous limestone deposited by hot springs. So-called Mexican onyx, familiar in pen stands and clock cases, is limestone marked by swirling patterns in attractive colors. Most cave stalactites and stalagmites are built of limestone.

MARBLE

KEYS: Minerals not easily seen with unaided eye. Stony appearance. Cannot be split into layers. Fizzes in acid.

Color: White. **Mineral Content:** Calcite, dolomite.

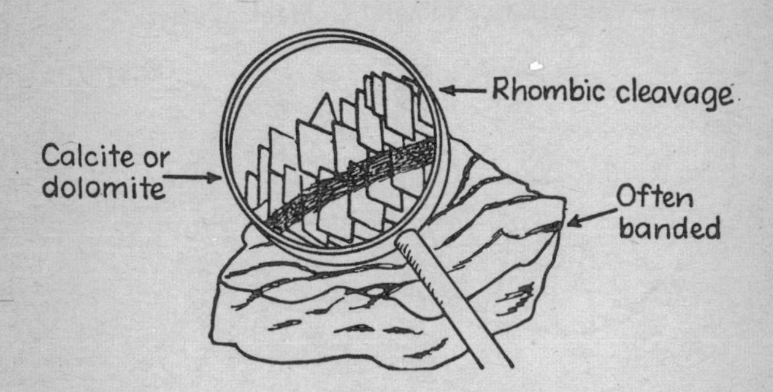

When either limestone or dolomite is drastically changed by heat, pressure, and water, the new metamorphic rock is termed marble. The agents that produce this transformation enable the grains of calcite or dolomite to grow larger and to give the surface a livelier sparkle than before. Any impurities that were present in the original rock or that were introduced during the change tend to be segregated into knots or spread out in wavy streaks, producing the varicolored "marbling" that is so appealing a feature of ornamental marble. North Africa produces superb examples of such stone. Snow-white marble, such as the famous stone from Carrara, Italy, is favored for statuary purposes. Similar Pentelic marble from Greece was sculptured into the priceless creations that are so enduring a heritage of Hellenic civilization. The Yule marble from Colorado, of which a single block weighing 56 tons was required for the Tomb of the Unknown Soldier, is equal to any from the Mediterranean region. Architectural marble is characterized by its uniform color. Vermont, Tennessee, and Georgia are states quarrying important amounts of marble.

SANDSTONE

KEYS: Minerals not easily seen with unaided eye. Stony appearance. Cannot be split into layers. Does not fizz in acid.

Color: White, brown. **Mineral Content:** Quartz.

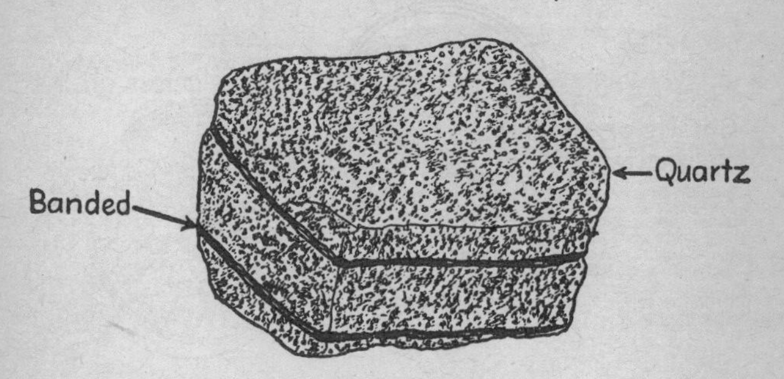

An accumulation of grains of quartz sand, cemented together more or less firmly to become rock, is called sandstone. As sandstone becomes coarse, it grades into conglomerate; as it becomes finer, it grades into siltstone. Some sandstone, such as the Potsdam sandstone of Wisconsin, is remarkably pure, consisting of little except quartz. Other specimens contain feldspar in increasing proportions, flakes of mica, and small grains of heavy minerals typical of placer deposits. The color of sandstone depends largely on the nature of the cement; iron oxide gives the red, yellow, and brown shades. A limy cement will fizz in acid but not the mineral grains. The shape of the individual particles likewise varies from perfectly round to sharply angular. Sandstone that splits readily into even slabs is known as flagstone. Brownstone, once the most fashionable building stone in Philadelphia, New York, and other Northeastern cities, is a sandstone containing considerable reddish feldspar. The most extraordinary kind of sandstone, called itacolumite, is actually flexible; a slab of it from North Carolina or Brazil will bend under its own weight.

QUARTZITE

KEYS: Minerals not easily seen with unaided eye. Stony appearance. Cannot be split into layers. Does not fizz in acid.

Color: White. Mineral Content: Quartz.

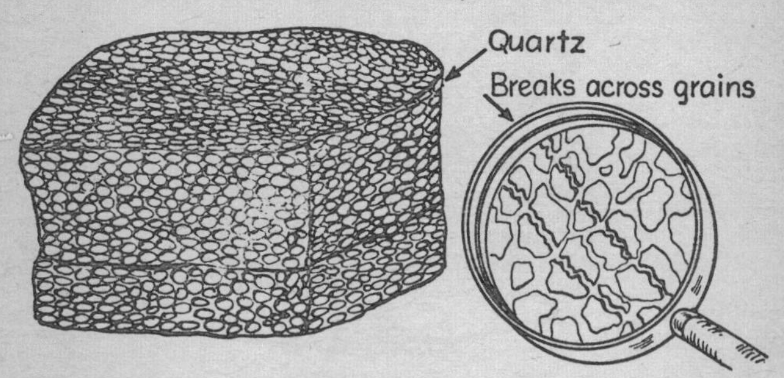

When subjected to enough pressure, sandstone is changed to the metamorphic rock know as quartzite. This name, which indicates that quartz is practically the sole mineral present, is also applied by many geologists to ordinary sandstone which has merely been cemented together more tightly than usual. A true quartzite, however—the toughest of all rocks—will break across the sand grains instead of having to break around them, because the former cementing material in the original sandstone has become as hard as the grains themselves. During the processes of change, moreover, some of the previous cement is likely to be recrystallized into small quantities of a number of new minerals, such as garnet, epidote, graphite, and muscovite mica. These may give color to an otherwise white rock. Quartzite used industrially as a heat-resisting material is called ganister. Burrstone is a porous variety of quartzite used for millstones. The Quartzite Range in British Columbia is named from its exposures of very old quartzite. The Baraboo quartzite is a handsomely crystalline rock, often deep-red in color, well exposed in Wisconsin.

FELSITE

KEYS: Minerals not easily seen with unaided eye. Stony appearance. Cannot be split into layers. Does not fizz in acid.

Color: White, gray. **Mineral Content:** Feldspar.

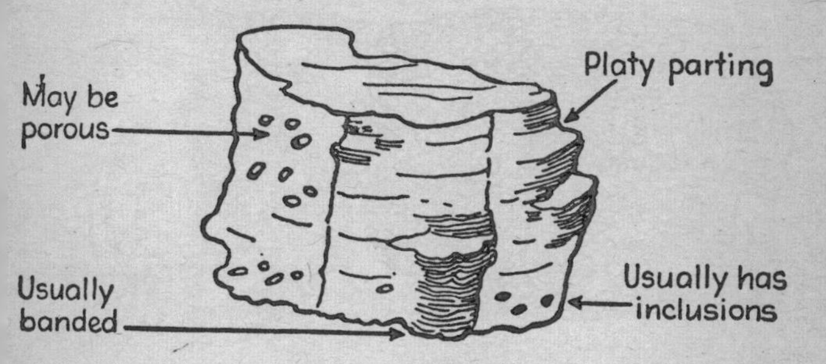

Light-colored igneous rocks that are so fine-grained that the constituent minerals can scarcely be recognized without a microscope are grouped together under the name felsite. They may be of any color but are light in tone, as contrasted with basalt, which is dark. The difference is basically due to the kinds of minerals that are present, and this is impossible to determine with the unaided eye. With a hand lens, however, perhaps the translucent edges of the feldspar, which is the chief mineral in felsite, can be observed even in some of the darker-looking specimens. Felsite originates mainly in lava flows and is abundant on a world-wide scale. One of the most important types is rhyolite, which makes up a large part of Yellowstone National Park. Phonolite contains the gold ores at Cripple Creek, Colo. It emits a ringing sound when struck; hence its name. Trachyte is prominent along the Rhine River, in central France, and in the Black Hills of South Dakota. Andesite is represented by a series of high volcanic cones stretching from Mount Rainier, Wash., through Mexico and Central America, all the way to the far tip of the Andes.

BASALT

KEYS: Minerals not easily seen with unaided eye. Stony appearance. Cannot be split into layers. Does not fizz in acid.

Color: Black. **Mineral Content:** Pyroxene, olivine.

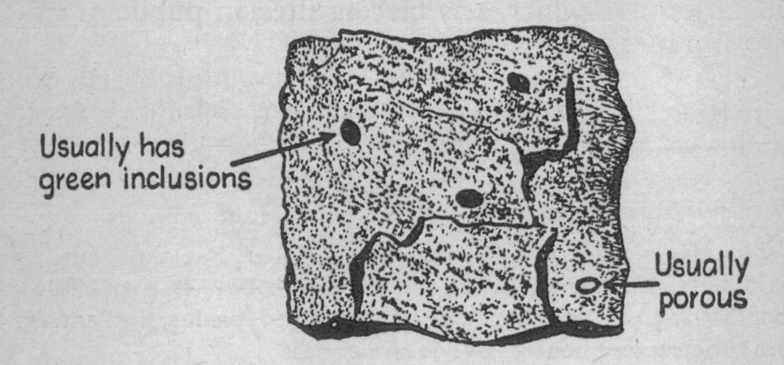

A heavy dark rock with a fine-grained texture, basalt is the most abundant of the rocks which have cooled from sheets or flows of lava. The gas escaping from the molten matter as it rises to the surface of the earth leaves oval cavities, which later are often lined or completely filled with minerals. The chief mineral that is readily visible against the dark background is olivine, which usually appears as green particles the size of buckshot. Of all the various kinds of rock, basalt is the one most likely to be divided by columnar jointing, which produces long upright pillars. The scenic Giant's Causeway on the north coast of Ireland is perhaps the most impressive example. Basalt occurs in small bodies as well, but the largest ones are of incredible extent. The Hawaiian Islands are built almost entirely of basalt, which erupted from numerous vents. The Columbia River region in the Northwestern section of the United States was blanketed by basalt, to create much of its present landscape. The Deccan Peninsula in India contains nearly one-half million square miles of basalt, which was piled as much as 10,000 feet thick.

Magazines for the Collector

The following magazines are national publications devoted to mineral and rock collecting and related hobbies. In addition there are various smaller but good periodicals of regional circulation and numerous specialized professional journals which may be consulted in public or college libraries.

Gems and Minerals, edited by Don MacLachlan and Ralph W. Dietz, has short illustrated articles on the various phases of mineral collecting. It is published monthly at Palmdale, Calif.; the subscription price is $3.00 per year.

The Mineralogist, edited since 1935 by Dr. H. C. Dake, deals interestingly with all aspects of the mineral hobby. It is published monthly (except in the summer) at 329 S.E. 32d Avenue, Portland 15, Ore.; the subscription price is $2.00 per year.

Northwest Mineral News, edited since 1954 by Kent K. Freeman, is the most recent general magazine of the mineral hobby. It is published bimonthly at 5606 Mount Tacoma Drive, S.W., Tacoma, Wash.; the subscription price is $1.50 per year.

Rocks and Minerals, edited since 1926 by Peter Zodac, covers in popular language the entire field of minerals and rocks. It is published bimonthly at Box 29, Peekskill, N. Y.; the subscription price is $3.00 per year.

Earth Science Digest, edited by Dr. Ben H. Wilson, includes worthwhile articles on minerals, rocks, and popular geology. It is published bimonthly at Box 1357, Chicago 90, Ill.; the subscription price is $2.00 per year.

The Lapidary Journal, edited since 1947 by Lelande Quick, specializes in the collecting and cutting of gems and ornamental stones. It is published bimonthly at Palm Desert, Calif.; the subscription price is $2.00 per year.

The Desert Magazine, edited since 1938 by Randall Henderson, features articles on mineral localities in Southwestern United States, illustrated with helpful maps. It is published monthly at Palm Desert, Calif.; the subscription price is $3.50 per year.

Books for the Collector

The following books are especially recommended for further reading and reference. The classifications and brief descriptive notes are intended to aid the purchaser.

INTRODUCTORY

Getting Acquainted with Minerals by George L. English, published by the McGraw-Hill Book Company, Inc., New York (1934). An attractive, nicely illustrated book to stimulate a beginner.

TEXTBOOK

Minerals and How to Study Them by Edward Salisbury Dana, revised by Cornelius S. Hurlbut, Jr., published by John Wiley & Sons, Inc., New York (3d ed., 1949). Well illustrated.

REFERENCE

Mineral Collectors Handbook by Richard M. Pearl, published by the Mineral Book Company, Colorado Springs, Colo. (1947). The standard reference book covering the care and preservation of specimens and giving extensive information on testing and classifying.

GEMS

Popular Gemology by Richard M. Pearl, published by John Wiley & Sons, Inc., New York (1948). A scientifically accurate, finely illustrated book on gems, clearly written in layman's language.

METEORITES

Out of the Sky by H. H. Nininger, published by the University of Denver Press, Denver (1952). Comprehensive illustrated survey.

LOCALITIES

The following volumes in the American Gem Trails Series are detailed locality guides for the mineral collector:

California Gem Trails by H. C. Dake, published by *The Mineralogist* magazine, Portland, Ore. (2d ed., 1952).

Colorado Gem Trails by Richard M. Pearl, published by the Mineral Book Company, Colorado Springs, Colo. (3d ed., 1953).

Northwest Gem Trails (Oregon, Washington, Idaho, Montana, Wyoming) by H. C. Dake, published by *The Mineralogist* magazine, Portland, Ore. (1950).

Index

ACKNOWLEDGMENTS

First, I'd like to thank my friend and editor, Joyce Johnson, for the countless hours, including much of her own time, spent helping construct this book, giving it the necessary shape and form. The book could not have been completed without her help and exceptional skills and talents.

Thanks also to Roger Steffens—actor, poetry-man, and friend—who gave freely of his time, effort, and energy, retyping almost the entire manuscript up in Mendocino. I'll remember his patience and understanding, his generosity and love, his faith in me and the book.

I'd also like to thank Mary and Sheila and my friend Waldo—a child at sixty—who gave me courage with his eyes and love with his wisdom.

And finally, thanks to Connie Panzarino—beautiful, strong, and brave woman—who believed in me and the book years before it had been written. She stood by me like no one else, listening through nights and days, caring and loving, understanding and encouraging, wiping the tears from my eyes. She was like a light shining from the darkness of what seemed to be an endless storm.

For my country
and its people,

happy birthday

Ask not what your country can do for you—ask what you can do for your country.

—PRESIDENT JOHN F. KENNEDY
JANUARY 20, 1961

I am the living death
the memorial day on wheels
I am your yankee doodle dandy
your john wayne come home
your fourth of july firecracker
exploding in the grave

1

THE BLOOD IS still rolling off my flak jacket from the hole in my shoulder and there are bullets cracking into the sand all around me. I keep trying to move my legs but I cannot feel them. I try to breathe but it is difficult. I have to get out of this place, make it out of here somehow.

Someone shouts from my left now, screaming for me to get up. Again and again he screams, but I am trapped in the sand.

Oh get me out of here, get me out of here, please someone help me! Oh help me, please help me. Oh God oh Jesus! "Is there a corpsman?" I cry. "Can you get a corpsman?"

There is a loud crack and I hear the guy begin to sob. "They've shot my fucking finger off! Let's go, sarge! Let's get outta here!"

"I can't move," I gasp. "I can't move my legs! I can't feel anything!"

I watch him go running back to the tree line.

"Sarge, are you all right?" Someone else is calling to me now and I try to turn around. Again there is the sudden crack of a bullet and a boy's voice crying. "Oh Jesus! Oh Jesus Christ!" I hear his body fall in back of me.

I think he must be dead but I feel nothing for him, I just want to live. I feel nothing.

And now I hear another man coming up from behind, trying to save me. "Get outta here!" I scream. "Get the fuck outta here!"

A tall black man with long skinny arms and enormous hands picks me up and throws me over his shoulder as bullets begin cracking over our heads like strings of firecrackers. Again and again they crack as the sky swirls around us like a cyclone. "Motherfuckers motherfuckers!" he screams. And the rounds keep cracking and the sky and the sun on my face and my body all gone, all twisted up dangling like a puppet's, diving again and again into the sand, up and down, rolling and cursing, gasping for breath. "Goddamn goddamn motherfuckers!"

And finally I am dragged into a hole in the sand with the bottom of my body that can no longer feel, twisted and bent underneath me. The black man runs from the hole without ever saying a thing. I never see his face. I will never know who he is. He is gone. And others now are in the hole helping me. They are bandaging my wounds. There is fear in their faces.

"It's all right," I say to them. "Everything is fine."

Someone has just saved my life. My rifle is gone and I don't feel like finding it or picking it up ever again. The only thing I can think of, the only thing that crosses my mind, is living. There seems to be nothing in the world more important than that.

Hundreds of rounds begin to crash in now. I stare up at the sky because I cannot move. Above the hole men are running around in every direction. I see their legs and frightened faces. They are screaming and dragging the wounded past me. Again and again the rounds crash in. They seem to be coming in closer and closer. A tall man jumps in, hugging me to the earth.

"Oh God!" he is crying. "Oh God please help us!"

The attack is lifted. They are carrying me out of the hole now—two, three, four men—quickly they are strapping me to a stretcher. My legs dangle off the sides until they realize I cannot control them. "I can't move them," I say, almost in a whisper. "I can't move them." I'm still carefully sucking the air, trying to calm myself, trying not to get excited, not to panic. I want to live. I keep telling myself, Take it slow now, as they strap my legs to the stretcher and carry my wounded body into an Amtrac packed with other wounded men. The steel trapdoor of the Amtrac slowly closes as we begin to move to the northern bank and back across the river to the battalion area.

Men are screaming all around me. "Oh God get me out of here!" "Please help!" they scream. Oh Jesus, like little children now, not like marines, not like the posters, not like that day in the high school, this is for real. "Mother!" screams a man without a face. "Oh I don't want to die!" screams a young boy cupping his intestines with his hands. "Oh please, oh no, oh God, oh help! Mother!" he screams again.

We are moving slowly through the water, the Amtrac rocking back and forth. We cannot be brave anymore, there is no reason. It means nothing now. We hold on to ourselves, to things around us, to memories, to thoughts, to dreams. I breathe slowly, desperately trying to stay awake.

The steel trapdoor is opening. I see faces. Corpsmen, I think. Others, curious, looking in at us. Air, fresh, I feel, I smell. They are carrying me out now. Over wounded bodies, past wounded screams. I'm in a helicopter now lifting above the battalion area. I'm leaving the war. I'm going to live. I am still breathing, I keep thinking over and over, I'm going to live and get out of here.

They are shoving tubes and needles in my arms. Now we are being packed into planes. I begin to believe more and more as I watch the other wounded packed around me on shelves that I am going to live.

I still fight desperately to stay awake. I am in an ambulance now rushing to some place. There is a man without any legs screaming in pain, moaning like a little baby. He is bleeding terribly from the stumps that were once his legs, thrashing his arms wildly about his chest, in a semiconscious daze. It is almost too much for me to watch.

I cannot take much more of this. I must be knocked out soon, before I lose my mind. I've seen too much today, I think. But I hold on, sucking the air. I shout then curse for him to be quiet.

"My wound is much worse than yours!" I scream. "You're lucky," I shout, staring him in the eyes. "I can feel nothing from my chest down. You at least still have part of your legs. Shut up!" I scream again. "Shut the fuck up, you goddamned baby!" He keeps thrashing his arms wildly above his head and kicking his bleeding stumps toward the roof of the ambulance.

The journey seems to take a very long time, but soon we are at the place where the wounded are sent. I feel a tremendous exhilaration inside me. I have made it this far. I have actually made it this far without giving up and now I am in a hospital where they will operate on me and find out why I cannot feel anything from my chest down anymore. I know I am going to make it now. I am going to make it not because of any god, or any religion, but because *I* want to make it, *I* want to live. And I leave the screaming man without legs and am brought to a room that is very bright.

"What's your name?" the voice shouts.

"Wh-wh-what?" I say.

"What's your name?" the voice says again.

"K-K-Kovic," I say.

"No!" says the voice. "I want your name, rank, and service number. Your date of birth, the name of your father and mother."

"Kovic. Sergeant. Two-oh-three-oh-two-six-one, uh, when are you going to . . ."

"Date of birth!" the voice shouts.

"July fourth, nineteen forty-six. I was born on the Fourth of July. I can't feel . . ."

"What religion are you?"

"Catholic," I say.

"What outfit did you come from?"

"What's going on? When are you going to operate?" I say.

"The doctors will operate," he says. "Don't worry," he says confidently. "They are very busy and there are many wounded but they will take care of you soon."

He continues to stand almost at attention in front of me with a long clipboard in his hand, jotting down all the information he can. I cannot understand why they are taking so long to operate. There is something very wrong with me, I think, and they must operate as quickly as possible. The man with the clipboard walks out of the room. He will send the priest in soon.

I lie in the room alone staring at the walls, still sucking the air, determined to live more than ever now.

The priest seems to appear suddenly above my head. With his fingers he is gently touching my forehead, rubbing it slowly and softly. "How are you," he says.

"I'm fine, Father." His face is very tired but it is not frightened. He is almost at ease, as if what he is doing he has done many times before.

"I have come to give you the Last Rites, my son."

"I'm ready, Father," I say.

And he prays, rubbing oils on my face and placing the crucifix to my lips. "I will pray for you," he says.

"When will they operate?" I say to the priest.

"I do not know," he says. "The doctors are very busy. There are many wounded. There is not much time for anything here but trying to live. So you must try to live my son, and I will pray for you."

Soon after that I am taken to a long room where there are many doctors and nurses. They move quickly around me. They are acting very competent. "You will be fine," says one nurse calmly.

"Breathe deeply into the mask," the doctor says.

"Are you going to operate?" I ask.

"Yes. Now breathe deeply into the mask." As the darkness of the mask slowly covers my face I pray with all my being that I will live through this operation and see the light of day once again. I want to live so much. And even before I go to sleep with the blackness still swirling around my head and the numbness of sleep, I begin to fight as I have never fought before in my life.

I awake to the screams of other men around me. I have made it. I think that maybe the wound is my punishment for killing the corporal and the children. That now everything is okay and the score is evened up. And now I am packed in this place with the others who have been wounded like myself, strapped onto a strange circular bed. I feel tubes going into my nose and hear the clanking, pumping sound of a machine. I still cannot feel any of my body but I know I am alive. I feel a terrible pain in my chest. My body is so cold. It has never been this weak. It feels so tired and out of touch, so lost and in pain. I can still barely breathe. I look around me, at people moving in shadows of numbness. There is the man who had been in the ambulance with me, screaming louder than ever, kicking his bloody stumps in the air, crying for his mother, crying for his morphine.

Directly across from me there is a Korean who has not even been in the war at all. The nurse says he was going to buy a newspaper when he stepped on a booby trap and it blew off both his legs and his arm. And all that is left now is this slab of meat swinging one arm crazily in the air, moaning like an animal gasping for its last bit of life, knowing that death is rushing toward him. The Korean is screaming like a madman at the top of his lungs. I cannot wait for the shots of morphine. Oh, the morphine feels so good. It makes everything dark and quiet. I can rest. I can leave this madness. I can dream of my back yard once again.

When I wake they are screaming still and the lights are on and the clock, the clock on the wall, I can hear it ticking to the sound of their screams. I can hear the dead being carted out and the new wounded being brought in to the beds all around me. I have to get out of this place.

"Can I call you by your first name?" I say to the nurse.

"No. My name is Lieutenant Wiecker."

"Please, can I . . ."

"No," she says. "It's against regulations."

I'm sleeping now. The lights are flashing. The black pilot is next to me. He says nothing. He stares at the ceiling all day long. He does nothing but that. But something is happening now, something is going wrong over there. The nurse is shouting for the machine, and the corpsman is crawling on the black man's chest, he has his knees on his chest and he's pounding it with his fists again and again.

"His heart has stopped!" screams the nurse.

Pounding, pounding, he's pounding his fist into his chest. "Get the machine!" screams the corpsman.

The nurse is pulling the machine across the hangar floor as quickly as she can now. They are trying to put curtains around the whole thing, but the curtains keep slipping and falling down. Everyone, all the wounded who can still see and think, now watch what is happening to the pilot, and it is happening right next to me. The doctor hands the corpsman a syringe, they are laughing as the corpsman drives the syringe into the pilot's chest like a knife. They are talking about the Green Bay Packers and the corpsman is driving his fist into the black man's chest again and again until the black pilot's body begins to bloat up, until it doesn't look like a body at all anymore. His face is all puffy like a balloon and saliva rolls slowly from the sides of his mouth. He keeps staring at the ceiling and saying nothing. "The machine! The machine!" screams the doctor, now climbing on top of the bed, taking the corpsman's place. "Turn on the machine!" screams the doctor.

He grabs a long suction cup that is attached to the machine and places it carefully against the

2

THE BUS TURNED off a side street and onto the parkway, then into Queens where the hospital was. For the first time on the whole trip everyone was laughing and joking. He felt himself begin to wake up out of the nightmare. This whole area was home to him—the streets, the parkway, he knew them like the back of his hand. The air was fresh and cold and the bus rocked back and forth. "This bus sucks!" yelled a kid. "Can't you guys do any better than this? I want my mother, I want my mother."

The pain twisted into his back, but he laughed with the rest of them—the warriors, the wounded, entering the gates of St. Albans Naval Hospital. The guard waved them in and the bus stopped. He was the last of the men to be taken off the bus. They had to carry him off. He got the impression that he was quite an oddity in his steel frame, crammed inside it like a flattened pancake.

They put him on the neuro ward. It was sterile and quiet. I'm with the vegetables again, he thought. It took a long while to get hold of a nurse. He told her that if they didn't get the top of the frame off his back he would start screaming. They took it off him and moved him back downstairs to another ward. This was a ward for men with open wounds. They put him there because of his heel, which had been all smashed by the first bullet, the back of it blown completely out.

He was now in Ward I-C with fifty other men who had all been recently wounded in the war—twenty-year-old blind men and amputees, men without intestines, men who limped, men who were in wheelchairs, men in pain. He noticed they all had strange smiles on their faces and he had one too, he thought. They were men who had played with death and cheated it at a very young age.

He lay back in his bed and watched everything happen all around him. He went to therapy every day and worked very hard lifting weights. He had to build up the top of his body if he was ever going to walk again. In Da Nang the doctors had told him to get used to the idea that he would have to sit in a wheelchair for the rest of his life. He had accepted it, but more and more he was dreaming and thinking about walking. He prayed every night after the visitors left. He closed his eyes and dreamed of being on his feet again.

Sometimes the American Legion group from his town came in to see him, the men and their wives and their pretty daughters. They would all surround him in his bed. It would seem to him that he was always having to cheer them up more than they were cheering him. They told him he was a hero and that all of Massapequa was proud of him. One time the commander stood up and said they were even thinking of naming a street after him. But the guy's wife was embarrassed and made her husband shut up. She told him the commander was kidding—he tended to get carried away after a couple of beers.

After he had been in the hospital a couple of weeks, a man appeared one morning and handed him a large envelope. He waited until the man had gone to open it up. Inside was a citation and a medal for Conspicuous Service to the State of New York. The citation was signed by Governor Rockefeller. He stuck the envelope and all the stuff in it under his pillow.

None of the men on the wards were civilian yet, so they had reveille at six o'clock in the morning. All the wounded who could get on their feet were made to stand in front of their beds while a roll call was taken. After roll call they all had to make their beds and do a general clean-up of the entire ward—everything from scrubbing the floors to cleaning the windows. Even the amputees had to do it. No one ever bothered him, though. He usually slept through the whole thing.

Later it would be time for medication, and afterward one of the corpsmen would put him in a wheelchair and push him to the shower room. The corpsman would leave him alone for about five minutes, then pick his body up, putting him on a wooden bench, his legs dangling, his toes barely touching the floor. He would sit in the shower like that every morning watching his legs become smaller and smaller, until after a month the muscle tone had all but disappeared. With despair and frustration he watched his once strong twenty-one-year-old body become crippled and disfigured. He was just beginning to understand the nature of his wound. He knew now it was the worst he could have received without dying or becoming a vegetable.

More and more he thought about what a priest had said to him in Da Nang: "Your fight is just beginning. Sometimes no one will want to hear what you're going through. You are going to have to learn to carry a great burden and most of your learning will be done alone. Don't feel frightened when they leave you. I'm sure you will come through it all okay."

I AM IN a new hospital now. Things are very different than in the last place. It is quiet in the early morning. There is no reveille here. The sun is just beginning to come in through the windows and I can hear the steady dripping of the big plastic bags that overflow with urine onto the floor. The aide comes in the room, a big black woman. She goes to Willey's bed across from me, almost stepping in the puddle of urine. She takes the cork out of the metal thing in his neck and sticks a long rubber tube in, then clicks on the machine by the bed. There is a loud sucking slurping sound. She moves the rubber tube around and around until it sucks all the stuff out of his lungs. After she is done she puts the cork back in his throat and leaves the room.

There are people talking down at the end of the hall. The night shift is getting ready to go home. They are laughing very loud and flushing the toilets, cursing and telling jokes, black men in white uniforms walking past my door. I shut my eyes. I try to get back into the dream I was having.

She is so pretty, so warm and naked lying next to me. She kisses me and begins to unbutton my hospital shirt. "I love you," I hear her say. "I love you." I open my eyes. Something strange is tickling my nose.

It is Tommy the enema man and today is my day to get my enema. "Hey Kovic," Tommy is saying. "Hey Kovic, wake up, I got an enema for you."

She kisses my lips softly at first, then puts her tongue into my mouth. I am running my hands through her hair and she tells me that she loves that. She is unbuttoning my trousers now and her hand is working itself deep down into my pants. I keep driving my tongue into her more furiously than ever. We have just been dancing on the floor, I was dancing very funny like a man on stilts, but now we are making love and just above me I hear a voice trying to wake me again.

"Kovic! I have an enema for you. Come on. We gotta get you outta here."

I feel myself being lifted. Tommy and another aide, a young black woman, picked me up, carefully unhooking my tube. They put my body into the frame, tying my legs down with long white twisted sheets. They lay another big sheet over me. The frame has a long metal bar that goes above my head. My rear end sticks out of a slit that I lie on.

"Okay," shouts Tommy in his gravel voice. "This one's ready to go."

The aide pushes me into the line-up in the hallway. There are frames all over the place now, lined up in front of the blue room for their enemas. It is the Six o'Clock Special. There are maybe twenty guys waiting by now. It looks like a long train, a long assembly line of broken, twisted bodies waiting for deliverance. It is very depressing, all these bodies, half of them asleep, tied down to their frames with their rear ends sticking out. All these bodies bloated, waiting to be released. Every third day I go for my enema and wait with the long line of men shoved against the green hospital wall. I watch the dead bodies being pushed into the enema room, then finally myself.

It is a small blue room and they cram us into it like sardines. Tommy runs back and forth placing the bedpans under our rear ends, laughing and joking, a cigarette dangling from the corner of his mouth. "Okay, okay, let's go!" he shouts. There is a big can of soapy water above each man's head and a tube that comes down from it. Tommy is jumping all around and whistling like a little kid, running to each body, sticking the rubber tubes up into them. He is jangling the pans, undoing little clips on the rubber tubes and filling the bellies up with soapy water. Everyone is trying to sleep, refusing to admit that this whole thing is happening to them. A couple of the bodies in the frames have small radios close to their ears. Tommy keeps running from one frame to the other, changing the rubber gloves on his hands and squirting the tube of lubricant onto his fingers, ramming his hands up into the rear ends, checking each of the bodies out, undoing the little clips. The aide keeps grabbing the bedpans and emptying all the shit into the garbage cans, occasionally missing and splattering the stuff on the floor. She places the empty pans in a machine and closes it up. There is a steam sound and the machine opens with all the bedpans as clean as new.

Oh God, what is happening to me? What is going on here? I want to get out of this place! All these broken men are very depressing, all these bodies so emaciated and twisted in these bedsheets. This is a nightmare. This isn't like the poster down by the post office where the guy stood with the shiny shoes; this is a concentration camp. It is like the pictures of all the Jews that I have seen. This is as horrible as that. I want to scream. I want to yell and tell them that I want out of this. All of this, all these people, this place, these sounds, I want out of this forever. I am only twenty-one and there is still so much ahead of me, there is so much ahead of me.

I am wiped clean and pushed past the garbage cans. The stench is terrible. I try to breathe through my mouth but I can't. I'm trapped. I have to watch, I have to smell. I think the war has made me a little mad—the dead corporal from Georgia, the old man that was shot in the village with his brains hanging out. But it is the living deaths I am breathing and smelling now, the living deaths, the bodies broken in the same war that I have come from.

I am outside now in the narrow hallway. The young black woman is pushing my frame past all the other steel contraptions. I look at her face for a moment, at her eyes, as she pushes my frame up against another. I can hear the splashing of water next door in the shower room. The sun has come up in the Bronx and people are walking through the hallways. They can look into all the rooms and see the men through the curtains that never close. It is as if we are a bunch of cattle, as if we do not really count anymore.

They push me into the shower. The black woman takes a green plastic container and squirts it, making a long thin white line from my head to my legs. She is turning on the water, and after making sure it is not too hot she hoses me down.

It's like a car wash, I think, it's just like a big car wash, and I am being pushed and shoved through with the rest of them. I am being checked out by Tommy and hosed off by the woman. It is all such a neat, quick process. It is an incredible thing to run twenty men through a place like this, to clean out the bodies of twenty paralyzed men, twenty bloated twisted men. It is an incredible feat, a stupendous accomplishment, and Tommy is a master. Now the black woman is drying me off with a big white towel and shoving me back into the hallway.

Oh get me back into the room, get me back away from these people who are walking by me and making believe like all the rest that they don't know what's happening here, that they can't figure out that this whole thing is crazy. Oh God, oh God help me, help me understand this place. There goes the nurse and she's running down the hall, hitting the rubber mat that throws open the big green metal door with the little windows with the wire in them. Oh nurse please help me nurse, my stomach is beginning to hurt again like it does every time I come out of this place and my head is throbbing, pounding like a drum. I want to get out of this hall where all of you are walking past me. I want to get back into my bed where I can make believe this never happened. I want to go to sleep and forget I ever got up this morning.

I never tell my family when they come to visit about the enema room. I do not tell them what I do every morning with the plastic glove, or about the catheter and the tube in my penis, or the fact that I can't ever make it hard again. I hide all that from them and talk about the other, more pleasant things, the things they want to hear. I ask Mom to bring me *Sunrise at Campobello*, the play about the life of Franklin Roosevelt—the great crisis he had gone through when he had been stricken with polio and the comeback he had made, becoming governor, then president of the United States. There are things I am going through here that I know she will never understand.

I feel like a big clumsy puppet with all his strings cut. I learn to balance and twist in the chair so no one can tell how much of me does not feel or move anymore. I find it easy to hide from most of them what I am going through. All of us are like this. No one wants too many people to know how much of him has really died in the war.

At first I felt that the wound was very interesting. I saw it almost as an adventure. But now it is not an adventure any longer. I see it more and more as a terrible thing that I will have to live with for the rest of my life. Nobody wants to know that I can't fuck anymore. I will never go up to them and tell them I have this big yellow rubber thing sticking in my penis, attached to the rubber bag on the side of my leg. I am afraid of letting them know how lonely and scared I have become thinking about this wound. It is like some kind of numb twilight zone to me. I am angry and want to kill everyone—all the volunteers and the priests and the pretty girls with the tight short skirts. I am twenty-one and the whole thing is shot, done forever. There is no real healing left anymore, everything that is going to heal has healed already and now I am left with the corpse, the living dead man, the man with the numb legs, the man in the wheelchair, the Easter Seal boy, the cripple, the sexlessman, the sexlessman, the man with the numb dick, the man who can't make children, the man who can't stand, the man who can't walk, the angry lonely man, the bitter man with the nightmares, the murder man, the man who cries in the shower.

In one big bang they have taken it all from me, in one clean sweep, and now I am in this place around all the others like me, and though I keep trying not to feel sorry for myself, I want to cry. There is no shortcut around this thing. It is too soon to die even for a man who has died once already.

I try to keep telling myself it is good to still be alive, to be back home. I remember thinking on the ambulance ride to the hospital that this was the Bronx, the place where Yankee Stadium was, where Mickey Mantle played. I think I realized then also that my feet would never touch the stadium grass, ever again; I would never play a game in that place.

The wards are filthy. The men in my room throw their breadcrumbs under the radiator to keep the rats from chewing on our numb legs during the nights. We tuck our bodies in with the sheets wrapped around us. There are never enough aides to go around on the wards, and constantly there is complaining by the men. The most severely injured are totally dependent on the aides to turn them. They suffer the most and break down with sores. These are the voices that can be heard screaming in the night for help that never comes. Urine bags are constantly overflowing onto the floors while the aides play poker on the toilet bowls in the enema room. The sheets are never changed enough and many of the men stink from not being properly bathed. It never makes any sense to us how the government can keep asking money for weapons and leave us lying in our own filth.

Briggs throws his bread over the radiator.

"There he goes again," says Garcia. "That goddamn rat's been there for the last two months."

Briggs keeps the rats in our room well fed. "It's a lot better than having the bastards nibble at your toes during the night," he says with a crazy laugh.

The nurse comes in and Garcia is getting real excited. "I think I pissed in my pants again," he cries. "Mrs. Waters, I think I pissed in my pants."

"Oh Garcia," the pretty nurse scolds, "don't say *piss*, say *urine*. *Urine* is much nicer."

Garcia tells her he is sorry and will call it urine from here on out.

Willey is clicking his tongue again and the nurse goes over to see. "What do you want?" she says to Willey. He is the most wounded of us all. He has lost everything from the neck down. He has lost even more than me. He is just a head. The war has taken everything.

He clicks three times. The nurse knows he wants the stuff sucked out of his lungs, so she does it. Garcia's radio is playing in the background. She slurps all of the stuff out, then walks out of the room. Now Briggs is getting the whiskey bottle out of his top drawer, taking big gulps and cursing out the rats that are still running under the radiator.

Someone please help me understand this thing, this terrible thing that's happening to me. I'm a brave man and I want to be brave even with this wound. I want to understand how I can live with it and with everything else that happened over there, the dead corporal from Georgia and all the other crazy things.

I find a place on the side of the hospital where the old men sit. The grass is very green and they feed the birds from their wheelchairs. They are the old men from the First World War, I am sure of that, and I sit next to them and feed the birds too. I just want to slow down, the whole thing has been moving much too fast, like some wild spinning top, and now I am trying to catch my breath, I am trying to figure out what this whole terrible thing is about.

I read the paper every morning and it always says the war is going on and the president is sending more troops, and I still tell people, whoever asks me, that I believe in the war. Didn't I prove it by going back a second time? I look them all right in the eye and tell them that we are winning and the boys' morale is high. But more and more what I tell them and what I am feeling are becoming two different things. I feel them tearing, tearing at my whole being, and I don't want to talk about the war anymore. I feed the birds and the squirrels. I want things to be simple again, things are just too confusing. The hospital is like the whole war all over again.

The aides, the big tall black guys who spit and sit on the toilet bowls all night, they're doing it again, they're picking up the paralyzed drunks from the hallways, they're wheeling them along the halls to the rooms. Now I see them strapping the men into big lifts, hoisting the drunken bodies back into their beds. And the aides are laughing, they're always laughing the way people laugh at a sideshow, it's all pretty funny to them. We are like a show of puppets dancing on strings for them, dancing to maddening music. They're wheeling all the guys in from the halls because it's late and it's time for all of the bodies to be put back into the beds, for all the tubes to be hooked up, and the drip of the piss bags to start all over again.

There's a train in the Bronx, somewhere out over the Harlem River, and it sounds so good, it sounds warm and wonderful like the heater back home, like the Long Island train that I used to hear as a kid. Pat, the new guy, is crying for help. He's puking into the cup again and he's cursing out everybody, he's cursing the place and the nurses, the doctors. He's asking me if I still have my Bible and he's laughing real loud now, he's laughing so loud the other men are telling him to shut up, to be quiet and let them go to sleep. It's a madhouse, it's a crazy house, it's a wild zoo, and we're the animals, we're the animals all neatly tucked into these beds, waking up every morning puking at the green walls and smelling the urine on the floor. We're hurting and we're praying that we can get out of this place. Somebody, give us back our bodies!

And each day I train in an exercise room that is very crowded with broken men, bodies being bent and twisted, put up on the parallel bars. Our therapists, Jimmy and Dick, train us hard. We put on braces and crawl on the floor. We're pissing in our pants and crawling into the bathtub. We're jumping up and down the curb, learning how to use our wheelchairs. There is a big wheel in the corner and they're strapping a puny guy with glasses to it. I'm watching the clock and the kid is trying to spin the big wheel around. There are machines like the wheel all over the place, and there's pain on all the faces. Some of us are trying to laugh, we're talking about the beer that comes into the hospital in the brown paper bags. But you cannot mistake the pain. The kid with the long hair is in the hallway again, the kid who looks in and never does anything but look in.

Now I'm grabbing the weights, twenty-five-pound weights, I'm grabbing them and lifting them up and down, up and down, until my shoulders ache, until I can't lift anymore. I'm still lifting them even after that, I'm still lifting them and Jimmy is talking about his model airplanes and then he and Dick are lifting me up to the high bar. There are newly invented machines sold to the hospital by the government to make the men well, to take all the Willeys and the Garcias and make them well again, to fix these broken bodies. There are machines that make you stand again and machines that fix your hands again, but the only thing is that when it's all over, when the guys are pulled down from the machines, unstrapped from them, it's the same body, the same shattered broken man that went up on the rack moments before, and this is what we are all beginning to live with, this is what the kid standing in the hallway is saying with his eyes.

It's early in the afternoon. I'm standing on my braces, holding on to the parallel bars. My mother and little sister have just come through the doorway. It is the first chance for them to see me try to stand again. My mother is frightened, you can tell by the look on her face, and my sister is standing next to her trying to smile. They are holding each other's hands.

My legs are shaking in terrible spasms. They're putting thick straps around my waist and around my legs and now my arms start to shake furiously. My mother and sister are still standing in the hallway. They haven't decided to come into the room yet. Jimmy is strapping my arms along the pole and my big oversized blue hospital pants are falling down below my waist. My rear end is sticking out and Jimmy is smiling, looking over to my mother in the corner.

"See," says Jimmy, "he's standing."

I start throwing up all over the place, all over the blue hospital shirt and onto the floor, just below the machine. Jimmy quickly undoes the straps and puts me back in the chair. My sister and my mother are clutching each other, holding real tight to each other's hands.

"It's really a great machine," Jimmy says. "We have a couple more coming in real soon."

I turn the chair toward the window and look out across the Harlem River to where the cars are going over the bridge like ants.

3

FOR ME IT began in 1946 when I was born on the Fourth of July. The whole sky lit up in a tremendous fireworks display and my mother told me the doctor said I was a real firecracker. Every birthday after that was something the whole country celebrated. It was a proud day to be born on.

I hit a home run my first time at bat in the Massapequa Little League, and I can still remember my Mom and Dad and all the rest of the kids going crazy as I rounded the bases on seven errors and slid into home a hero. We lost the game to the Midgets that night, 22 to 7, and I cried all the way home. It was a long time ago, but sometimes I can still hear them shouting out in front of Pete's house on Hamilton Avenue. There was Bobby Zimmer, the tall kid from down the street, Kenny and Pete, little Tommy Law, and my best friend Richie Castiglia, who lived across from us on Lee Place.

Baseball was good to me and I played it all I

could. I got this baseball mitt when I was seven. I had to save up my allowance for it and cash in some soda bottles. It was a cheap piece of shit, but it seemed pretty nice, I mean it seemed beautiful to me before Bobby and some of the other guys tore the hell out of it.

I remember that I loved baseball more than anything else in the world and my favorite team was the New York Yankees. Every chance I got I watched the games on the TV in my house with Castiglia, waiting for Mickey Mantle to come to the plate. We'd turn up the sound of the television as the crowd went wild roaring like thunder. I'd run over to Richie's house screaming to his mother to tell Richie that Mantle was at bat.

And Richie would come running over with his mitt making believe we were at Yankee Stadium sitting in our box seats right in back of the Yankee dugout and when Mantle hit a homer you could hear the TV halfway down the block. Richie and I would go completely nuts hugging each other and jumping up and down with tears streaming down our faces. Mantle was our hero. He was like a god to us, a huge golden statue standing in center field. Every time the cameras showed him on the screen I couldn't take my eyes off him.

Back then the Yankees kept winning like they would never stop. It was hard to remember them ever losing, and when we weren't watching them on TV or down at the stadium, Kenny Goodman and I were at Parkside Field playing catch-a-fly-you're-up for hours with a beat-up old baseball we kept together with black electrician's tape. We played all day long out there, running across that big open field with all our might, diving and sliding face-first into the grass, making one-handed, spectacular catches. I used to make believe I was Mel Allen, screaming at the top of my lungs, "Did you see that?! Did you see that, folks?! Kovic has just made a tremendous catch and the crowd is going wild! They're jumping up and down all over the stadium! What a catch, ladies and gentlemen, what a tremendous catch by Kovic!" And I did that all afternoon, running back and forth across the gigantic field. I was Mickey Mantle, Willie Mays, and all my heroes, rolled into one.

When we weren't down at the field or watching the Yankees on TV, we were playing whiffle ball and climbing trees checking out birds' nests, going down to Fly Beach in Mrs. Zimmer's old car that honked the horn every time it turned the corner, diving underwater with our masks, kicking with our rubber frog's feet, then running in and out of our sprinklers when we got home, waiting for our turn in the shower. And during the summer nights we were all over the neighborhood, from Bobby's house to Kenny's, throwing gliders, doing handstands and backflips off fences, riding to the woods at the end of the block on our bikes, making rafts, building tree forts, jumping across the streams with tree branches, walking and balancing along the back fence like Houdini, hopping along the slate path all around the back yard seeing how far we could go on one foot.

And I ran wherever I went. Down to the school, to the candy store, to the deli, buying baseball cards and Bazooka bubblegum that had the little fortunes at the bottom of the cartoons.

When the Fourth of July came, there were fireworks going off all over the neighborhood. It was the most exciting time of year for me next to Christmas. Being born on the exact same day as my country I thought was really great. I was so proud. And every Fourth of July, I had a birthday party and all my friends would come over with birthday presents and we'd put on silly hats and blow these horns my Dad brought home from the A&P. We'd eat lots of ice cream and watermelon and I'd open up all the presents and blow out the candles on the big red, white, and blue birthday cake and then we'd all sing "Happy Birthday" and "I'm a Yankee Doodle Dandy." At night everyone would pile into Bobby's mother's old car and we'd go down to the drive-in, where we'd watch the fireworks display. Before the movie started, we'd all get out and sit up on the roof of the car with our blankets wrapped around us watching the rockets and Roman candles going up and exploding into fountains of rainbow colors, and later after Mrs. Zimmer dropped me off, I'd lie on my bed feeling a little sad that it all had to end so soon. As I closed my eyes I could still hear strings of firecrackers and cherry bombs going off all over the neighborhood.

The whole block grew up watching television. There was Howdy Doody and Rootie Kazootie, Cisco Kid and Gabby Hayes, Roy Rogers and Dale Evans. The Lone Ranger was on Channel 7. We watched cartoons for hours on Saturdays—Beanie and Cecil, Crusader Rabbit, Woody Woodpecker—and a show with puppets called Kukla, Fran, and Ollie. I sat on the rug in the living room watching Captain Video take off in his spaceship and saw thousands of savages killed by Ramar of the Jungle.

I remember Elvis Presley on the Ed Sullivan Show and my sister Sue going crazy in the living room jumping up and down. He kept twanging this big guitar and wiggling his hips, but for some reason they were mostly showing just the top of him. My mother was sitting on the couch with her hands folded in her lap like she was praying, and my dad was in the other room talking about how the Church had advised us all that Sunday that watching Elvis Presley could lead to sin.

I loved God more than anything else in the world back then and I prayed to Him and the Virgin Mary and Jesus and all the saints to be a good boy and a good American. Every night before I went to sleep I knelt down in front of my bed, making the sign of the cross and cupping my hands over my face, sometimes praying so hard I would cry. I asked every night to be good enough to make the major leagues someday. With God anything was possible. I made my first Holy Communion with a cowboy hat on my head and two six-shooters in my hands.

On Saturday nights, Mrs. Jacket drove us to confession, where we waited in line to tell the priest our sins, then walked out of the church feeling refreshed and happy with God and the world again. And then Dad and I and the rest of the kids went to church on Sundays. The church was a big place. It was the most enormous place I'd ever seen, with real quiet people sitting up straight and mumbling things. And I remember smelling this stuff and seeing the priest moving back and forth behind the altar, speaking in words we never understood.

And the Sunday comics and Dad cooking big breakfasts of hash brown potatoes and eggs, filling our bellies and making us feel warm and good inside. After breakfast I read the colorful comics on the living-room rug. There was Dick Tracy and Beetle Bailey, Dagwood and Blondie, Terry and the Pirates, Prince Valiant and Donald Duck, Dondi and Mickey Mouse, Bugs Bunny, Uncle Scrooge and Gasoline Alley.

My father was a checker at the A&P. He worked real hard. He was like a big hurricane, always moving with his big strong arms, raking the leaves in the back yard or building new parts to our little house. One summer I remember hammering nails on the roof with him and feeling proud to be up there with him doing all that hard work. Sometimes, he'd get angry because all of us weren't working, or cleaning or just acting busy. It seemed important to be moving whenever he was around and acting busy if you didn't have anything to do.

We were always moving, all the kids on the block and me, like there was no tomorrow. We cut up our mothers' broomsticks, hiding the brooms in the basement and taking the sticks out to

Hamilton Avenue for that night's stickball game, where we'd belt high-bouncing Spalding balls for hours off Kenny's roof and into little Tommy Law's hedge. We hit eggballs that used to spin crazily sideways with everyone screaming "Eggball! Eggball!" seeing if the guy who was pitching on one bounce could handle the lopsided pop-up. Whoever hit the ball past the second telephone pole right in back of Kenny's father's station wagon, or over Tommy Law's hedge, made a home run. We played every night in the spring and the summer until it was dark and the only light left on Hamilton Avenue was the street lamp.

We collected Topps baseball cards of our favorite players and traded them and flipped them and scaled them down against the wall at Turner's Bar.

In the spring we dug up worms and went fishing with Bobby Zimmer. I made a Morse code set with Castiglia, stringing the telegraph wires across the street to his house. We did science experiments with his chemistry set and Bobby and I played red-light-green-light on summer nights when Mom was taking the clothes off the line. And when it got dark my sister Sue and I chased fireflies with glass jars.

In the fall we played touch football in the streets and raked the summer leaves that had turned brown and fallen from the trees. We and our fathers swept them and piled them and packed them into wire baskets by the sides of our houses, burning them and watching the bright embers swirl in the wind. And the trees again stood naked in the back yard like they did every fall and winter and the air became fresh and cold and soon there was ice on the puddles in the streets outside our houses.

We'd all go back to school and for me it was always a frightening experience. I could never understand what was happening there. I remember once they called my mother and told her I had been staring out the window. I tried to listen to them, and sit in the chair behind the desk like they told me to, but I kept looking out that window at the trees and the sky. I couldn't wait until the last day of school when we all ran out of our classrooms, jumping up and down, throwing our books in the air, singing and shouting "No more pencils, no more books, no more teachers' dirty looks!" We were free. And another summer vacation began for all of us on the block.

When the first snow came we'd get our sleds out of the basement and belly-whop on sheets of ice out on Lee Place in front of Richie's house. We had snowball fights and built snow forts and snowmen. Castiglia and I and Bobby Zimmer used to grab the back bumpers of cars and see how far we could slide down the street on our shoes. Kenny and I would hide in Parkside Woods plastering the cars that passed along the boulevard with ice balls, then get Bobby and Pete and the rest of the guys and go down to Suicide Hill, a tremendous steep hill by the woods, frozen like glass, with a tree stump at the bottom you had to swerve around. Me and Bobby would head straight for it, and just before we were about to hit it,

I'd jam the wooden steering bar with my foot, throwing up sparks and ice, just missing the stump by inches. Then both of us would spin off the sled, rolling down the hill on top of each other, around and around, laughing into a huge snowdrift. We made winter gloves out of our father's socks, packing snowballs with them until they became soaked and frozen and our fingers would become numb and we'd have to take them off. I loved when it snowed, and so did all the rest of the guys on the block.

Every Saturday afternoon we'd all go down to the movies in the shopping center and watch gigantic prehistoric birds breathe fire, and war movies with John Wayne and Audie Murphy. Bobbie's mother always packed us a bagful of candy. I'll never forget Audie Murphy in *To Hell and Back.* At the end he jumps on top of a flaming tank that's just about to explode and grabs the machine gun blasting it into the German lines. He was so brave I had chills running up and down my back, wishing it were me up there. There were gasoline flames roaring around his legs, but he just kept firing that machine gun. It was the greatest movie I ever saw in my life.

Castiglia and I saw *The Sands of Iwo Jima* together. The Marine Corps hymn was playing in the background as we sat glued to our seats, humming the hymn together and watching Sergeant Stryker, played by John Wayne, charge up the hill and get killed just before he reached the top. And then they showed the men raising the flag on Iwo Jima with the marines' hymn still playing, and Castiglia and I cried in our seats. I loved the song so much, and every time I heard it I would think of John Wayne and the brave men who raised the flag on Iwo Jima that day. I would think of them and cry. Like Mickey Mantle and the fabulous New York Yankees, John Wayne in *The Sands of Iwo Jima* became one of my heroes.

We'd go home and make up movies like the ones we'd just seen or the ones that were on TV night after night. We'd use our Christmas toys—the Matty Mattel machine guns and grenades, the little green plastic soldiers with guns and flamethrowers in their hands. My favorites were the green plastic men with bazookas. They blasted holes through the enemy. They wiped them out at thirty feet just above the coffee table. They dug in on the front lawn and survived countless artillery attacks. They burned with high-propane lighter fluid and a quarter-gallon of gasoline or were thrown into the raging fires of autumn leaves blasting into a million pieces.

On Saturdays after the movies all the guys would go down to Sally's Woods—Pete and Kenny and Bobbie and me, with plastic battery-operated machine guns, cap pistols, and sticks. We turned the woods into a battlefield. We set ambushes, then led gallant attacks, storming over the top, bayonetting and shooting anyone who got in our way. Then we'd walk out of the woods like the heroes we knew we would become when we were men.

The army had a show on Channel 2 called "The

Big Picture," and after it was over Castiglia and I crawled all over the back yard playing guns and army, making commando raids all summer into Ackerman's housing project blasting away at the imaginary enemy we had created right before our eyes, throwing dirt bombs and rocks into the windows, making loud explosions like hand grenades with our voices then charging in with our Matty Mattel machine guns blazing. I bandaged up the German who was still alive and had Castiglia question him as I threw a couple more grenades, killing even more Germans. We went on countless missions and patrols together around my back yard, attacking Ackerman's housing project with everything from bazookas to flamethrowers and baseball bats. We studied the Marine Corps Guidebook and Richie brought over some beautiful pamphlets with very sharp-looking marines on the covers. We read them in my basement for hours and just as we dreamed of playing for the Yankees someday, we dreamed of becoming United States Marines and fighting our first war and we made a solemn promise that year that the day we turned seventeen we were both going down to the marine recruiter at the shopping center in Levittown and sign up for the United States Marine Corps.

We joined the cub scouts and marched in parades on Memorial Day. We made contingency plans for the cold war and built fallout shelters out of milk cartons. We wore spacesuits and space helmets. We made rocket ships out of cardboard boxes. And one Saturday afternoon in the basement Castiglia and I went to Mars on the couch we had turned into a rocket ship. We read books about the moon and Wernher von Braun. And the whole block watched a thing called the space race begin. On a cold October night Dad and I watched the first satellite, called *Sputnik,* moving across the sky above our house like a tiny bright star. I still remember standing out there with Dad looking up in amazement at that thing moving in the sky above Massapequa. It was hard to believe that this thing, this *Sputnik,* was so high up and moving so fast around the world, again and again. Dad put his hand on my shoulder that night and without saying anything I quietly walked back inside and went to my room thinking that the Russians had beaten America into space and wondering why we couldn't even get a rocket off the pad.

It seemed that whole school year we talked about nothing but rockets and how they would break away into stages and blast their satellites into outer space. I got all the books I could on rockets and outer space and read them for hours in the library, completely fascinated by the drawings and the telescopes and the sky charts. I had an incredible rocket I got for Christmas that you had to pump compressed water into. I pulled back a plastic clip and it would send the thing blasting out across Castiglia's lawn, then out onto Hamilton Avenue in a long arc of spurting water. Castiglia and I used to tape aluminum-foil rolls from Mom's kitchen to the top of the plastic rocket then put ants and worms in the nosecone with a secret message wrapped in tissue paper. We had hundreds of rocket launchings that year. Though none of our payloads made it into orbit like the Sputniks, we had a lot of fun trying.

In the spring of that year I remember the whole class went down to New York City and saw the movie *Around the World in Eighty Days* on a tremendous screen that made all of us feel like we were right there in the balloon flying around the world. After the movie we went to the Museum of Natural History, where Castiglia and I walked around staring up at the huge prehistoric dinosaurs billions of years old, and studied fossils inside the big glass cases and wondered what it would have been like if we had been alive back then. After the museum they took us to the Hayden Planetarium, where the whole sixth-grade class leaned back in special sky chairs, looking up into the dome where a projector that looked like a huge mechanical praying mantis kept us glued to the sky above our heads with meteor showers and comets and galaxies that appeared like tremendous snowstorms swirling in the pitch darkness of the incredible dome. They showed the whole beginning of the earth that afternoon, as we sat back in our chairs and dreamed of walking on the moon someday or going off to Mars wondering if there really was life there and rocketing off deeper and deeper into space through all the time barriers into places and dreams we could only begin to imagine. When we got on the school bus afterward and were all seated, Mr. Serby, our sixth-grade teacher, turned around and in a soft voice told us that someday men would walk upon the moon, and probably in our lifetime, he said, we would see it happen.

We were still trying to catch up with the Russians when I heard on the radio that the United States was going to try and launch its first satellite, called *Vanguard,* into outer space. That night Mom and Dad and me and the rest of the kids watched the long pencil-like rocket on the television screen as it began to lift off after the countdown. It lifted off slowly at first. And then, almost as if in slow motion, it exploded into a tremendous fireball on the launching pad. It had barely gotten off the ground, and I cried that night in my living room. I cried watching *Vanguard* that night on the evening news with Mom and all the rest. It was a sad day for our country, I thought, it was a sad day for America. We had failed in our first attempt to put a satellite into orbit. I walked slowly back to my room. We were losing, I thought, we were losing the space race, and America wasn't first anymore.

When *Vanguard* finally made it into space, I was in junior high school, and right in the middle of the class the loudspeaker interrupted us and the principal in a very serious voice told us that something very important was about to happen. He talked about history, and how important the day was, how America was finally going to launch its first satellite and we would remember it for a long time.

There was a long countdown as we all sat on the edge of our seats, tuning our ears in to the radio. And then the rocket began to lift off the edge of the launching pad. In the background there was the tremendous roar of the rocket engines and a guy was screaming like Mel Allen that the rocket was lifting off. "It's lifting off! It's lifting off!" he kept screaming crazily. All the kids were silent for a few seconds, still straining in their chairs, waiting to see whether the rocket would make it or not, then the whole room broke into cheers and applause. America had done it! We had put our first satellite into space. "We did it! We did it!" the guy was screaming at the top of his lungs.

And now America was finally beginning to catch up with the Russians and each morning before I went to school I was watching "I Led Three Lives" on television about this guy who joins the Communists but is actually working for us. And I remember thinking how brave he was, putting his life on the line for his country, making believe he was a Communist, and all the time being on our side, getting information from them so we could keep the Russians from taking over our government. He seemed like a very serious man, and he had a wife and a kid and he went to secret meetings, calling his friends comrades in a low voice, and talking through newspapers on park benches.

The Communists were all over the place back then. And if they weren't trying to beat us into outer space, Castiglia and I were certain they were infiltrating our schools, trying to take over our classes and control our minds. We were both certain that one of our teachers was a secret Communist agent and in our next secret club meeting we promised to report anything new he said during our next history class. We watched him very carefully that year. One afternoon he told us that China was going to have a billion people someday. "One billion!" he said, tightly clenching his fist. "Do you know what that means?" he said, staring out the classroom window. "Do you know what that's going to mean?" he said in almost a whisper. He never finished what he was saying and after that Castiglia and I were convinced he was definitely a Communist.

About that time I started doing push-ups in my room and squeezing rubber balls until my arms began to ache, trying to make my body stronger and stronger. I was fascinated by the muscle-men ads in the beginnings of the Superman comics, showing how a skinny guy could overnight transform his body into a hulk of fighting steel, and each day I increased the push-ups, more and more determined to build a strong and healthy body. I made muscles in the mirror for hours and checked my biceps each day with a tape measure, and did pull-ups on a bar in the doorway of my room before I went to school each morning. I was a little guy, back then, and used to put notches with a penny on the door of my room, little scratches with the coin to remind myself how tall I was and to see each week whether I'd grown.

"The human body is an amazing thing," the coaches told us that fall when we started high school. "It is a beautiful remarkable machine that will last you a lifetime if you care for it properly." And we listened to them, and worked and trained our young bodies until they were strong and quick.

I joined the high-school wrestling team, practicing and working out every day down in the basement of Massapequa High School. The coaches made us do sit-ups, push-ups, and spinning drills until sweat poured from our faces and we were sure we'd pass out. "Wanting to win and wanting to be first, that's what's important," the coaches told us. "Play fair, but play to win," they said. They worked us harder and harder until we thought we couldn't take it anymore and then they would yell and shout for us to keep going and drive past all the physical pain and discomfort. "More! More!" they screamed. "If you want to win, then you're going to have to work! You're going to have to drive your bodies far beyond what you think you can do. You've got to pay the price for victory! You can always go further than you think you can."

Wrestling practice ended every day with wind sprints in the basement hallways that left us gasping for air and running into the showers bent over in pain, and I honestly wondered sometimes what I was doing there in the first place and why I was allowing myself to go through all this.

The wrestling coach was very dedicated and held practice every day of the week including Saturdays and Sundays and I can even remember having practice once on Thanksgiving. I came in first in the Christmas wrestling tournament. There's still a picture of me in one of the old albums in the attic that shows me with two other guys holding a cardboard sign with the word *Champion* on it. I won most of my matches that year. When I lost, I cried just like when I lost my Little League games and I'd jump on the bus and ride back to Massapequa with tears in my eyes, not talking to anyone for hours sometimes.

I was very shy back then and dreamed of having a girlfriend, or just someone to hold my hand. Even though I was on the wrestling team and had won all those matches and wore my sweater with the big *M* on it, I still dreamed of the day I could have a girlfriend like all the rest of the guys. I wanted to be hoisted aloft in the arms of other young men like myself and carried off the field for scoring the winning touchdown, or winning the wrestling match that brought the championship to my school.

I wanted to be a hero.

I wanted to be stared at and talked about in the hallways.

"Hey look," said one of the kids. "There goes Kovic!"

I was the great silent athlete now, who never had to say anything, who walked through the halls of Massapequa High School, sucking the air deeply into my chest and pumping up the blood into my arms.

"There goes Kovic," a pretty freshman said. "Boy, he sure is cute." And as I walked through the crowded halls I was sure everyone was noticing me, staring at my varsity letter, and looking at my wrestler's shoulders.

And it was also during my freshman year that I started to get pimples on my face. I remember coming home from school and seeing what looked like a tremendous blackhead on my forehead. It was right smack-dab in the middle of my forehead and it was just like the things that were all over my sister Sue's face. The more I looked in the mirror, the more scared I got. Stevie Jacket's face was covered with the things, he had the worst case of them of anyone I ever knew in my life. In gym I saw him once taking a shower, and his face and neck, all over his arms and back, his whole body was covered with blackheads and whiteheads and thousands of pimples. And now I was catching them, I was getting them just like Stevie Jacket and my sister. There it was, right in front of me in the mirror, a big goddamn blackhead, and after staring at it for almost an hour, I still didn't know what to do. I remembered this girl in the sixth grade who used to have them all over her face and it looked like somebody hit her with a rake. It was awful and she used to put this disgusting filmy cream on, to try and hide them, but it looked worse.

I looked in the medicine cabinet for the little metal thing that my sister used, with tiny openings on each end that you were supposed to press against the pimples and pop them out of your skin forever. So I pressed it up against the blackhead real hard like I was going to take my head off, until it finally oozed out of the pore like a tiny white dot. I kept popping those things all year, and I finally broke down and bought that filmy crap, and started to put it on my face too.

It was about the same time I started to get these ugly hairs under my lip and up in my armpits. I was getting these things all happening at once, and I couldn't stop them, no matter how hard I tried, they all kept coming. I put some Nair under my lip one night because one of the guys in boy scout camp had said that if you shaved with a razor it would grow back twice as fast. So I put on this underarm stuff I found in the closet, it was the stuff that was supposed to take the hair off your legs. Well, I put it under my nose and waited about an hour and then I wiped it off, leaving a big red rash. It looked like a huge gigantic red mustache and I went to school the next week using a handkerchief, trying to hide it and making believe I had a real bad cold. Most of the year was like that, with the pimples all over my face, and by the time the spring came all sorts of other difficult things began to happen.

I felt strange feelings in places I had never discovered before. The part of me that had just been there like everything else now began to get hard and excited every time I looked at a pretty girl. I had never felt anything like it before in my life. That thing, my penis, was getting hard, every time I watched the girls on "American Bandstand" or saw them walking down the streets. They'd even be in my dreams at night. I'd wake up in the mornings with the whole sheet soaked. I felt guilty at first. I actually thought I was committing a sin, dreaming it, thinking it, just watching them. But then one afternoon I crawled on top of a Rawlings basketball in my bedroom and did it for the sheer pleasure of doing it. And it felt good. It felt so good that I did it again after that, and again, and again—with teddy bears in my bed making believe they were Marilyn Monroe, in the bathroom in the bathtub, in the basement laying the side pocket of the pool table seventeen times, in the back yard against trees. I did it everywhere. And no matter how hard I tried I couldn't stop. It got so bad after a while, I started saying Acts of Contrition after doing it. I asked God to forgive me for feeling this thing and then I couldn't understand why I'd be asking God to forgive me for doing something that felt so good.

For some reason Mom and I just didn't get along back then. I was being sent to my room for punishment almost every night after dinner. "Take a bath," "Clean your room," "Take out the garbage." . . . It was always something like that, and after battling it out with Mom in the kitchen and getting hit with the egg turner I'd be back in my room cursing her out under my breath as she'd be shouting, "God's going to punish you, Ronnie! God's going to punish you!" Later she'd come in and tell me she was sorry for yelling at me and I'd give her a big hug and tell her I was sorry too for making her so angry.

Mom always wanted me to be the best at whatever I did, especially at school. "If you fail any subjects this year," she'd tell me, "you're not going out for any sports." I kept telling her I was trying to do my best, but the only thing I could think of was baseball and instead of doing my homework every night I read every sports book I could get my hands on. For hours I'd swing the baseball bat in front of the mirror in my room. I still wanted to play for the New York Yankees more than anything else in the world.

I joined the track team in the spring. I wanted to be the greatest pole-vaulter in the history of the school and so I worked out every day until dark on the parallel bars Dad had built the summer before in the back yard. I remember Mom in the kitchen cheering me on, turning on the porch lights so I could work out even more. I loved those bars and when my brother Tommy was home from school, we'd both get on them together. We'd call Mom and Dad out to watch us perform, doing handstands together, back to back, with both of us touching each other's feet. "The amazing Kovics," I'd shout to Mom. "Ladies and gentlemen, the amazing Kovics are about to perform their death-defying feats." I can still remember both of them standing below us with pride in their eyes as we turned and balanced on those bars. I'd swing my body back and forth, back and forth, until I had swept myself into a perfect handstand, my body in a strong beautiful arc above my back yard. I'd look out around me, holding the handstand as long as I could, and swing down, dismounting with a beautiful twist, thumping onto the ground, stinging my bare feet. It was perfect, I'd say to myself, beautiful, just beautiful.

I was a natural athlete, and there wasn't much of anything I wasn't able to do with my body back then. I was proud and confident and there was always a tremendous energetic bounce in the way I moved. I knew what it was to walk and run and I loved it. After climbing the ropes in school, I'd go out to the track. I remember the feel of the long, lightweight, fiberglass pole in my hands and the black Permatrack beneath my feet; even in the meets I'd jump without shoes. I'd start running from the very end of the long track toward the pit, with the sleek pole gently vibrating up and down in my hands and my face full of determination. I'd hit the hole with the end of my pole, swinging like a pendulum, then kick high into the air, twisting, clearing the bar by inches, falling into the pit on my back, looking at the bar still up there.

As I got older Mom would kid me a lot because I wasn't interested in girls, but I was still dreaming about them all the time. I thought constantly about Joan Marfe, the girl who'd sat next to me in sixth grade, but I was too shy to ever ask her for a date.

I'd heard a priest at some kind of church conference warn us how a thing called petting could lead to sin. Kissing was all right, the priest said in a serious voice, but petting or heavy petting almost always led to sex, and sex, he said, was a mortal sin. I remember listening to him that day and promising myself and God I'd try never to get too close to a girl. I wanted to do all the things the guys in the study hall whispered about, but I didn't want to offend God. I never even went to the senior or junior prom. I just wanted to be a great athlete and a good Catholic and maybe even a priest someday or a major leaguer.

In the spring of the year before I graduated I actually wrote a letter to the New York Yankees management telling them I would give anything in the world for a tryout at the stadium. Castiglia's sister Arlene typed it up for me and for weeks I walked around in a daze waiting for an answer, daydreaming about how Dad and Castiglia would drop me off at the Long Island Railroad station that day and shake my hand and wish me luck. I'd be looking at them, pounding my fist into my new baseball mitt: "I'm gonna make it. Don't worry about it, Castig. I'm gonna make it." Then there'd be the great moment after the tryout when one of the coaches would come up to me: "Well, Kovic, you really looked good out there today. We think you've got what it takes."

It never happened that way. Even though the letter from the Yankees finally came in the mail and I ran over to Castiglia's house shouting that I had made the tryouts, I chickened out when the morning came to leave for the station. I decided I didn't want to go after all. Richie and Bobby Zimmer were all over me for weeks, and I was sorry I'd ever told them anything. I still played after that, but it was different. I was thinking about other things, other things I wanted to be.

By that fall it seemed the guys on the block were almost grown up. In the halls at school we still gave each other the old Woodchuck Club signal we had started in sixth grade, sticking our hands under our chins, moving our fingers up and down, shouting, "Woodchuck, woodchuck." It was crazy but it kept us together. And we went from class to class just waiting for each day to end so we could get back home and play touch out on the street after our homework. Still everything was different. Castiglia was still talking about being a priest or joining the marines, but we weren't seeing as much of each other anymore. Bobby Zimmer told me one afternoon that Richie was growing his hair long and smoking cigarettes with Peter Weber in some abandoned cement tunnel in the woods at the end of the block.

Bobby's hair was long too. My mother said he had a pompadour just like Elvis Presley's. Whenever I saw him in the hallways, he had a pretty girl by his side and he was the first one of the guys on the block to get a driver's license. I was still shy with girls. While I'd be waiting at the bus stop every morning with Kenny and Mike Lamb, Bobby Zimmer would drive past honking the horn of his car with one arm around his girlfriend. He'd turn the corner on Hamilton Avenue, roaring off down Broadway to the high school, leaving the rest of us still jumping up and down at the bus stop trying to stay warm. Peter Weber and Castiglia also drove to school every morning or got rides with their new friends.

I remember for a long time Mike and Bobby Zimmer were a lot taller than me and Castiglia. Then all of a sudden I was taller than all three of them. We'd stand back to back over at Kenny's house as his mother checked to see who was the tallest and it was so good for little guys like me and Castiglia to be taller than the other guys. And when we weren't trying to see who was the tallest, we'd be out on the lawn still playing tag and wrestling on the grass.

Steve Jacket was still throwing screwdrivers into his front lawn across from Pete's house on Hamilton Avenue, telling us all he was going to become a TV sports announcer just like Mel Allen, and Pete was still coming over to my house every once in a while after school to steal beer out of my father's locker in the garage. Little Tommy Law was hanging out with Billy Meyers, trying to stay out of trouble and graduate from high school like the rest of us.

High school was just about over for me and the rest of the guys. We had been on the block together for almost twelve years, running and moving from Toronto Avenue to Lee Place to Hamilton Avenue. No one could remember how we all first got together back then, but we had become friends, "as close as real brothers," Peter told me one afternoon, and we wanted to believe it would always be that way.

President Kennedy got killed that last year and we played football in the huge snowdrifts that had settled on the Long Island streets that afternoon. We played in silence, I guess because you're supposed to be silent when someone dies. I truly felt I had lost a dear friend. I was deeply hurt for a long time afterward. We went to the movies that

Sunday. I can't remember what was playing, but how ashamed I was that I was even there, that people could sit through a movie or have the nerve to want to go to football games when our president had been killed in Dallas. The pain stuck with me for a long time after he died. I still remember Oswald being shot and screaming to my mother to come into the living room. It all seemed wild and crazy like some Texas shootout, but it was real for all of us back then, it was very real. I remember Johnson being sworn in on the plane and the fear in the eyes of the woman judge from Texas. And then the funeral and the casket. I guess all of us, the whole country, watched it like a big football game. Down the street the black horses came and his little boy saluting the way he did, the perfect way he did. Soon after he died there was a memorial picture of him that went up in the candy store down the block. At the bottom of it it said he had been born in 1917 and had died in 1963. It stayed up in the candy store on the wall for a long time after we all went to the war.

That spring before I graduated, my father took me down to the shopping center in Levittown and made me get my first job. It was in a supermarket not far from the marine recruiting station. I worked stacking shelves and numbing my fingers and hands unloading cases of frozen food from the trucks. Working with Kenny each day after school, all I could think of, day after day, was joining the marines. My legs and my back ached, but I knew that soon I would be signing the papers and leaving home.

I didn't want to be like my Dad, coming home from the A&P every night. He was a strong man, a good man, but it made him so tired, it took all the energy out of him. I didn't want to be like that, working in that stinking A&P, six days a week, twelve hours a day. I wanted to be somebody. I wanted to make something out of my life.

I was getting older now, I was seventeen, and I looked at myself in the mirror that hung from the back of the door in my room and saw how tall and strong I had suddenly become. I took a deep breath, flexing my muscles, and stared straight into the mirror, turning to the side and looking at myself for a long time.

In the last month of school, the marine recruiters came and spoke to my senior class. They marched, both in perfect step, into the auditorium with their dress blue uniforms and their magnificently shined shoes. It was like all the movies and all the books and all the dreams of becoming a hero come true. I watched them and listened as they stood in front of all the young boys, looking almost like statues and not like real men at all. They spoke in loud voices and one of them was tall and the other was short and very strong looking.

"Good afternoon men," the tall marine said, "We have come today because they told us that some of you want to become marines." He told us that the marines took nothing but the best, that if any of us did not think we were good enough, we should not even think of joining. The tall marine spoke in a very beautiful way about the exciting history of the marines and how they had never lost and America had never been defeated.

"The marines have been the first in everything, first to fight and first to uphold the honor of our country. We have served on distant shores and at home, and we have always come when our country has called. There is nothing finer, nothing prouder, than a United States Marine."

When they were finished, they efficiently picked up their papers and marched together down the steps of the stage to where a small crowd of boys began to gather. I couldn't wait to run down after them, meet with them and shake their hands. And as I shook their hands and stared up into their eyes, I couldn't help but feel I was shaking hands with John Wayne and Audie Murphy. They told us that day that the Marine Corps built men—body, mind, and spirit. And that we could serve our country like the young president had asked us to do.

We were all going in different directions and we had our whole lives ahead of us, and a million different dreams. I can still remember the last stickball game. I stood at home plate with the sun in my face and looked out at Richie, Pete, and the rest. It was our last summer together and the last stickball game we ever played on Hamilton Avenue.

One day that summer I quit my job at the food

store and went to the little red, white, and blue shack in Levittown. My father and I went down together. It was September by the time all the paperwork was completed, September 1964. I was going to leave on a train one morning and become a marine.

I stayed up most of the night before I left, watching the late movie. Then "The Star-Spangled Banner" played. I remember standing up and feeling very patriotic, chills running up and down my spine. I put my hand over my heart and stood rigid at attention until the screen went blank.

"AWRIGHT, LADIES!" SHOUTED the sergeant again. "My name is Staff Sergeant Joseph. This—" he said, pointing to the short sergeant at the end of the formation, "this is Sergeant Mullins. I am your senior drill instructor. You will obey both of us. You will listen to everything we say. You will do everything we tell you to do. Your souls today may belong to God, but your asses belong to the United States Marine Corps!" The sergeant swaggered sharply back and forth in front of the formation, almost bouncing up and down on his heels, his long thin hands sliding up and down against his hips. "I want you swinging dicks to stand straight at attention, do you hear me? I don't want you people to look left or right, I want you people to stand straight ahead."

It was unbearably hot. He could feel the sweat rolling off his face. He was afraid to look either way and he stared straight ahead like he'd been told.

"Left face!" screamed the sergeant.

"You goddamned idiots!" screamed the short sergeant again. "You're turned the wrong way. You goddamned fucking people, you goddamned scum, when are you people gonna listen, when are you people gonna learn? You came here to be marines."

The short sergeant was laughing now. He took a deep breath and stepped forward, picking out one of the young boys, the tips of his shiny shoes almost touching the tips of the ones the boy wore. "You no good fucking civilian maggot," he screamed in the boy's ears. "You're worthless, do you understand? And I'm gonna kill you. There are eighty of you, eighty young warm bodies, eighty sweet little ladies, eighty sweetpeas, and I want you maggots to know today that you belong to me and you will belong to me until I have made you into marines."

The formation was very sloppy. It didn't look to him like a military formation at all. He was trying so hard, standing straight and looking ahead and cupping his hands right along the seams of his trousers the way the guidebook had taught him, the way Richie and he had practiced it so many times. He was straining till he felt his hands almost go numb, he was trying so hard to be a good marine and do what they said and boot camp hadn't even started yet. But he was determined, even though he didn't understand why they had to be so angry and so mean, why they had to scream and shout and curse the way they did. He couldn't understand that, but it didn't matter. He was going to make it, he was going to do what they said, like a good marine.

They took them from the place where they had stayed that night and marched them and ran them shouting and screaming, eighty of them, dressed in suits and ties and sweatshirts and T-shirts, long-haired and short-haired, short ones and fat ones, kids from New Jersey, kids from Detroit, the drill instructor almost stepping on the boys' heels, taunting and threatening, "Let's go! Let's go!" He looked up at the sky as he ran; he could hardly breathe.

"Awright, awright, all you maggots, get in there!"

They had come to what looked like a large hangar. And they marched, all eighty, single file, with their heads straight ahead, into the aluminum structure, with the chrome-domes they had just gotten spinning on their heads, their cartridge belts loosely fitted, jumping and dangling from their waists. They didn't look like marines, he thought, they looked like Richie and Pete and the rest of the guys, running into Sally's Woods for a game of guns. What was going on here? he thought. What was happening? It wasn't anything like he thought it would be. Why did they have to push them and shove them and kick them and scream and shout? But before he could even get his thoughts together, they put them in a long line and made them face a line of large wooden boxes. He saw that each box had a number painted on it.

"I want you to take your clothes off," the sergeant shouted. "I want you to take off everything that ever reminded you of being a civilian and put it in the box. Do you see that box in front of you and that number? I want everything!" he said. "Now do it, ladies! Quickly, now, quickly!"

As soon as the sergeant had said it, all the young boys began tearing their clothes off, unbuckling their belts, pulling off their shirts, their pants, their shoes, their socks. Everything went. Everything. And as they took their last bits of clothing off, the short sergeant began racing back and forth along the line, screaming into the ears of the young boys, cursing them and jabbing his hands hard into their backs.

He had a small medal around his neck. It was the one Mom had given him for Christmas. He had kept it on for years, all through high school, and even down in the basement wrestling practice, he had never taken it off. And now the short sergeant was pointing at it with his finger, laughing, then shouting for him to throw it in the box that had the number painted on the side.

"Can I keep it?" he said.

"Don't talk back to me," screamed the sergeant. "You fucking maggot. Don't you ever talk back to me!" The sergeant grabbed the medal from his hand and threw it in the box. And now he found himself turning slowly to where the thunderous sound of the drill instructor's voice came from, and he was moving now, stepping and marching, almost running, and then stepping again. He didn't know what to do. They were screaming in his ears again, shouting, cursing. The short guy punched him again and again, and he felt his breath burst from his lungs, twisting and bending him over.

"I'm trying," he said.

"Get in step!" screamed the sergeant.

Stepping, marching, running. "Get in step, people! Come on, people! Let's go, people!" He didn't know what to do. He didn't know how to do it. He wanted to go home, then he didn't. Then he wanted to, then he didn't know what he wanted to do. They were driving him and pushing him and shoving him, screaming and bullying him through this whole crazy thing. He kept thinking over and over and over again that this day, this place, the screaming shouting voices in his ears, in all their ears, roaring like thunder were like angry hate! Oh get us out! Get us out! God, help us!

And they threw them into a barbershop that was more like a factory where there was hair flying all over the place, his hair, everyone's hair, all the hair of the boys who had come to be marines that day. Men as angry and as cold as the sergeants shaved the hair off their heads until he could feel the warm soft wind that swept through the hangar on his head too. They had made them completely bald, and he looked around as he sat on the chair, and the guys who were cutting, the guys who were shaving all their hair off, weren't even looking at the heads, but just cutting like guys shearing sheep.

"Get the fuck up!" screamed the barber. "Next!" he shouted, and the next young boy jumped into the chair staring straight ahead.

He found himself being swept along with all the

young boys, now strange looking, naked like himself. Young bodies tense and twisted naked together, grasping on to each other, holding on like children. Where were they going? he thought. What were they becoming? Shoved and pushed by the drill instructors, they continued to move, from the barbershop where their heads had been shaved, through the long metal hallways of the hangar into the showers.

"Wash all that scum off!" screamed the sergeant. "I want you maggots to wash all that civilian scum off your bodies forever!" And now he felt the soothing hot water streaming down his back and onto his legs. Oh, he could feel it splash hot against his bald head. It felt so good, so warm and different from their angry screams. And before he could begin to even feel comfortable, someone was shouting at him again and telling him to get out of the shower, back into the place where he had been before, in front of his box again. And he ran with the others, their bodies naked and dripping with water, all eighty shaved and washed clean and their clothing packed tightly to be mailed home. And now they all stood rigid at attention, their hands at their sides, facing the boxes with the painted numbers.

"Awright people, awright people!" said the sergeant. "We're gonna issue you clothing." There were marine privates walking past the boxes throwing in green belts and trousers, utility caps and long black socks. "Awright ladies!" screamed the sergeant. "We are going to begin today by learning how to dress. I want you to look down into your boxes and I want you to look for a pair of black socks. Do you see that pair of black socks, ladies?"

"Yessir!" screamed the eighty boys.

"Again!" shouted the sergeant.

"Yessir!" screamed the young men.

"Now I want you to grab that pair of black socks, when I tell you to," he said, almost hesitating. "And when I tell you to grab them I want you to put them on. Do you understand that, ladies?"

"Yessir!"

"Do it!" shouted the short sergeant. And one hundred and sixty hands reached into the boxes, searching for the black socks and putting them on their feet as quickly as they could.

"Grab your trousers!" shouted the sergeant. "These are trousers," he shouted. "Not pants! Pants are for little girls! *Trousers* are for marines! Put your trousers on!" he commanded.

"Yessir!" they screamed and they grabbed their trousers and then their belts and then their skivvy shirts and jackets and utility caps, until they all stood dressed together inside that hangar. Many of the uniforms didn't fit. He could feel his cap covering his face, he was almost swimming in it, and his enormous pants hung down below his boots that didn't fit either. He felt like a ragamuffin doll. He thought he must look like some kind of painter, with his painting cap turned all sideways on his head. He felt so silly. He looked around him and some of the others looked worse than he did. There was one short kid who seemed to have his belt buckle up to his chest and his hat seemed to cover his whole face too.

Why, there was a tall guy, to the right of him down at the end, yeah there was a tall guy whose pants were way too short and his shirt, he thought, belonged on the little kid who was swimming in his stuff. There was a fat kid who couldn't get his pants on at all and the drill instructor was screaming at him, cursing him, and telling him he'd never make it through boot camp alive, he'd never become a marine.

They were all crowding around the fat guy, all the drill instructors, there must have been six of them standing all around that fat kid, circling him for the kill with their angry stares and one at a time they'd scream into his ears, laughing at him and cursing him because he couldn't fit into his pants.

He kept looking from the corner of his eye, and all of them, all of them on the other side of the fat kid, they all seemed to be looking the way he was, trying to see what was going to happen next. And now he remembered that kid, he was the same one on the bus after they had landed in Raleigh, he was the same kid that had stood up and boasted on the bus, with both hands on his hips, that his father had won a whole lot of medals in World War II and he'd killed a whole bunch of Germans. Yeah, it was the same kid. The same one who told everyone he wasn't afraid of anything. Now they had him surrounded so you couldn't see what was happening, and they were punching him, yeah punching, he could hear that fat kid shout every time they jabbed their tight fists into his gut. And now he sounded like a little whining three-year-old, he sounded like a little baby, he was just like a little frightened baby.

"Are you gonna cry?" screamed the sergeant. "Is that what's gonna happen? Everybody, I want you to look at this, look over here, people, I want you to see the baby cry!"

Everyone looked over to where the fat kid was.

"Are those tears?" screamed the sergeant. They were all laughing now, laughing, rocking back and forth on their heels, their hands on their hips.

"Cry!" screamed the sergeant. "Cry Cry Cry you little baby! That's what we want, we want you people to cry like little babies because that's all you maggots are. You are nothing!"

The fat kid was now kneeling on the floor. His whole body was shaking; he had his hands against his face like he was praying. "I don't want this," he was saying. "I . . . I want . . . to go home. I want to go home." He was saying it over and over again now, "I want to go home, I want to go home, I want to go home." He hadn't even gotten there, it was the first day and he wanted to go home. And as he watched, the drill instructors, having had all the fun they could, slowly stepped back from where the fat boy was kneeling, laughing and scorning him, pitying him and cursing him, running back and forth screaming in the ears of the other young boys, cursing them and jabbing them again and again, until the whole maddening thunderous echo of cursing sounds and raging angry voices began to deafen his ears and turn his head around and around till he wondered who he was and what was happening and what was this place.

"He's not gonna make it, he's not gonna make it!" screamed the short sergeant, almost dancing in front of them. "He's not gonna hack it. He's a baby. He's nothing but a baby, ladies!"

"He can't even fit into his pants!" screamed the tall sergeant, laughing.

"Yeah," said the southern sergeant. "He's nothin' but a goddamned little baby and you know what we do with babies," he said. "We kick 'em in their fucking asses and send 'em home. You people, you better listen up!" said the southern sergeant. "You are in Parris Island. You are now in Platoon One Hundred Eighty-one. You are in my platoon and if you people wanna be marines, y'all gonna hafta work harder than you have ever worked before in your lives and you are gonna listen to me and you are gonna do everything I tell you to do if you want to get your asses off this island alive and become marines you better listen to me."

It was beginning to get dark on the island. It had been a long day for him. It had seemed like a hundred days, a thousand days! The day had been endless. It was the longest day of his life. But, he thought, if this is what it takes to become a marine, he was ready to take it, and if this is what he would have to go through in the days and weeks ahead, then he was ready for it. Ready for it!

Like the young president had said, they would have to bear many burdens, many sacrifices, and now he was in this place, and as crazy and depressing as it seemed, he would face it like a man. He would not let his president, or his family, or any of them down. He could take it, he was tough, he knew it. He could make it through these thirteen weeks.

And now they shouted for them to move out of the hangar that they seemed to have been in forever.

"Right—face!" screamed the short sergeant. "Double time . . . MARCH!" screamed the sergeant again. And they began to move now, all eighty of them, with their fresh new clothing and their utility caps, their oversized belts hanging from their waists. They ran, dragging heavy sea bags packed full of new clothing and uniforms, like men bent in a gale. They stumbled and gasped across the huge parade deck past the great statue of the marines raising the flag at Iwo Jima, and he thought of John Wayne and the movies and Castiglia and for a moment his heart quickened. He felt good inside. He was proud of being on the island and getting the chance to become a marine.

They looked like little schoolchildren being herded toward the long wooden barracks, all eighty of them now, stretched out in a long line, tripping over their pants, their caps spinning crazily around their heads, gasping for air, choking and spitting and coughing in the heat, their oversized boots thumping against the parade deck again and again, thumping until they sounded like a train slowly rolling into the station. He felt he couldn't go on any farther and the drill instructors were still screaming. They had been screaming all day, all afternoon, all morning, ever since he got to that place they were screaming, screaming and shouting, cursing, screaming again, until it all sounded like one tremendous scream. He had to keep pushing, he thought. He had to make it to the long wooden squad bay. He had come this far, he thought. He hadn't cried like the fat boy, he hadn't fallen to his knees like a baby. He had come this far and he was gonna make it the rest of the way, with all of them.

But now some were dropping out in back of him. He could hear the drill instructors shouting at them. They were falling to their knees in the evening heat onto the parade deck and he looked back and watched, still gasping for air, still not believing he had made it this far. There were boys on their knees—three, four, five, six—he couldn't count them all, but they were on their knees with their sea bags still over their shoulders like Christs, and they were crawling, he saw them crawling! trying not to quit, trying to catch up with the rest. And he was thankful now he was still on his feet. Oh his legs ached and his chest felt like it was going to explode and his head was pounding now and his eyes were burning and he was getting closer and closer.

Some men were cursing now, swearing and cursing like the drill instructors, cursing the heat, cursing the sweat. They began to shout and curse the shock, the shock of this day. They dragged themselves, exhausted, in a single file into the squad bay. It was a long hallway painted green with double racks on each side making the place seem tighter than it was. He found a rack at the end near the window that looked out into the swamps. He stood rigid at attention in front of his rack, dropping his sea bag at his side, staring straight ahead like they had told him, staring directly into the eyes of another young man. All of them now were coming in, their big boots banging against the wooden deck, cursing and sweating and dragging their sea bags up to their racks.

"Get in there! Hurry up! Hurry up! Get in there!" screamed the sergeant who came running through the open door of the squad bay. "I want each one of you to get in front of a rack!" screamed the sergeant. "And now I want you to listen to me!" And he told them that this place, this squad bay, would be their home for the next three months. They would live here and sleep here and shower here and work here until they became marines.

"It's late!" screamed the short sergeant. "And I know how tired you ladies are tonight. Are you tired ladies?" screamed the sergeant.

"Yessir!" shouted the men.

"I can't hear you!" screamed the sergeant. "Louder!"

"Yessir!" the young men screamed again.

"That's more like it."

The sergeant repeated a long list of names including the president and vice president of the United States and everyone else right on down to the senior drill instructor himself, and after completing the list, he shouted to the men that every night from here on out they would repeat those names. And then he shouted, "Ready—Mount!" And they shouted back "Ready—Mount! Aye aye, sir!" And all eighty jumped into bed, still standing at attention, lying in their racks.

"Awright! I want you to stand at attention all night! I think it's good practice for you."

And as they lay in their racks at attention, one of the sergeants had a young black boy from Georgia sing the Lord's Prayer: "Our Father, Who art in heaven, hallo-o-wed be Thy name," he sang. "Thy kingdom come, Thy will be done, on earth as it is in hea-ven." And when he was finished the lights went out and they slowly closed their eyes.

And the first day had ended.

(Lights flash, flash, flash standing by my rack now) sir! the private requests to make an emergency sitting head call WHAT DO YOU WANT KOVIC? sir! o god o jesus yessir aye aye sir one two aye aye sir If I die in a combat zone pack me up and ship me home *COUNTDOWN—READY—SEATS! GET IN THE PASSAGEWAY SWEETPEA AND GIVE ME FIVE HUNDRED BENDS AND THRUSTS—DO IT! BY THE LEFT FLANK*—one two three four I love the Marine Corps *THIS IS YOUR RIFLE LADIES I WANT YOU TO KNOW IT ALL OF IT EVERY PART OF IT! CAN'T YOU READ SWEETPEA?* this is my rifle this is my gun this is for fighting this is for fun, Ask not what your country *(the formation now) remember i can talk no i can't talk no i can't bring back by the river—with the rifle*—America. America. God

shed His grace on thee, Eenie meenie mynie moe catch a nigger by the toe *EYES RIGHT! I WANT YOU TO BELIEVE THIS AFTERNOON THAT THIS THING OUT THERE IS A COMMIE SONOFABITCH and wops and spics and chinks and japs and GET IN FRONT OF YOUR RACKS!! THAT'S NOT QUICK ENOUGH! (never quick enough, eighteen i'm eighteen now) UP! DOWN! GET IT! OUT! GET IT! o mom o please o someone somone help now somebody BY THE RIGHT FLANK! GET DOWN! GET UP! (hot deck parades faces mirror face still pimples now boots and socks) o lights flashes GET THE FUCK UP!* We will bear any burden *by your leave sir excuse me sir pardon me sir* suffer any hardships *i'm sorry sir o yessir no sir aye aye sir, sir! (push-ups push-ups clanking sounds steel) READY—SEATS! (plates forks and) EAT AND HURRY UP AND RUN AND HURRY UP AND EAT AND HURRY UP AND RUN AND HURRY UP HURRY UP!* There is something I believe—we'll be home by Christmas Eve *sir my service number is two-oh-three-oh-two-six-one sir the president of the united states is the honorable lyndon baines johnson sir the vice president is* Our Father, Who art in heaven *PREPARE TO MOUNT aye aye sir* hallowed be Thy name *MOUNT!* Thy kingdom come, if I die on the Russion front bury me with a Russian cunt *DO IT! DO IT! DO IT! DO IT!* Thy will be done *DO IT! DO IT! DO IT IN YOUR SLEEP ON THE FLOOR ON YOUR HEAD DO IT NOW WANT TO BECOME MEN WANT TO BECOME MEN WANT TO BECOME MEN oh, become, marines oh god bless the marine corps god bless america TIGHTEN UP! TIGHTEN UP! god bless my senior drill instructor god bless the president PLATOON HALT! god bless the battalion commander god bless chesty puller god bless john wayne* From the halls of Montezuma *BY THE RIGHT FLANK! AWRIGHT WHEN I TELL YOU PEOPLE YOU GOT TWO FUCKIN MINUTES TO SHIT SHOWER AND SHAVE I MEAN EXACTLY THAT NOW GET DOWN SCUMBAGS! MAIL CALL! (eighty chests hitting the deck) i want the flag SECOND'S AS GOOD AS LAST LADIES! can't you see, Father, the tests in spring shots GOTTA BE FIRST GOTTA BE FIRST! STARBOARD SIDE MAKE A HEAD CALL PORTSIDE MAKE A HEAD CALL* oh hail Mary full of grace the Lord is *motherfucking cocksuckers!* oh Our Father *KILL! KILL! KILL! KILL!* Who art in *COMMIES CHINKS JAPS AND DINKS* hallowed be *IF YOU WANT TO BE MARINES . . . HAVE TO PAY THE PRICE PAY THE PRICE PAY THE PRICE* If I die in a combat zone box me up and ship me home, Thy kingdom come *private kovic sir two-oh-three-oh-two-six-one sir yessir no sir one two aye aye sir* Thy will be done *the private requests permission to speak to his senior drill instructor oh god oh jesus help me help me* on earth as it is in heaven *SCHOOL CIRCLES! aye aye sir* as it is *WHAT DO YOU WANT MAGGOT? READY—SEATS! aye aye sir DO IT! aye aye sir THIS IS YOUR RIFLE I WANT YOU TO SLEEP WITH IT GET UP GET DOWN GET UP GET DOWN DO YOU HEAR ME? DO YOU HEAR ME PEOPLE? (we are moving now) GET OUT OF*

THE PASSAGEWAY GIMME FIVE HUNDRED BENDS AND THRUSTS aye aye sir one two aye aye sir one two DON'T STOP PEOPLE KEEP RUNNING PEOPLE SCUM SCUM SWINE SWINE THERE WILL BE NO DROPOUTS TODAY THERE WILL BE NO QUITTERS IN MY MARINE CORPS! RUN! RUN! RUN! RUN! YOU BETTER BE DEAD IF YOU DROP OUT There is nothing finer *QUICKLY! QUICKLY! and when i grow up i'm going to TEN!NINE!EIGHT!SEVEN!-SIX!FIVE!FOUR!THREE!TWO!ONE! YOU'RE LATE! LATE LATE LATE LATE LATE LATE! (raising the flag) DON'T MOVE DON'T SIT DON'T STAND DO IT DO IT DO IT DO IT! FORWARD—MARCH! o mary mother of jesus you gotta help me WE ARE THE BEST WE ARE THE BEST WE ARE THE BEST platoon one eighty-one is the best KILL THEM AT THREE HUNDRED FEET! DRESS RIGHT! AT THIRTY FEET! in the trenches on the benches in the butts o get me outta here god (cracking strings and pasting holes and making hits) i'm an expert mom i'm an expert! oh make this time this time i want to scream i want to scream oh no oh wait, hey i'm, wait, i'm just, wait i'm just going to screamscreamscreamscream screamscreamscreamscreamscream GOTTA GRADUATE GOTTA GRADUATE! BY THE LEFT FLANK—MARCH! YOU'LL NEVER MAKE IT! BY THE RIGHT FLANK EIGHTY PLATOON ONE EIGHTY! platoon one eighty-one sir! the colors guidons guide posts guide posts oh god goal posts touchdown touchdown jackets green utility's fresh smell one-two-three-four-one-two-three-four (his voice the voices they them letters) hi mom and hi dad! MARINE CORPS MARINE CORPS MARINE CORPS PORK CHOP HILL* From the halls of Montezuma *the vice president of the united states is WE HAVE NEVER LOST! EMPTY THOSE SEA BAGS! I WANT YOU TO CRAWL WORMS CRAWL WORMS CRAWL! GET THOSE LOCKER BOXES ABOVE YOUR HEADS! WE HAVE NEVER LOST! (tear apart racks tear apart racks) YOU'RE EITHER GONNA SINK OR SWIM PEOPLE! LOOK STRAIGHT AHEAD LOOK STRAIGHT AHEAD! RUN!RUN!RUN!RUN!RUN! RUN!RUN!RUN!!!*

4

THEY CAME FOR him early that morning, walking up the wooden ramp and knocking on the front door of his house. He could hear them in the living room talking to his mom and dad about the parade and how important it was to have him marching with them on Memorial Day in his wheelchair.

"Parade time," his father said, walking into his room.

"I'll be right with you, Dad," he said, looking up from his bed. "I've got to get my pants on."

It was always hard getting dressed, but he was getting better at it. He turned from his back to his stomach, grabbing his pants and pulling them up until they reached his waist. Turning on his back again, he buckled his belt. Then he pushed himself with both hands in back of him until he was sitting up in the bed next to his wheelchair. He grabbed the chair with one hand, dragging his body across in a quick sweeping motion until he was seated, his legs still up on the bed.

Now his father knew it was time to help. He took each leg, carefully lowering them one at a time to the chair, spreading them apart to make sure the rubber tube wasn't twisted.

"Ready?" shouted the boy.

"Ready!" said his dad. And his father went in back of the chair as he always did and lifted him up underneath his arms so that he could pull his pants up again.

"Good," said the boy.

His father let him slowly down back onto the cushion and he turned around in his wheelchair to face the door and pushed his chair down the long, narrow hallway to the living room. His mom was there with a tall man he immediately remembered from the hospital; right next to him was a heavy guy. Both of them had on their American Legion uniforms with special caps placed smartly on their heads. He sat as straight in his chair as he could, holding on with one hand so he wouldn't lose his balance. He shook hands with the tall commander and with the heavy guy who stood beside him.

"You sure look great," said the tall commander, stepping forward. "Same tough marine we visited in the hospital," he said, smiling, "You know, Mr. Kovic—" he was looking at his father now— "this kid of yours sure has a lot of guts."

"We're really proud of him," said the heavy guy.

"The whole town's proud of him and what he did," said the tall commander, smiling again.

"He's sacrificed a lot," said the heavy guy, putting his hand on the boy's shoulder.

"And we're gonna make certain," the tall commander said, "we're gonna make certain that his sacrifice and any of the others weren't in vain. We're still in that war to win," he said, looking at the boy's father. His father nodded his head up and down, showing the commander he understood.

It was time to go. The heavy guy had grabbed the back handles of the chair. Acting very confident, he reminded the boy that he had worked in the naval hospital.

The boy said goodbye to his mom and dad, and the heavy guy eased the wheelchair down the long wooden ramp to the sidewalk in front of the house. "I've been pushin' you boys around for almost two years now," he said.

The boy listened as the heavy guy and the commander stood for a moment in the front yard trying to figure out how they were going to get him into the back seat of the Cadillac convertible.

"You're goin' in style today," shouted the commander.

"Nothing but the best," said the heavy guy.

"I haven't learned how to . . ."

"We know, we understand," said the commander.

And before he could say another word, the heavy guy who had worked at the hospital lifted him out of the chair in one smooth motion. Opening the door with a kick of his foot, he carefully placed him in the back seat of the big open car.

"All right, Mr. Grand Marshal." The heavy guy patted him on the shoulder, then jumped into the car with the commander, beeping the horn all the way down Toronto Avenue.

"We're goin' over to Eddie Dugan's house," said the commander, turning his head. "Ya know Eddie?" He was talking very fast now. "Good boy," said the commander. "Lost both legs like you. Got plastic ones. Doin' great, isn't he?" He jabbed the heavy man with his fist.

"Got a lot of guts that kid Eddie Dugan," the heavy man said.

"I remember him . . ." The commander was turning the corner now, driving slowly down the street. "Yeah, I remember Eddie way back when he was . . . when he was playin' on the Little Leagues. And as God is my witness," said the commander, turning his head back toward him again, "as God is my witness, I seen Eddie hit a home run on his birthday. He was nine or ten, something like that back then." The commander was laughing now. "I was coaching with his dad and it was Eddie's birthday. A lot of you guys got messed up over there." He was still talking very fast.

"Remember Clasternack? You heard of Clasternack, didn't you? He got killed. They got a street over in the park named after him." He paused for a long time. "Yeah . . . he got killed. He was the first of you kids to get it. And there were others too," said the commander. "That little guy, what was his name? Yeah I got it . . . Johnny Heanon . . . little Johnny Heanon . . . he used to play in the Little League with you guys."

He remembered Johnny Heanon.

"He tripped a land mine or something and died on the hospital ship during the operation. I see his folks every once in a while. They live down by the old high school. Fine kid," said the commander.

"He used to deliver my paper," said the heavy guy.

"There was the Peters family too . . . both brothers, . . ." said the commander again, pausing for a long time. "Both of them got killed in the same week. And Alan Grady. . . . Did you know Alan Grady? He used to go to the boy scouts when you kids was growing up."

The boy in the back seat nodded. He knew Alan Grady too.

"He drowned," said the commander.

"Funny thing," said the heavy guy. "I mean, terrible way to go. He was on R and R or something and he drowned one afternoon when he was swimming."

"And Billy Morris," said the commander, "he used to get in all sorts of trouble down at the high school. He got killed too. There was a land mine or something and he got hit in the head with a tree. Isn't that crazy?" The commander was laughing almost hysterically now.

"He goes all the way over there and gets killed by a fucking tree."

"We've lost a lot of good boys," the heavy guy said. "We've been hit pretty bad. The whole town's changed."

"And it's been goin' on a long time." The commander was very angry now. "If those bastards in Washington would stop fiddlefucking around and drop a couple of big ones in the right places, we could get that whole thing over with next week. We could win that goddamn thing and get all our kids out of there."

When they got to Eddie Dugan's house, both of the men got out, leaving him in the back seat, and ran up to Eddie's doorstep. A few minutes passed, then Eddie came out the front door rocking back and forth across the lawn like a clown on his crutches until he had worked himself to the car door.

"I can do it," Eddie said.

"Sure," said the tall commander, smiling.

They watched as Eddie stretched leaning on his crutches, then swung into the car seat.

"Not bad," said the commander.

The commander and the heavy guy jumped back into the car and the boy could feel the warm spring air blowing on his face as they moved down Eddie's block. The leaves on the trees had blossomed full. They glistened in the sun, covering the streets in patches of morning shadow.

"You're not going to believe this," Eddie said to him, looking down at his legs. "I got hit by our own mortars." He was almost laughing now. "It was on a night patrol. . . . And you?" he asked.

"I got paralyzed from the chest down. I can't move or feel anything." He showed Eddie with his hand how far up he could not feel and then showed him the bag on the side of his leg. Usually he didn't like telling people how bad he had been hurt, but for some reason it was different with Eddie.

Eddie looked at the bag and shook his head, saying nothing.

"Let me see your new legs," he said to Eddie.

Eddie pulled up his trousers, showing his new plastic legs. "You see," he said, tapping them with his knuckles. He was very sarcastic. "As good as new."

They got to the place where the march was to begin and he saw the cub scouts and the girl scouts, the marching bands, the fathers in their Legion caps and uniforms, the mothers from the Legion's auxilliary, the pretty drum majorettes. The street was a sea of red, white, and blue. He remembered how he and all the rest of the kids on the block had put on their cub scout uniforms and marched every Memorial Day down these same streets. He remembered the hundreds of people lining the sidewalks, everyone standing and cheering and waving their small flags, his mother standing with the other mothers on the block shouting for him to keep in step. "There's my Yankee Doodle boy!" he'd hear her shouting, and he'd feel embarrassed, pulling his cap over his eyes like he always did.

There were scouts decorating the Cadillac now with red, white, and blue crepe paper and long paper banners that read WELCOME HOME RON KOVIC AND EDDIE DUGAN and SUPPORT OUR BOYS in VIETNAM. There was a small sign, too, that read: OUR WOUNDED VIETNAM VETS . . . EDDIE DUGAN AND RON KOVIC.

When the scouts were finished, the commander came running over to the car with a can of beer in his hand. "Let's go!" he shouted, jumping back in with the heavy guy.

They drove slowly through the crowd until they were all the way up in the front of the parade. He could hear the horns and drums behind him and he looked out and watched the pretty drum majorettes and clowns dancing in the street. He looked out onto the sidewalks where the people from his town had gathered just like when he was a kid.

But it was different. He couldn't tell at first exactly what it was, but something was not the same, they weren't waving and they just seemed to be standing staring at Eddie Dugan and himself like they weren't even there. It was as if they were ghosts like little Johnny Heanon or Billy Morris come back from the dead. And he couldn't understand what was happening.

Maybe, he thought, the banners, the ones the boy scouts and their fathers had put up, the ones telling the whole town who Eddie Dugan and he were, maybe, he thought, they had dropped off into the street and no one knew who they were and that's why no one was waving.

If the signs had been there, they'd have been flooding into the streets, stomping their feet and screaming and cheering the way they did for him and Eddie at the Little League games. They'd have been swelling into the streets, trying to shake their hands just like in the movies, when the boys had come home from the other wars and everyone went crazy throwing streamers of paper and confetti and hugging their sweethearts, sweeping them off their feet and kissing them for what seemed forever. If they really knew who they were, he thought, they'd be roaring and clapping and shouting. But they were quiet and all he heard whenever the band stopped playing was the soft purr of the American Legion's big Cadillac as it moved slowly down the street.

Even though it seemed very difficult acting like heroes, he and Eddie tried waving a couple of times, but after a while he realized that the staring faces weren't going to change and he couldn't help but feel like he was some kind of animal in a zoo or that he and Eddie were on display in some trophy case. And the more he thought about it, the more he wanted to get the hell out of the back seat of the Cadillac and go back home to his room where he knew it was safe and warm. The parade had hardly begun but already he felt trapped, just like in the hospital.

The tall commander turned down Broadway now, past Sparky the barber's place, then down to Massapequa Avenue, past the American Legion hall where the cannon they had played on as kids sat right across from the Long Island Railroad station. He thought of the times he and Bobby and Richie Castiglia used to sit on that thing with their plastic machine guns and army-navy store canteens full of lemonade; they'd sit and wait until a train pulled into the Massapequa station, and then they'd all scream "Ambush!" with Castiglia standing up bravely on the cannon barrel, riddling the train's windows.

He was beginning to feel very lonely. He kept looking over at Eddie. Why hadn't they waved, he thought. Eddie had lost both of his legs and he had come home with almost no body left, and no one seemed to care.

When they came to where the speakers' platform had been erected, he watched Eddie push himself out of the back seat, then up on his crutches while the heavy guy helped him with the door. The commander was opening the trunk, bringing the wheelchair to the side of the car. He was lifted out by the heavy guy and he saw the people around him watching, and it bothered him because he didn't want them to see how badly he had been hurt and how helpless he was, having to be carried out of the car into the chair like a baby. He tried to block out what he was feeling by smiling and waving to the people around him, making jokes about the chair to ease the tension, but it was very difficult being there at all and the more he felt stared at and gawked at like some strange object in a museum, the more difficult it became and the more he wanted to get the hell out of there.

He pushed himself to the back of the platform where two strong members of the Legion were waiting to lift him up in the chair. "How do you lift this goddamn thing?" shouted one of the men, suddenly staggering, almost dropping him. He tried to tell them how to lift it properly, the way they had shown him in the hospital, but they wanted to do it their own way and almost dropped him a second time.

They finally carried him up the steps of the stage where he was wheeled up front next to Eddie, who sat with his crutches by his side. They sat together watching the big crowd and listening to one speaker after the other, including the mayor and all the town's dignitaries; each one spoke very beautiful words about *sacrifice and patriotism and God,* crying out to the crowd to support the boys in the war so that their brave sacrifices would not have to be in vain.

And then it was the tall commander's turn to speak. He walked up to the microphone slowly, measuring his steps carefully, then jutted his head up and looked directly at the crowd. *"I believe in America!"* shouted the commander, shaking his fist in the air. *"And I believe in Americanism!"* The crowd was cheering now. *"And most of all . . . most of all, I believe in victory for America!"* He was very emotional. Then he shouted that the whole country had to come together and support the boys in the war. He told how he and the boys' fathers before them had fought in Korea and World War II, and how the whole country had been behind them back then and how they had won a great victory for freedom. Almost crying now, he shouted to the crowd that they couldn't give up in Vietnam. *"We have to win . . ."* he said, his voice still shaking; then pausing, he pointed his finger at him and Eddie Dugan, *". . . because of them!"*

Suddenly it was very quiet and he could feel them looking right at him, sitting there in his wheelchair with Eddie all alone. It seemed everyone—the cub scouts, the boy scouts, the mothers, the fathers, the whole town—had their eyes on them and now he bent his head and stared into his lap.

The commander left the podium to great applause and the speeches continued, but the more they spoke, the more restless and uncomfortable he became, until he felt like he was going to jump out of his paralyzed body and scream. He was confused, then proud, then all of a sudden confused again. He wanted to listen and believe everything they were saying, but he kept thinking of all the things that had happened that day and now he wondered why he and Eddie hadn't even been given the chance to speak. They had just sat there all day long, like he had been sitting in his chair for weeks and months in the hospital and at home in his room alone, and he wondered now why he had allowed them to make him a hero and the grand marshal of the parade with Eddie, why he had let them take him all over town in that Cadillac when they hadn't even asked him to speak.

These people had never been to his war, and they had been talking like they knew everything, like they were experts on the whole goddamn thing, like he and Eddie didn't know how to speak for themselves because there was something wrong now with both of them. They couldn't speak because of the war and had to have others define for them with their lovely words what they didn't know anything about.

He sat back, watching the men who ran the town as they walked back and forth on the speakers' platform in their suits and ties, drinking their beer and talking about patriotism. It reminded him of the time in church a few Sundays before, when Father Bradley had suddenly pointed to him during the middle of the sermon, telling everyone he was a hero and a patriot in the eyes of God and his country for going to fight the Communists. "We must pray for brave boys like Ron Kovic," said the priest. "And most of all," he said, "we must pray for victory in Vietnam and peace throughout the world." And when the service was over, people came to shake his hand and thank him for all he had done for God and his country, and he left the church feeling very sick and threw up in the parking lot.

After all the speeches, they carried him back down the steps of the platform and the crowd started clapping and now he felt more embarrassed than ever. He didn't deserve this, he didn't want this shit. All he could think of was getting out of there and going back home. He just wanted to get out of this place and go back right away.

But now someone in the crowd was calling his name. "Ronnie! Ronnie!" Over and over again he heard someone shouting. And finally he saw who it was. It was little Tommy Law, who had grown up on Hamilton Avenue with all the rest of the guys. He used to hit home runs over Tommy's hedge. Tommy had been one of his best friends like Richie and Bobby Zimmer. He hadn't seen him for years, not since high school. Tommy had joined the marines too, and he'd heard something about him being wounded in a rocket attack in the DMZ. No one had told him he was back from the war. And now Tommy was hugging him and they were crying, both of them at the bottom of the stage, hugging each other and crying in front of all of them that day. He wanted to pull away in embarrassment and hold back his feelings that seemed to be pouring out of him, but he could not and he cried even harder now, hugging his friend until he felt his arms go numb. It was so wonderful, so good, to see Tommy again. He seemed to bring back something wonderfully happy in his past and he didn't want to let go. They held on to each other for a long time. And when Tommy finally pulled away, his face was bright red and covered with tears and pain. Tommy held his head with his hands still shaking, looking at him sitting there in disbelief. He looked up at Tommy's face and he could see that he was very sad.

The crowd had gathered now watching the two friends almost with curiosity. He tried wiping the tears from his eyes, still trying to laugh and make Tommy and himself and all the others feel more at ease, but Tommy would not smile and he kept holding his head. Still crying, he shook his head back and forth. And now, looking up at Tommy's face, he could see the thin scar that ran along his hairline, the same kind of scar he'd seen on the heads of the vegetables who had had their brains blown out, where plates had been put in to replace part of the skull.

But Tommy didn't want to talk about what had happened to him. "Let's get out of here," he said. He grabbed the back handles of the chair and began pushing him through the crowd. He pushed him through the town past the Long Island Railroad station to the American Legion hall. They sat in the corner of the bar, watching the mayor and all the politicians. And Tommy tried to keep the drunken Legion members from hanging all over him and telling him their war stories.

The tall commander, who was now very drunk, came over asking Tommy and him if they wanted a ride back home in the Cadillac. Tommy said they were walking home, and they left the American Legion hall and the drunks in the bar, with Tommy pushing his wheelchair, walking back through the town where they had grown up, past the baseball field at Parkside School where they had played as kids, back to Hamilton Avenue, where they sat together in front of Peter Weber's house almost all night, still not believing they were together again.

I AM WATCHING THE young couple walk along the beach. They are walking on the wet sand just where the waves wash up to the shore. The girl is holding his hand and she is laughing. Oh I want so badly to be that guy with her. I want to feel, I want to feel again, I want to walk with a woman, I want to be just like that guy who is walking with her along the beach. Please God, I say, I want it back so bad. I will give anything, anything, just to be inside a woman again. I think of approaching them. It would be so difficult. What could I say? "Excuse me, would you like to pull my chair across the sand? Or maybe you'd like to carry me over your shoulders and I could hold your hand laughing . . ." NO NO NO NO, that's not right! That's not fair! I want it back! They have taken it, they have robbed it, my penis will never get hard anymore. I didn't even have time to learn how to enjoy it and now it is gone, it is dead, it is as numb as the rest of me.

I watch the other women now. I see their long

slim legs standing pretty. I start to get excited, my mind racing with fantasies, and then the hurt comes. . . .

Oh God, I never dreamed that this could possibly happen, that this part of me that had made me feel so good when I was young, that this wonderful thing that no one ever seems to want to talk about . . . has gone, has suddenly disappeared. It has happened so fast, so quickly. What can I do, how can I ever get it back? Everyone says it is such an important thing, but nobody wants to talk about it. The Church says if you play with it, it is a sin. Now I can't even roll on top of a basketball, I can't do it in the bathtub or against the tree in the yard. It is over with. Gone. And it is gone for America. I have given it for democracy. It is okay now. It is all right. Yes it is all right. I have given my dead swinging dick for America. I have given my numb young dick for democracy. It is gone and numb, lost somewhere out there by the river where the artillery is screaming in. Oh God oh God I want it back! I gave it for the whole country, I gave it for every one of them. Yes, I gave my dead dick for John Wayne and Howdy Doody, for Castiglia and Sparky the barber. Nobody ever told me I was going to come back from this war without a penis. But I am back and my head is screaming now and I don't know what to do.

Every night after he had been to Arthur's Bar, he would push up his old man's wooden ramp. He would stop at the top in his chair, knocking the big blue milk can into the bushes, cursing under his breath and opening the screen door that his old man would leave unbolted. It was always two or three in the morning by then and he would try to slip into the house without waking anybody even though he could barely push the chair. Every night he stopped next to the crucifix and stuck his fingers into the holy water. Oh Jesus, he mumbled to himself, you gotta help me, you gotta find me a woman, someone to love this broken body of mine. He would make the sign of the cross with the holy water just as he had done when he was a kid. Oh Jesus, please Jesus, you gotta help me, you gotta give me strength. This broken body ain't gonna mend and it's gonna be this way for a long time and you gotta help me now Jesus you gotta help me somehow. Sometimes the dog would come up to him and he would tap it softly on the head. Well, here's a real friend, someone I can count on. He would turn the chair and push it down the narrow hallway, past the bookshelf, banging his hand against the wall, cursing, then pushing the chair angrily into his room. He would stay up all night sometimes, sitting by the typewriter, trying to forget the war, the wound, by putting words down on paper.

there was a soldier
tapdancing softly in the rain
above the coffin
six feet above, the people praying

They had to carry him out of Arthur's Bar one

night. The people were still dancing and the band was blasting really loud and he was screaming. There was a girl. He wanted to dance with her and squeeze her, kiss her soft face and take her home. *Here, don't worry about the chair, we can leave it here, we can go to your apartment and I can take your clothes off. I can lie with you and stroke your long slim body. I can kiss you and make love to you. We can make babies and I can tell you about the war. We can make lots of babies.*

He was very drunk, drunker than he had ever been. The whole place was spinning and it became very hard to hear anything but a great rushing sound that roared in his ears like a terrific storm. "You got to get out of here," they were telling him. "You got to get in the car and go home." They slowly lifted the body into the small car. He was laughing now, laughing and singing Irish songs. "Hurry up now," he could hear them saying. "Hurry up now and we'll get you back home." They all seemed to look like funny cartoon characters moving the numb limbs of his lower part into the front seat of the car. "That's right, that's good now," they were saying. Some girl was laughing in the back seat and the driver told her to shut up. "Are you okay, is everything all right?" said his friend.

"He's really drunk, really smashed," said the girl. "We got to get him home right away."

"How are his legs? Are his legs okay?"

The rubber urine bag. He moved his hand slowly down his leg to the rubber urine bag. It was as hard as a rock and his pants were soaked and it was all slowly soaking into the seat.

"He's pissed all over the fucking seat," said the girl. "What should we do?"

"Get him home. Drop him off."

They got him to the house and lifted him out into his chair and there was the front seat of the car all soaked. It was very late and the young girl almost seemed in a panic. The two boys pushed him up the wooden ramp his father had built with his own hands. He had put it all together just before he came home from the hospital. His old man had worked long and hard on the ramp to make it just right for his son who had just come home from the war. It was a piece of art, just like the special room with the shower. Every piece had been cut to fit and there were two long smooth handrails. The whole thing was painted red like the house. The old man had worked hard on the ramp, like he had worked hard in the food store for twenty-five years, like he worked hard at everything he ever did in his life.

His mother screamed when he came in. She was still screaming hysterically when the old man bent down and lifted him up onto the little bed. He laid the body gently down and began to hook up the plastic tube. Then he took the piss-soaked pants off and undid the rocklike rubber piss bag from his boy's leg.

"I'm fucked up, I'm fucked up," the boy was saying.

His mother went racing in and out of the room.

"He's drunk, he's drunk," she repeated to the old man. "We've got a drunk for a son."

The old man didn't seem to hear her. He grabbed a warm washcloth and began scrubbing his son. The last thing he did was to connect the rubber tube that went into the boy's penis to the long plastic tube that went into the bag on the side of the bed. That was what the nurses in the hospital had taught him to do. It was very important to connect the rubber tube in the boy's penis to the plastic tube when he went to bed at night. So that everything would run okay. So that everything would be all right. So he did it just the way they had told them and after pulling the sheets and covers up over the body and just below the shoulders of his son, the old man walked out of the room.

The lights went out in the house. The boy turned slowly over until he had propped himself up on both elbows with his head pushed down into his pillow. He wanted to forget the terrible night. He wanted to forget it and everything else, the numb legs, the unfeeling numbness. He was lost, more lost than he had ever been in his life. Lost in some kind of limbo land of the dead. He wanted to explode, to get out of this crazy numb body and be a man again. He wanted to be free again, to walk in his back yard on the grass. He wanted to run down to Sparky's and get a haircut, he wanted to play stickball with Richie, to swing the bat, to feel the gravel on Hamilton Avenue beneath his feet again. He wanted to stand up in the shower every morning with the hot water streaming down his back and off his legs.

It was now very clear that this thing was final like death.

No one, he thought, ever wanted to think about final things, dead things, things that ended abruptly or could not be explained. Once someone died, he thought, people just put them in the ground, they put them in the ground and stood above the grave saying words that helped explain why there was an end to the person, words that were beautiful like the flowers and the big stone, words that helped others realize that it wasn't the end, but only the beginning of a wonderful thing. It was so easy for them to say the words, to deny the finality. Why weren't they saying the words over his bed? Why weren't they telling him that this whole thing, this whole crazy numb thing, wasn't final? But for him there were no words and no people, nothing to tell him things would be beautiful again. This end was no beginning. It was starting to become very clear that there would be no change in his condition, no reconciliation with the half of his body that seemed so utterly lost forever. He was in the rain, trapped, and there was no one. It was ugly and cold and final.

HE WATCHED THE island disappear as the plane took off from Kennedy Airport. For the first time since he had come home from the war, he was getting away, going off somewhere by himself. His chair was safely packed in the belly of the plane, and he was just one of the other passengers, sitting there just like everybody else. Sometimes when he was out in his car, driving around, cruising up and down the block and into the town with his hand controls, he would get the same kind of feeling. It was a really free feeling that he couldn't get unless he was out of the chair.

He had been thinking about going to Mexico for a long time. In the hospital there had been a brochure that said there was this place down there where people like himself were cared for. It was a place called the Village of the Sun. He'd even met one guy who'd been there and talked about a whorehouse he'd gone to where the whores were very understanding, where even paralyzed men could get fucked. He thought about the Village of the Sun all the time after that. He just knew inside he could make love again, even though all the parts had been destroyed by the war.

It was night by the time he arrived in Guadalajara. A man named Rahilio met him at the airport and put him in his Ford pickup. It had been a long trip and now it was going to be a long ride to Las Fuentes and the Village, but he was happy to be in Mexico. Rahilio's small son lay on the seat next to him singing a song he couldn't understand. He opened up his window and looked out into the dark Mexican countryside.

The long dining hall full of wheelchairs was an exciting place for him the next morning. There were a lot of people talking and laughing and the sun was very bright on the white walls and the colorful tile tables. There were old and young, veterans from all the wars. Aides ran back and forth helping the men who couldn't use their hands to eat. It made him feel good to be with so many others who were like himself. He felt accepted here. He thought he might be able to feel human again.

It was the Fourth of July and that night after dinner Rahilio's wife came up to him with a big cake and everybody began to sing "Happy Birthday." Somehow they had found out it was his birthday.

He could see you could have a nice life here if you wanted to. Some of the veterans he met were planning to stay at the Village of the Sun until they died. He could see there were a lot of reasons not to go back to the States again. A lot of the men would play cards all day long and some would drink heavily and have to be carried back into their rooms. They got pretty loud during the card games with their women hanging over their shoulders, big-busted Mexican women. It was something you would never see back home. Some of the others just stayed in their little rooms writing letters to people or reading the newspaper.

It was a week before he got really restless, before he got tired of sitting around the Village. It was a Sunday and he asked Rahilio if he could go to church with him and his children. It was very quiet in the little Spanish chapel, the men sitting on one side and the women on the other. He listened to the small birds that flew above the altar during the Mass, chirping and singing. After church he told Rahilio he wanted to go into the city.

He was lonely and he wanted to move around. . . . He had come almost three thousand miles and now, finally, he was riding in a cab and maybe in one of the houses in the city he was going to find a woman like the women they had told him about, a woman who would love him and make his broken body come alive again, who would lie down next to the disfigurement and love it like there was not anything the matter with him at all. He cried inside for a woman, any woman, to lie close to him. In the hospital there were so many times when he had looked at the nurses and all the visitors and it would seem so crazy that the same government that provided a big check for the wounded men couldn't provide someone warm, someone who cared for him.

The cabdriver left him off at the Hilton Hotel. For a long time after that he had lunch there every day. After lunch he would wheel all over the city, taking cabs and pushing the chair as far as he could until his arms began to ache. There would always be people to help him up and down the big Mexican curbs. There were beautiful cathedrals and statues everywhere he looked, and the sky was clear most of the time.

Finally one afternoon he went up to the guy who worked behind the desk at the Hilton and asked him where the biggest whorehouse in town was. The guy behind the desk wrote down the address for him and he wheeled out to the street and caught a cab.

The girl was very beautiful and the jukebox was playing as she pushed his chair into the small room. There was an old mattress on the floor and he got himself onto it and began to take his shirt off, watching the girl as she took off all her clothing. She lay down in the bed next to him and asked him why he wasn't taking off his pants.

"I can't." He hesitated. It was very hard for him to talk about. "I can't take them off," he said. He pointed to his legs. "They were paralyzed in the war."

She looked at him and seemed very confused.

"The war," he said. "Vietnam. Have you ever heard of Vietnam?"

"Vietnam, yes."

"I can't move it," he said, showing her his penis. "You see this?" he said, pointing at the yellow catheter tube. "It doesn't move anymore and I have to use this tube. You see this tube," he said, pointing to it again. "It's okay," he said. "Don't worry about it, *senorita* is *muy bonita*," he said, staring at her dark eyes. "We can still love," he said.

The tears began to roll down her face. She was sitting in the bed next to him crying.

"You see?" he said, pointing to the scar on his chest. "This is where they stuck a chest tube. . . ."

She was getting up now and putting her clothes back on. She was still crying. She was so very beautiful and he wanted so much to lie with her body warm and soft against the top of him, where he could still feel. But now she was walking out the door, leaving for good. She didn't even ask for his money, she didn't even want that.

He lay there for a long time until the madam came in and said it was time for him to leave. It was getting very late, she said. He put on his shirt and dragged his body across the bed, back into the wheelchair. The madam helped him out into the street.

It was early in the morning and the sun was about to come up and he sat crying outside the whorehouse. A cab came by. The driver stopped and asked him if he needed anything. "Do you need a woman?" he said. "Hey, want to go to a great whorehouse? There's a woman in there that will knock you out, really knows how to fuck."

There wasn't anything left to lose, he thought.

The driver got out of his cab and pushed him down the street to a place that was still open. "Wait a minute out here. I'll be right back," he told him. He came back with a big smile on his face. "Maria will be right out," he said, and pushed him into the bar.

A very young girl came into the room, walking past all the tables and then up to his. She had long brown hair down to her waist. "Do you want to sleep with me?" she said. He looked at her and said, "Yes." She seemed very excited, her brown eyes as bright as a little child's. He thanked the cabdriver and gave him some money and followed the girl into one of the tiny cubicles.

She was so much more relaxed than the other woman. He didn't have to explain anything to her. She lay down and touched his face gently. She kissed him and pushed her breasts next to his chest. She felt warm and good. She didn't seem to notice his pants were still on, or the catheter, the rubber urine bag, or any of that. She loved him, they loved each other on the bed in the little room, for what seemed a very long time. She didn't care about the war or any of the other things. They laughed and rolled on top of each other, hiding under the blankets, and talked about a lot of things. She told him she had a kid, a little girl, and they lived in the city. It was very lonely she told him and she really didn't want to do what she was doing, but it was the only way she could make money for herself and her baby. He held her in his arms as if she were his sister as well as his lover.

There was a loud knock on the door and the cabdriver yelled in a taunting voice that it was time for him to get out. But she laughed and said something in Spanish and they stayed in bed almost an extra ten minutes over the limit. When she was getting dressed she asked him if he wanted to get married. She told him she loved him very much and wrote down her address on a small piece of paper. "Here. You take this," she said. She helped him put on his shirt and buttoned each one of the buttons for him. "Come see me tomorrow at four," she said. "You can live with me. *Dinero*," she said, and he gave her fifteen dollars and she helped him into the chair.

All the way back to the village he thought about her and how they would live together and learn each other's language. He saw them sitting naked in bed together studying their books, the child playing at their feet. But then he began to think she hadn't really meant it and he didn't go back the next day at four. He went to a different place and lay with a different girl.

He went out almost every night after that, coming in every morning just after the sun came up and sleeping until four in the afternoon. Then he would get up and get ready to go into the city. Rahilio would call a cab for him and he would wait for it outside the gate of the Village of the Sun.

He would go from whorehouse to whorehouse, wheeling the chair in past the pretty painted Mexican women. He would find a table and wait for one to come up and talk to him. Usually they were kind and did not pity him. They would smile back, very interested, very curious, and he would smell their perfume and look at their breasts. He would sleep with a different one every night. He wanted to sleep with as many as he could, trying one after the other.

One night another Vietnam veteran from the Village came in with him, a guy named Charlie. Charlie had some good weed and said he wanted to have a real party. They got very stoned and very drunk together, and in the last whorehouse they went to Charlie got into a wild fight with one of the whores. He punched her in the face because she laughed at him when he pulled down his pants and told her he couldn't feel his penis or move it anymore. He was crazy drunk and he kept yelling and screaming, swinging his arms and his fists at the crowd who had gathered around him. "That goddamn fucking slut! I'm gonna kill that whore for ever laughing at me. That bitch thinks it's funny I can't move my dick. Fuck you! Fuck all of you goddamn motherfuckers! They made me kill babies! They made me kill babies!" Charlie screamed again and again.

The owner was shaking his fist, telling them both to get out and never come back, and he knew someone was going to kill them if they didn't leave right away. But he just sat there in the middle of the bar, unable to move. What Charlie was saying was what he had been feeling for a long time.

Finally the owner got a couple of guys and threw them out into the street. They managed to get a cab, but halfway home Charlie got into another fight with the driver over the money he was charging, and they both had to get out in the middle of the highway.

They sat by the edge of the road for a long time until a Mexican truckdriver picked them up. He just picked them up as if there was nothing at all unusual about finding the two of them out there. He lifted them out of their chairs and put them into the cab of his truck. Charlie was singing by the time they got to the Village and had pissed all over the seat; the driver opened his window but never complained.

Somehow that was the end of it for him. The whole thing was over. He had a real cold feeling about it now. He didn't go back to the city the next night. He spent one more day in the Village, then told Rahilio he'd had enough. He caught the next plane back to New York.

IT IS THE END of the summer when I get back. The days are long and hot and there is still so much restlessness in me. I sit in my parents' living room and try to watch the baseball game on television. I keep going down to Arthur's Bar. I begin to think about getting an apartment. I have never lived alone, but I decide to try it now.

I get a place in Hempstead near the university. The rent is two hundred dollars, but I never think much about money anymore. I just spend the big checks I get from the government. I go all over Hempstead buying out the furniture stores. I buy an electric typewriter, a huge expensive stereo, a bunch of paintings. I don't care what things cost.

Every morning I wheel into the bathroom of my new apartment and throw up. It frightens me to live alone with my paralyzed body and my thoughts of Vietnam. I am dreaming too often of the dead corporal. The tension and fear are twisted up inside me like a loaded spring. I get into my car and drive around for hours. Sometimes I drive very fast.

I have registered at the university and it is much better when classes begin. Maybe all I needed was to be with people again. I begin to look back and think about the summer, about Mexico. Even with all the loneliness, there were times that had been good. My first summer without the war. I tell myself the war and the hospital are behind me now. The best years of my life are still ahead of me.

I am more determined than ever to learn to walk on braces and I exercise for hours every day. In the hospital they have shown me a way to stretch my legs a little and I am doing it one evening in my second week of school when I hear something snap. It sounds like the branch of a tree breaking off—and there is my right leg all twisted under me. I panic for the first few minutes, then call my father. He drives over right away and takes me to the hospital, the V.A. hospital in the Bronx. I spend the next six months there.

I am alone again. I have been lying in Room 17 for almost a month. I am isolated here because I am a troublemaker. I had a fight with the head nurse on the ward. I asked for a bath. I asked for the vomit to be wiped up from the floor. I asked to be treated like a human being.

My leg has swollen to twice its original size. The thigh bone had been completely shattered in the break, leaving the bone sticking out just beneath the surface of my skin. It sticks out like a knife and every few minutes my leg jumps in violent spasms, the bone cutting and stabbing back and forth. The big clumsy cast I have been encased in isn't doing any good. It is not going to heal. Again and again I wonder why it has happened, why I am back in the same place I fought so hard to leave before.

The doctor never seems to be around. When he does show up it is only for a minute to see if I am still alive. He walks in and out, mumbles a few words. Once he calls me by the wrong name. It frightens me.

It is like being in a prison. But it is not a prison, it is a hospital. The tall skinny man who brings my breakfast calls me Seventeen. "Seventeen!" he screams, waking me out of a doped sleep. "Seventeen! It's time to eat." Up and down the hall the nurses move like programmed robots, pushing their metal carts, giving shots, handing out medication. There is one nurse who always tells me I am crazy. She gives me extra doses of a drug to make me drowsy.

It is so easy to lose it all here. The whole place functions so smoothly, but somewhere along the way I am losing, and all the rest of the people whom I can't see in the rooms around me are losing too. Even if I make it out of this place, I think, even if I heal the leg, I will lose. No one ever leaves this place without losing something.

Early one morning the doctor comes into my room and tells me he's been thinking it might be a good idea to cut my leg off. He tells me that to cut the leg off would be a very simple thing. He makes it sound so easy, like there would be nothing to it. It's they who are all crazy in here, I think. They are all moving so quickly, all of them in such a fantastic hurry. This place is more like a factory to break people than to mend them and put them back together again. I don't want them to cut my leg off. It is numb and dead but it still means something to me. It is still mine. It is a part of me and I am not going to give it away that easily. Why isn't anyone helping me? I think over and over again. Why am I being forgotten in this place?

Something is happening to me in Room 17. I lie and stare at the walls of the small green box they have put me in. The walls are almost as dirty as the floor and I cannot even see out of the window. I feel myself changing, the anger is building up in me. It has become a force I cannot control. I push the call button again and again. No one comes. I am lying in my own excrement and no one comes. I begin shouting and screaming. I grab an ice pack and my water pitcher. I throw them out of the open door into the hallway, splashing water and ice all over the floor. I have been screaming for almost an hour when one of the aides walks by. He sticks his head in the door, taunting me and laughing. "I'm a Vietnam veteran," I tell him. "I fought in Vietnam and I've got a right to be treated decently."

"Vietnam," the aide says loudly. "Vietnam don't mean nothin' to me or any of these other people.

You can take your Vietnam and shove it up your ass."

I am in the intensive-care ward. It is so quiet I can hear the big round clock ticking on the green wall. There are mostly old men here. They are all attached to complicated machines. The clock keeps ticking. I look down. There are big stitches on my leg and two plastic tubes—one runs a clear fluid in and the other carries a bright red fluid back out of the wound. There is some kind of machine on the side of the bed that keeps clanking and pumping, keeping everything flowing nicely. I realize I have made it, I have lived through the operation. I am not going to die and they haven't cut my leg off. They have put a steel plate in. They have screwed in all the screws and sewn the whole thing up. I will be out of this place soon. The leg will heal and I will get out of this hospital. I will get out of it for good and never come back.

The pump stops suddenly. An aide comes over and kicks it. He curses at it and kicks it very hard. It still doesn't work, and I am frightened now that I will lose the leg. "Goddamn thing," he says. "This hospital doesn't ever have nothing but old equipment." He runs to look for a doctor.

The doctor who comes in isn't the one who did the operation. He is a younger man from a big university in the city. He tells me the pump is old and probably will not work anymore. "Well, doesn't this hospital have another one?" I say. "I can't believe that a modern veterans' hospital like this doesn't have an extra pump." The young doctor explains in a very matter-of-fact way that this is the only pump they have. It all has to do with the war, he explains. It is all because of the war. "The government is not giving us money for things that we need. It's really too bad. It's not fair at all."

"I've tried so hard to keep this leg," I tell him. "I've done everything. . . ." I'm trying to be calm, as calm as he is.

"Yes," he says, nodding his head. "I completely understand."

An hour or so later the pump starts going again. No one even kicks it. It just starts up by itself. They tell me I am very lucky.

The leg heals slowly. I am weak and sick for a long time, but I continue to survive in the Bronx V.A. hospital. There are times I scream and shout and throw things out my door. I get a bath and an enema every four days. I have to watch the pump all the time to make sure it doesn't stop. I am so tired, so weary. One day the doctor comes and pulls the two plastic tubes out of my leg and puts small bandages over the holes. He and an aide put me on a gurney and strap me down. They are very careful with my leg. I have two hospital canes and am able to push myself and the gurney up and down the hospital ward. It is the first freedom I have had in months and I am very careful not to go too fast.

I lie in the hall a lot. I do not talk to anyone. I am very quiet. My mother and father come down to see me every week. I do not even want to talk to them. I do not tell them what I have been thinking about the war and the wound and the hospital—that the whole thing is beginning to go round and round in my head. I am just beginning to see what it all adds up to. It would only hurt them if they knew.

I WAS IN VIETNAM when I first heard about the thousands of people protesting the war in the streets of America. I didn't want to believe it at first—people protesting against *us* when we were putting our lives on the line for our country. The men in my outfit used to talk about it a lot. How could they do this to us? Many of us would not be coming back and many others would be wounded or maimed. We swore they would pay, the hippies and draftcard burners. They would pay if we ever ran into them.

But the hospital had changed all that. It was the end of whatever belief I'd still had in what I'd done in Vietnam. Now I wanted to know what I had lost my legs for, why I and the others had gone at all. But it was still very hard for me to think of speaking out against the war, to think of joining those I'd once called traitors.

I settled into my apartment again and went back to classes at the university. It was the spring of 1970. I still wore a tie and sweater every day to school and had a short haircut. I was very sensitive to people looking at me in the wheelchair. I buried myself in my books, cutting myself off from the other students. It was as if they threatened me—particularly the activists, the radicals.

I was sitting alone in my apartment listening to the radio when I first heard the news about Kent State. Four students had just been shot in a demonstration against the invasion of Cambodia. For a moment there was a shock through my body. I felt like crying. The last time I had felt that way was the day Kennedy was killed. I remember saying to myself, The whole thing is coming down now. I wheeled out to my car. I didn't know where I was going but I had to find other people who felt the way I did. I drove down the street to the university. Students were congregating in small groups all over the place. The campus looked as if it were going to explode. Banners were going up and monitors with red armbands were walking up and down handing out leaflets. There was going to be a march and demonstration. I thought carefully for a moment or two, then decided to participate, driving my car past the hundreds of students marching down to the big parking lot where the rally was to be held. I honked my horn in support but I was still feeling a little hesitant. I stayed in my car all during the rally, listening intently to each speaker and cheering and shouting with the crowd. I was still acting like an observer. The last speaker was a woman who said there would be a huge rally in Washington that Saturday and that it was hoped that everyone would make it down. I decided I would go.

That night I called my cousin Ginny's husband Skip. He used to come and visit me at the hospital when I first came back and after I got out we became good friends. Sometimes we'd stay up all night at his house playing cards and talking about Vietnam and what had happened to me. Skip's views were very different from mine back then. He was against the war. And each time I left his house to go home, he'd give me books to read—books about the black people and poor people of the country. I laughed at him at first and didn't take the books too seriously, but it was lonely in my room and soon I began to read. And before long, every time I went to his house I asked for more books. Skip seemed surprised when I asked him to go to the rally with me but he said yes, and early Saturday morning we left for Washington.

The New Jersey Turnpike was packed with cars painted with flags and signs, and everywhere there were people hitching, holding up big cardboard peace symbols. You didn't have to ask where anyone was going. We were all going to the same place. Washington was a madhouse with buses and trucks and cars coming in from all directions.

We got a parking space and I gave up my tie and sweater for no shirt and a big red bandana around my head. Skip pushed the wheelchair for what seemed a mile or so. We could feel the tremendous tension. People were handing out leaflets reminding everyone that this was a nonviolent demonstration, and that no purpose would be served in violent confrontation. I remember feeling a little scared, the way I did before a firefight. After reading the leaflet I felt content that no one was going to get hurt.

Skip and I moved as close to the speakers' platform as we could and Skip lifted me out of my chair and laid me on my cushion. People were streaming into the Ellipse from all around us—an army of everyday people. There was a guy with a stereo tape deck blasting out music, and dogs running after Frisbees on the lawn. The Hari Krishna people started to dance and the whole thing seemed like a weird carnival. But there was a warmth to it, a feeling that we were all together in a very important place. A young girl sat down next to me and handed me a canteen of cool water. "Here," she said, "have a drink." I drank it down and passed it to Skip who passed it to someone else. That was the feeling that day. We all seemed to be sharing everything.

We listened as the speakers one after another denounced the invasion of Cambodia and the slaying of the students at Kent State. The sun was getting very hot and Skip and I decided to move around. We wanted to get to the White House where Nixon was holed up, probably watching television. We were in a great sea of people, thousands and thousands all around us. We finally made it to Lafayette Park. On the other side of the avenue the government had lined up thirty or forty buses, making a huge wall between the people and the White House. I remember wondering back then why they had to put all those buses in front of the president. Was the government so afraid of its own people that it needed such a gigantic barricade? I'll always remember those buses lined up that day and not being able to see the White House from my wheelchair.

We went back to the rally for a while, then went on down to the Reflecting Pool. Hundreds of people had taken off their clothes. They were jumping up and down to the beat of bongo drums and metal cans. A man in his fifties had stripped completely naked. Wearing only a crazy-looking hat and a pair of enormous black glasses, he was dancing on a platform in the middle of hundreds of naked people. The crowd was clapping wildly. Skip hesitated for a moment, then stripped all his clothes off, jumping into the pool and joining the rest of the people. I didn't know what all of this had to do with the invasion of Cambodia or the students slain at Kent State, but it was total freedom. As I sat there in my wheelchair at the edge of the Reflecting Pool with everyone running naked all around me and the clapping and the drums resounding in my ears, I wanted to join them. I wanted to take off my clothes like Skip and the rest of them and wade into the pool and rub my body with all those others. Everything seemed to be hitting me all at once. One part of me was upset that people were swimming naked in the national monument and the other part of me completely understood that now it was their pool, and what good is a pool if you can't swim in it.

I remember how the police came later that day, very suddenly, when we were watching the sun go down—a blue legion of police in cars and on motorcycles and others with angry faces on big horses. A tall cop walked into the crowd near the Reflecting Pool and read something into a bull-horn no one could make out. The drums stopped and a few of the naked people began to put their clothes back on. It was almost evening and with most of the invading army's forces heading back along the Jersey Turnpike, the blue legion had decided to attack. And they did—wading their horses into the pool, flailing their clubs, smashing skulls. People were running everywhere as gas canisters began to pop. I couldn't understand why this was happening, why the police would attack the people, running them into the grass with their horses and beating them with their clubs. Two or three horses charged into the crowd at full gallop, driving the invading army into retreat toward the Lincoln Memorial. A girl was crying and screaming, trying to help her bleeding friend. She was yelling something about the pigs and kept stepping backward away from the horses and the flying clubs. For the first time that day I felt anger surge up inside me. I was no longer an observer, sitting in my car at the edge of a demonstration. I was right in the middle of it and it was ugly. Skip started pushing the chair as fast as he could up the path toward the Lincoln Memorial. I kept turning, looking back. I wanted to shout back at the charging police, tell them I was a veteran.

When we got to the memorial, I remember looking at Lincoln's face and reading the words carved on the walls in back of him. I felt certain that if he were alive he would be there with us.

I told Skip that I was never going to be the same. The demonstration had stirred something in my mind that would be there from now on. It was so very different from boot camp and fighting in the war. There was a togetherness, just as there had been in Vietnam, but it was a togetherness of a different kind of people and for a much different reason. In the war we were killing and maiming people. In Washington on that Saturday afternoon in May we were trying to heal them and set them free.

IT WILL BE my turn to speak soon. They have put me up on the platform of this auditorium in this high school that is so much like the one I went to, in this town that is like the one I grew up in. I am looking at all the young faces. Kids. They were laughing, horsing around when they came in, just the way we used to. Now they are silent, looking at me and Bobby Muller, my friend from the V.A. hospital who is speaking to them from his wheelchair.

It is like the day the marine recruiters came. I remember it like it was yesterday—their shiny shoes and their uniforms, their firm handshakes, all the dreams, the medals, the hills taken with Castiglia by my side his army-navy store canteen rattling, the movies the books the plastic guns, everything in 3-D and the explosive spiraling colors of a rainbow. Except this time, this time it is Bobby and me. What if I had seen someone like me that day, a guy in a wheelchair, just sitting there in front of the senior class not saying a word? Maybe things would have been different. Maybe that's all it would have taken.

Bobby is telling his story and I will tell mine. I am glad he has brought me here and that all of them are looking at us, seeing the war firsthand—the dead while still living, the living reminders, two young men who had the shit shot out of them.

I have never spoken before but it is time now. I am thinking about what I can tell them. I wheel myself to the center of the platform. I begin by telling them about the hospital.

5

AFTER THE SPEECH in the high school I spent less and less time going to classes at the university. Suddenly school no longer seemed important. What I really wanted to do was to go on speaking out. Bobby and I made a couple of other speeches at high schools together and once I did one by myself at a university. It was November and turning cold. Ever since I'd been wounded, I'd hated the cold weather. Snow was like a jailer for me. It made it so hard for me to get out of the house, to move around. I felt I'd stayed in one place for a very long time—I'd never lived more than a few miles from my parents' house except for the years when I was in Vietnam. For a while I thought of taking another trip to Mexico, but then just before Christmas my friend Kenny came home from California and asked me if I wanted to drive back across with him and live out there. I jumped at the idea of going. California seemed like such a warm and beautiful place, another planet. I cleaned my whole apartment out in one Sunday afternoon and gave all the furniture I owned to Mom and Dad. My car was packed that night and the next morning Kenny and I were on the road.

Three days later we'd gotten all the way to Texas. It was New Year's Eve. We celebrated it in a bar in Longview shooting a game of pool. The next day we got up early and drove straight through to Las Cruces, New Mexico. I remember big bramble bushes blowing in front of the car and dust all over everything. I wanted to push straight on to L.A., but Kenny and I hadn't eaten more than a few sandwiches in the last few days and we needed a good night's sleep. We stopped at a motel overnight and had a big breakfast of hot coffee and scrambled eggs before we started driving again. Even Kenny got excited later that afternoon when we passed the Great Salt Lake. He took the car the rest of the way in and I sat by the open window watching the orange groves and green trees begin to appear as we came out of the desert. It's California, I kept saying to myself, it's California. It got dark just as we came into L.A. and the lights went on all over the sprawling city like flickering little candles. No matter what Kenny or anybody said to me, this was Paradise, and like the pioneers before me I was going to make it my home. We got to Heliotrope Avenue and parked the car in front of Kenny's house. We went into his tiny apartment, turned the air conditioner on and fell asleep exhausted.

We rented a larger apartment down by the

ocean later that week, and after a while Kenny quit school. We hung out together all the time. It was so good to be with someone who'd known me all my life. Every day we went swimming with two girls who lived next door and Kenny bought himself a brand-new motorcycle. He strapped me on the back and took me riding on it the first day he brought it home.

I had been in California for about a month when one day there was a big photo on the front page of the *L.A. Times*—a group of vets had gone to Washington and thrown away their medals. It was one of the most moving antiwar demonstrations there had been. I would have given anything to have been there with them. I read about it sitting by the pool of the Santa Monica Bay Club, wearing a ridiculous Mickey Mouse shirt. Suddenly I knew my easy life could never be enough for me. The war had not ended. It was time for me to join forces with other vets.

I went home and called a couple of people I knew. One of them told me there was going to be a meeting of Vietnam Veterans Against the War that night in an apartment in L.A. I was still a bit unsure of myself but I couldn't wait to get into my car and drive over.

I remember how kind they were to me from the moment I arrived. When I got there, a bunch of vets were in front of the house waiting to carry me up the stairs in my chair. "Hi brother," they said to me warmly. "Can we help you brother? Is there anything we can do?"

All of a sudden everything seemed to change—

the loneliness seemed to vanish. I was surrounded by friends. They were the new veterans, the new soldiers with floppy bush hats and jungle uniforms right here on the streets of America. I began to feel closer to them than I ever had to the people at the university and at the hospital and all the people who had welcomed me back to Massapequa. It had a lot to do with what we had all been through. We could talk and laugh once again. We could be honest about the war and ourselves. Before each meeting there was the thumb-and-fist handshake—it meant you cared about your brother.

We were men who had gone to war. Each of us had his story to tell, his own nightmare. Each of us had been made cold by this thing. We wore ribbons and uniforms. We talked of death and atrocity to each other with unaccustomed gentleness.

I remember being very nervous and anxious at that first meeting. I told them, Give me a speech, give me a place to show this wheelchair. I really wanted to get going immediately. The brothers told me to calm down and not to worry, there would be plenty of chances to speak, it was time to get the organization together.

Afterward I went into the kitchen for a cup of coffee and one of the guys came up to me and gave me a big hug. He held me for a long time and when he let go there were tears streaming down his face. "I love you, brother," he said, wiping his eyes. And then he said, "I'm sorry, I'm really sorry I did that."

"It's okay," I said. "I love you too. Now when's my first speaking gig?"

They told me to go to a rally in Pasadena the next day. I would be speaking at noon with a couple of other people.

The VVAW sent me to do a lot of speeches after that and soon I was on television all the time. On one network there was a big argument with a producer who didn't want a disfigured veteran on her show. "We've seen enough of that," she told me over the phone. "Every night for the last couple of years people have seen it on the six o'clock news and they're tired of it." She tried to be nice and told me that she had read a book called *Johnny Got His Gun,* so she knew what I was all about, but she didn't think it would be tasteful at all to let the people of L.A. see a crippled kid on a Sunday morning.

I was at a rally a few weeks later when Donald Sutherland began to read the last couple of pages of the book the woman had talked to me about, the one about the kid in World War I who gets blown to hell like myself and loses almost everything, he's just a hulk, a slab of meat. Sutherland began to read the passage and something I will never forget swept over me. It was as if someone was speaking for everything I ever went through in the hospital. It was as if the book was speaking about me, my wound and the hell it had been coming back and learning to live with it. I began to shake and I remember there were tears in my eyes. Just before Sutherland was finished I found myself pushing my chair toward the stage and telling them that I wanted to be lifted up the steps. "I have a poem," I told them. "I have a poem I wrote about the vets who threw their medals away and I want to read it."

They broke all the rules and hoisted my chair up on the stage. I went up to the microphone and started reading. The crowd cheered when I was finished and again I had tears in my eyes. I said a couple of words I can't remember.

For the next couple of weeks the phone wouldn't stop ringing. There were all sorts of clubs and schools wanting to hear me speak. I wrote the names and addresses down on pieces of paper and all over the walls of the apartment.

I went totally into speaking out against the war after that. I went into it the same way I'd gone into everything else I've wanted to do in my life—the way I'd gone into pole vaulting or baseball or the marines. But this was something that meant much more than being an athlete or a marine. I could see that this thing—this body I had trained so hard to be strong and quick, this body I now dragged around with me like an empty corpse—was to mean much more than I had ever realized. Much more than I'd known the night I cried into my pillow in Massaqequa because my youth had been desecrated, my physical humanity defiled. I think I honestly believed that if only I could speak out to enough people I could stop the war myself. I honestly believed people would listen to me because of who I was, a wounded American veteran. They would have to listen. Every chance I had to get my broken body on the tube or in front of an audience I went hog wild. Yes, let them get a look at me. Let them be remined of what they'd done when they'd sent my generation off to war. One look would be enough —worth more than a thousand speeches. But if they wanted speeches I could give them speeches too. There was no end to what I had to tell them.

"I'm the example of the war," I would say. "Look at me. Do you want your sons to look like this? Do you want to put on the uniform and come home like me?" Some people could not believe the conditions I told them about in the hospitals. Others could not believe anything at all. After one of the TV shows a cameraman called me a commie traitor to my face. He was pushing me down the studio steps in my chair and I wondered if he was going to drop me. I kept receiving letters from people calling me names and telling me what they would do if I didn't stop aiding the enemy.

The speaking went on and on, and so did the war, and after a while it all began to seem endless. My friends told me I was starting to sound like a broken record. Even Kenny got disgusted with my new role of activist and antiwar veteran and left for New York. I went a little crazy staying alone in the apartment, answering the phone that never stopped ringing and scrawling more names all over the walls. One night I tore the place apart.

I thought of stopping but I was afraid of the loneliness. The speaking had brought back everything—the hospital, Vietnam. Each time I spoke about an experience it was just like reliving it. And there were some things I never talked about—like the corporal from Georgia and the ambush in the village and the dead children lying on the ground.

I can't remember one time when I even came close to telling anyone exactly what had happened over there. Back then it was still deep inside of me and I shared it with no one—not even the men I had come to know as my brothers.

THE NOON TRAFFIC is moving along Wilshire Boulevard just as if the line of veterans and ordinary citizens picketing Nixon's campaign headquarters were not there. "Join us!" we cry. "Stop the war!" Heavy curtains are drawn over the windows of the campaign headquarters where volunteers are working for the reelection of the president. We have been there for two days and not one of the volunteers has ever looked out. The people in their cars pass us quickly, intent on their steering wheels. Who are these people going to work, going to lunch, as if nothing is more important than that? "Here!" I scream. "Look at the war!" They never so much as turn their heads. I wheel out into the traffic, pushing myself in front of cars. "Take a good look at the war!" I cry, racing with my wheelchair in front of a truck. I do not think—or even care—about getting killed. I am screaming at them to look at me. Up on the rooftop of the headquarters the hidden police cameras are taking pictures, and I know that all by myself I have at least succeeded in stopping traffic.

One by one the other demonstrators are breaking from the line. They sit down among the cars, banging their picket sticks and yelling, their voices hoarse—"One, two, three, four. We don't want your fucking war"—tying up the traffic for blocks. We have taken the streets. People are honking their horns now, workers and secretaries hanging out their windows, busdrivers shouting their approval. Some of the demonstrators are dancing and I grab both wheels of my chair, then let go with one hand and raise my middle finger in the air as a salute to the cops and the FBI. I spin on my two wheels in front of everyone, as the shouting goes on for the war to end, for the killing to be stopped forever. I keep doing my wheelies as the police look on with envy and utter contempt, frozen on their side of the street. They seem torn between wanting to kill us and wanting to tear off their uniforms and throw away their guns. "Come join us!" we shout to them, but they do not take us up on our invitation.

Finally a tall lieutenant announces over a bullhorn that the demonstration has ended and that everyone is to clear out immediately. "How are you doing, brother?" says a man with long red hair in back of me. "Is everything okay?" He is someone I have seen at other demonstrations, but I do not know his name. "You look like you could use some help," he says, and offers to push me for a while.

The police are moving now, closing in on us. I can hear sirens in the distance. I begin yelling and screaming directions to the people around me. "Get back on the sidewalk into the line! Come on now!" I try to wheel my chair forward, but it will not move. I try again.

Suddenly the man with the red hair is leaning over from behind me, grabbing my hands. "You're under arrest." Another man whom I recognize from the picket line runs up to help him. "Come on you bastard. You're going to jail!"

I am fighting to keep them from handcuffing me, screaming for the other demonstrators to help me.

The red-headed man lifts up the handles of my chair and dumps me into the street. I fall forward on my face, my legs twisted under me.

"Get your fucking hands behind you!" The red-headed man jabs his knee into my back.

There is a tremendous commotion all around me. Someone is kicking the dead part of my body that can't feel anymore. People are yelling and screaming and clubs are flying everywhere.

"I'm a Vietnam veteran! Don't you know what you're doing to me? Oh God, what's happening." They are holding my arms. They twist them behind my back, clamp handcuffs around my wrists.

"Don't you understand? My body's paralyzed. I can't move my body, I can't feel my body."

"Get him the fuck out of here!" yells someone.

Kicking me and hitting me with their fists, they begin dragging me along. They tear the medals I have won in the war from my chest and throw me back into the chair, my hands still cuffed behind me. I feel myself falling forward because I cannot balance and the red-headed man keeps pushing me back against the chair, yelling and cursing at me to stay put.

"I have no stomach muscles, don't you understand?"

"Shut up you sonofabitch!"

There are women standing on the sidewalk nearby crying, and all around me people are being beaten and handcuffed. The two men begin dragging me in the chair to an unmarked car on the other side of the street.

The red-headed man throws my body into the back seat, my dead limbs flopping underneath me. "Get in there you fucking traitor!"

I am feeling hurt all over and I can hardly breathe. I lie bleeding in the back seat as a discussion goes on between the two of them about whether or not they have broken any of my bones. I hear them say they are going to take me to the county jail hospital for x-rays.

Something happens to them when I take my clothes off in the admitting room. They stand there looking at me. They see my scars and the rubber catheter tube going into my penis and they begin to think they have made a mistake. I can see the fear in their faces. They have just beaten up a half-dead man, and they know it. They are very careful now, almost polite. They help me put my clothes back on when the doctor is through with me.

"I was in Vietnam too," the red-headed man says, hesitating.

"We don't want the war either," says the other cop. "No one wants war."

They help me back into the chair and take me to another part of the prison building to be booked.

"What's your name?" the officer behind the desk says.

"Ron Kovic," I say. "Occupation, Vietnam veteran against the war."

"What?" he says sarcastically, looking down at me.

"I'm a Vietnam veteran against the war," I almost shout back.

"You should have died over there," he says. He turns to his assistant. "I'd like to take this guy and throw him off the roof."

They fingerprint me and take my picture and put me in a cell. I have begun to wet my pants like a little baby. The tube has slipped out during my examination by the doctor. I try to fall asleep but even though I am exhausted, the anger is alive in me like a huge hot stone in my chest. I lean my head up against the wall and listen to the toilets flush again and again.

They lead me out of the cell the next morning around ten o'clock. I am to be moved to another part of the prison until someone comes to bail me out. They have arrested seventeen other vets at the demonstration. They take them out of the cells one by one, handcuffing and chaining them together in a long line like a chain gang. I look at their faces and wonder which one of them is like the guy with long red hair and the other cop who'd pretended to be veterans the day before. Which one is the informer now? I think to myself.

They tell me to move out of the way. They cannot fit me into the line with the others. "It's too difficult with that chair of yours," one of the cops complains.

"Don't you want to put the cuffs on me again?" I say. "Don't you think I need leg chains like the others?"

He looks at me surprised, then turns away and screams, "Let's go!"

The veterans clank their chains against the cold cement floor as they file past me out of the cellblock. Seventeen of America's veterans dragging those chains, handcuffed together—America's children. I cry because I want to be walking with them and because I want so much to trust them. But after what has happened I don't know whether I will be able to trust anyone, even my closest friends now. What are they doing to me? I think. They have taken so much from me already and still they are not satisfied. What more will they take?

AFTER A SPEECH in a church in Compton I met a woman. I had the whole congregation in tears and a pretty woman in a long dress came up to me afterward and we started talking. We went outside and we kept talking until late that night. She gave me her phone number and told me she had two kids and if I wasn't doing anything the next week to drop by. She was a schoolteacher and her name was Helen. We called each other every day that week and one night I went over to her house. I kissed her in the driveway with the motor still running in my fancy Oldsmobile. It was the first time I had been close to a woman since Mexico. She called me the next day and told me she loved me. I thought it was pretty silly at first.

I went up to the mountains with a group of Quakers soon after that. I remember staying up all night at a house near their training school. It was a house that belonged to this crippled guy—I think he'd had polio. His wife had divorced him, but she was up there that weekend in his house with her boyfriend, making it on the couch. The guy in the wheelchair wasn't there, but even if he had been, they said he wouldn't have minded. I remember they gave me his room to stay in, and there were shelves in it with hundreds of books. I stayed awake all night and when I finally got up the next morning I threw up in the toilet bowl. I was thinking about the guy's wife on the couch with her boyfriend, and about Helen who said she loved me.

I called her up as soon as I got back. It was really nice to have someone love me, I said, and I listened to her tell it to me again. I went over to her house that night and slept with her in her bed. She had this little room that was near the kitchen and she had a photograph in it, a wedding photograph of herself and her ex–old man all dressed up in the finest things. She said he was a drifter but she still cared about him. He just wasn't responsible enough to take care of her and the two kids. I remember she played soft music on the radio. The whole thing gave me a funny empty feeling. I slept with her the second time just before I went back to New York. I told her I was leaving and that I would see her in a month or two. I didn't tell her it bothered me that she was calling me all the time now telling me she loved me. I said I'd had enough of California.

I remember freaking out a couple of times when I got home, crying in front of my mother, telling her about the babies I had killed. I thought

I was losing my mind. The dead corporal from Georgia was finally catching up with me and hanging me in almost all my dreams. Every day I woke up with a pain in my chest. I felt scared and shaky. I broke down one night and called Helen. "I think I want to marry you," I remember saying.

"Are you sure?" I heard her say over and over on the phone. "Are you sure you want to marry me?"

"Yeah," I said. "I love you baby and I want to marry you."

Next thing I knew she was flying across the country with two screaming kids to meet my family.

I met her at the airport. She was wearing red tights and I remember she had cut her hair. I'd really liked her hair long but when I went to the airport her hair was short and the kids looked terrible too. I didn't know how to tell her about her hair.

I remember she wanted to go to church that day to say a few prayers for something or other. I drove her over there but I wouldn't go in. I sat in the car and turned up the radio. A song was playing called "Bye-Bye Miss American Pie" and I remember listening to it and feeling real sad inside, real low like I wanted to cry or kill someone.

She came back into the car and we drove all over the neighborhood. I kept stopping and introducing her to people I knew. "Helen and I are getting married," I said. I even introduced her to Castiglia, who was visiting his folks that weekend, pushing away from him in the wheelchair after I told him I was going to marry her.

By the time we left Massapequa we were fighting about everything all the time and I was getting sick of the whole thing. She was always talking to me about going back to church and meeting married couples and building a strong family for the future. We hadn't even been able to sleep together much. I'd had to stay on the couch on the porch and she was down in Sue's room with the kids. My mother and dad never wanted a man and woman that weren't married sleeping together even if the woman was divorced and had two kids.

We tried living together for a while when we got back to California, first at my house and then at hers. I don't know why I ever did it or why I ever asked her to marry me, but back then it seemed really important to have someone like Helen to hold on to. I even ended up going down to the V.A. hospital in Long Beach and seeing a marriage counselor for paralyzed men. The counselor and I sat out in the sun a lot and fed birds and shouted at each other but it never worked. Every time I came home from the sessions I threw up and finally I couldn't even sleep near Helen anymore. I knew I had to be alone for a while. I found a small house on Hurricane Street in Santa Monica and moved into it.

WHEN I FIRST MOVED to Hurricane Street it was quiet. I wanted to get away not only from Helen but from everything that reminded me of the war. I was going to grow plants and cook my own food. I had a lot of dreams about how it was going to be. I even wanted to write a book. I bought an old rolltop desk and spent an afternoon with a couple of friends going to pick it up and moving it into the house.

It was a beautiful little house a block from the ocean—more a small neat shack tucked into an alleyway. The windows were wooden hurricane slats, which gave the place the appearance of always being ready for a hurricane or a big storm. There was a shower that had been adjusted for me so I could fit the wheelchair in comfortably, and I loved being so close to the ocean. I went out one afternoon and bought a big waterbed, the first one I'd ever had.

I never talked too much to my neighbors, except when I was emptying garbage or something.

I used to sit at the window and stare at a dog that was always on the roof of the house in front of me. After the first couple of days I gave up cooking and started eating out at the Jack-in-the-Box hamburger stands. The food was awful, but it was better to be out in the car than stuck alone in the house all the time.

Sometimes I'd have terrible nightmares about the war. I'd wake up scared in my room in the middle of the night. There was no one to hold on to, just myself there inside my frozen body. I remember watching flowers bloom outside my window and feeling good when the ants would come into the house. Well, at least I've got some company, I thought.

I wrote a poem once at my rolltop desk. It was called "Hurricanes/in the eye of the hurricane." I wrote about the loneliness and the silence of my house, how being there was like a sudden pause in the middle of a wild swirling storm. A lot of times I couldn't take it. I'd get into my car and drive as far and fast as I could. But after a while I learned to stay by myself for a long time.

The time since the war was passing so fast now and he wasn't in the hospital anymore and they weren't smiling down by his bedside and the priests weren't there and he wasn't in the streets speaking out against the men who had made all the terrible things that happened to him possible. They weren't cheering and clapping or even putting the handcuffs on him anymore. He wasn't in jail and in jail at least he knew there were other people around to talk to but now there was no one and all the cheering and all the clapping had stopped and now he was more alone than he had ever been in his life.

What kind of miserable life was this, no friends, no legs, people staring at him wherever he went. The depression sometimes was awesome, like he was drowning in it, and no matter how hard he tried he wasn't ever getting out. He had tried so hard for years to hold on. He had even sometimes invented things that weren't true, made believe so the feelings would go away. But now he wasn't making things up anymore, he was too tired to do that, in too much pain. Where were his legs that used to run? he thought.

He wanted people around him. He wanted someone to call him on the phone. He wanted just one friend he could talk to about the real things, the painful truths about his miserable existence that would make most people walk away from him—"Sorry I gotta run now. I'm late already." Other people always seemed able to laugh and joke about the whole thing, but they weren't the one who was living in this angry numb corpse, they didn't have to wake up each morning and feel the dead weight of these legs and strain the yellow urine into the ugly rubber bag, they didn't have to put on the rubber gloves each morning over the bathroom bowl and dig into his rear end to clean the brown chunks of shit out. They lived very easy lives, why their lives were disgustingly easy compared to his and they acted sometimes like everything was equal and he was the same as them, but he knew they were lying and especially the women, when they lay with him and told him how much they loved his body, how it wasn't any different than any other man's, that they didn't care if his dick was numb and dead and he couldn't feel warm and good inside a woman ever again. He was a half-dead corpse and no one could tell him any different. They could use the fancy medical words like they had in the hospital but he knew who they had brought back with all their new helicopters and wonderful new ways of killing people, all that incredible advancement in technology. He would never have come back from any other war. But now here he was. He was back and dead and breathing. Oh Mom, oh Dad, somebody, Jesus, somebody please help me. No one to love him, no one to touch him the way he had been touched before the war. He was a little speck now, he was a tiny little dot and he had to do something fast because he felt himself getting smaller and smaller. He had to live again, feel again.

He had been born on the Fourth of July, he had been their Yankee Doodle Dandy, their all-American boy. He had given them almost his whole being in the war and now, after all that, they weren't satisfied with three-quarters being gone, they wanted to take the rest of him. It was crazy but he knew that's what they wanted. They wanted his head and his mind, the numb legs and the wheelchair, they wanted everything. It had all been one big dirty trick and he didn't know what to think anymore. All he had tried to do was tell the truth about the war. But now he just wanted it to be quiet, to be where they weren't cursing at him and beating him and jailing him, lying and calling him a traitor. He had never been anything but a thing to them, a thing to put a uniform on and train to kill, a young thing to run through the meat-grinder, a cheap small nothing thing to make mincemeat out of.

And somewhere along the way he had forgotten to be polite anymore, and how to be a nice person. Somewhere through it all they had taken even that and he wanted it back so much, so very desperately, he would give almost anything to be able to be kind to people again, but the big machine, the one that had given him the number and the rifle, had sucked it out of him forever. They had made him confused and uncertain and blind with hate. They wanted to make him hide like he was hiding now. How many more, he thought, how many more like him were out there hiding on a thousand other Hurricane Streets? He was a living reminder of something terrible and awful. No matter what they said to him, no matter how much they tried to twist and bend things, he held on to what he knew and all the terrible things he had seen and done for them. They had buried the corporal and the children he had killed in the ground, but he was still sitting and breathing in his wheelchair, and now the last thing he could do for them if he wasn't going to die was to disappear.

He knew too much about them. He knew, goddamn it, like no one else would ever know. They were small men with small ideas, gamblers and hustlers who had gambled with his life and hustled him off to the war. They were smooth talkers, men who wore suits and smiled and were polite, men who wore watches and sat behind big desks sticking pins in maps in rooms he had never seen, men who had long-winded telephone conversations and went home to their wives and children. They were like the guy on television who hid the little pea under the three cups, moving them back and forth, back and forth, until you got real confused and didn't know where the hell anything was. They had never seen blood and guts and heads and arms. They had never picked up the shattered legs of children and watched the blood drip into the sand below their feet. It was they who were the little dots, the small cheap things, not him and the others they had sent to do their killing.

He had to rise up out of this deep dark prison. He had to come back. He knew the power he had. Maybe he had forgotten it for a while but it was still there and he could feel it growing in his mind, bigger and bigger—the power to make people remember, to make them as angry as he was every day of his life, every moment of his existence. He would come back very soon and he would make it like all the stories of the baseball players he had read when he was a kid. *"He's picking up the ball. He's running across the field. Kovic is making a terrific comeback, folks! A terrific comeback. . . ."*

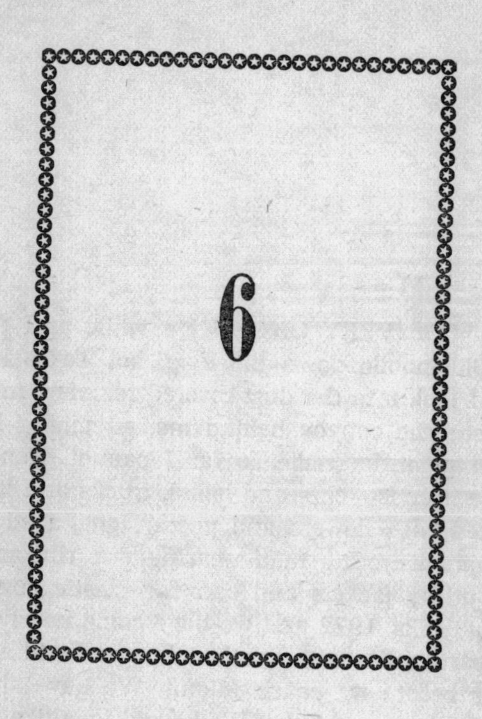
6

EVERY ONCE IN a while as I drive the Oldsmobile down the long, hot Texas highway, I look into the dust-covered rearview mirror and see the convoy behind me, stretching back like a gigantic snake so far I cannot even tell where it ends—cars and buses, trucks and jeeps, painted with flowers and peace signs, a strange caravan of young men wearing war ribbons on torn utility jackets and carrying plastic guns. It is August of 1972 and we have come nearly two thousand miles with another thousand still ahead of us before we reach Miami. We have shared food and cans of Coke. We have driven like madmen across the desert and lain down in the sand in our sleeping bags. We have played and laughed around campfires. It is our last patrol together, and I know I will remember it as long as I live. It is a historic event like the Bonus March of thousands of veterans upon the Capitol in the thirties. And now it is we who are marching, the boys of the fifties. We are going to the Republican National Convention to reclaim America and a bit of ourselves. It is war and we are soldiers again, as tight as we have ever been, a whole lost generation of dope-smoking kids in worn jungle boots coming from all over the country to tell Nixon a thing or two. We know we are fighting the real enemies this time—the ones who have made profit off our very lives. We have lain all night in the rain in ambush together. We have burned anthills with kerosene and stalked through Sally's Woods with plastic machine guns, shooting people out of trees. We have been a generation of violence and madness, of dead Indians and drunken cowboys, of iron pipes full of match-heads.

There is a tremendous downpour just outisde of Houston that almost tears the windshield wipers off the car. And after the rain there is one of the most beautiful rainbows I have ever seen, and then a second rainbow appears—a magnificent double rainbow above our heads. I am certain I want to be alive forever. I know that no matter what has happened the world is a beautiful place, and I am here with my brothers.

We drive into Louisiana through the little towns, past waving schoolchildren and smiling gas-station attendants flashing the peace sign and faces looking curiously at us from windows, not angry just curious and friendly, surprisingly friendly—the ordinary working people who want the war to end too, the glory John Wayne war. But I am scared in Louisiana. Like a lot of the other guys I think the KKK is all over the place and someone says there is no difference between the Klan and the cops, they are both the same thing.

He probably hated niggers, the corporal from Georgia. All through the South, these roads, the memories are talking.

He probably hated niggers. Pushing shoving, moving grooving, sliding diving into the coffin, into the soft earth of Georgia. Brought him back in and some guys sent him down the river where all of the dead went to, all the nineteen-year-old corpses who had to be fixed up, shot full of stuff and preserved real good so they could be packaged like meat in the deli to be sent home where their mothers and their sisters and their fathers and their wives could stand and pray and talk about what they were like when they were alive. She'd probably remember better than most of them what it was like to hold his hand, walk with him, kiss him on his soft lips that were now cold and dead, planted six feet in the Georgia mud. Nothing will bring him back, nothing on earth will bring him back. The corporal's dead and he's dead because of me. Oh god, oh Jesus, I want to cry, I want to scream, I want him to be alive again, I want him to be alive again I want him to be alive again oh god oh Jesus oh god o god ogod help me, make him feel, bring him back, bring him back wailing and talking, breathing and laughing again. Who who who who who is he? Now he's finished in the earth, in the ground. Try not to think about it, the thought, the dead thought. Goddamn, goddamn, goddamn fuckin' southern bigot. They were all that way in boot camp. Yes yes I remember. I want school and sitting on the fence and where's Mom and the heater, Richie and me stringing high-tension stickballs, eggballs, baseballs, r r r r r r run the bases to Castiglia's basement. I want out, I want out, I want out mom mom mom mom mom mom. Take a drag of the cigarette Yes thank you. Can't move, can't you see Richie, can't move, no more posters, teacher's dirty looks, no more warm good red checkered table . . . let me out let me out.

And the Last Patrol moved into the silence and darkness of Louisiana, the long snake, long line of us packed together, moving slower and slower, following the cops under the swaying beautiful trees, the warm muggy night, so warm and muggy and nice and getting ready to rain. Okay okay everybody! Someone screaming into a bullhorn and we are easing into the campsite, circling around like Gabby Hayes and the wagon trains, like a big 360 in the Nam. People crawling into their sleeping bags all over the tall swampy grass, crawling in and pulling them up over their heads dreaming of illumination canisters, or popping red flares in the DMZ, they make love like morphine, rolling and driving together like tomorrow will never come. *What gave them the right to beat me, the war, the scar, the scar in the chair, in the road, for whose trophy case this time Mr. President?*

There is a bridge that goes into Miami and we moved over it like a returning army, like a returning army we moved together slowly across the bridge, our horns blasting, our flags waving, shouting into the wind that blew from the ocean. Once we crossed the bridge we headed through the city, headlights burning on all the cars and trucks. A quick decision was made and we went through every red light and stop sign in the town. I remember hanging out of the Oldsmobile with the big upside-down flag flapping, screaming and shouting as we came nearer and nearer to Flamingo Park. This was the end of the journey and as we approached the park we were beseiged by hundreds and hundreds of well-wishers yelling and cheering and clapping the arrival of the veterans. People were dancing in the streets, playing flutes, running up to us, Yippies and Zippies shoving handfuls of joints into our laps and all the brothers were climbing out of their cars hugging and jumping on top of each other, singing and screaming and carrying on like we had just won the war.

A couple of vets from New York who knew me ran up and hugged me, welcoming me to the enormous tent city. "Yeah man," one of them said, "I read about you in New York when they beat you up. Good to see you down here, good to have you down." I found a place to put my rubber mattress and plant my upside-down American flag. I sat down and looked at all the wild activity around me. Later in the afternoon one of the first reporters came by. "I've got a few things to say," I told her, and we talked for about two hours until she had to go. It got dark and all of us went to sleep. The Yippies and the Zippies were still smoking dope and carrying on in a wild pot party but the Last Patrol was tired. It had been a long journey across America.

IT WAS THE night of Nixon's acceptance speech and now I was on my own deep in his territory, all alone in my wheelchair in a sweat-soaked marine utility jacket covered with medals from the war. A TV producer I knew from the Coast had gotten me past the guards at the entrance with his press pass. My eyes were still smarting from teargas. Outside the chain metal fence around the Convention Center my friends were being clubbed and arrested, herded into wagons. The crowds were thick all around me, people dressed as if they were going to a banquet, men in expensive summer suits and women in light elegant dresses. Every once in a while someone would look at me as if I didn't belong there. But I had come almost three thousand miles for this meeting with the president and nothing was going to prevent it from taking place.

I worked my way slowly and carefully into the huge hall, moving down one of the side aisles. "Excuse me, excuse me," I said to delegates as I pushed past them farther and farther to the front of the hall toward the speakers' podium.

I had gotten only halfway toward where I wanted to be when I was stopped by one of the convention security marshals. "Where are you going?" he said. He grabbed hold of the back of my chair. I made believe I hadn't heard him and kept turning my wheels, but his grip on the chair was too tight and now two other security men had joined him.

"What's the matter?" I said. "Can't a disabled veteran who fought for his country sit up front?"

The three men looked at each other for a moment and one of them said, "I'm afraid not. You're not allowed up front with the delegates." I had gotten as far as I had on sheer bluff alone and now they were telling me I could go no farther. "You'll have to go to the back of the convention hall, son. Let's go," said the guard who was holding my chair.

In a move of desperation I swung around facing all three of them, shouting as loud as I could so Walter Cronkite and the CBS camera crew that was just above me could hear me and maybe even focus their cameras in for the six o'clock news. "I'm a Vietnam veteran and I fought in the war! Did you fight in the war?"

One of the guards looked away.

"Yeah, that's what I thought," I said. "I bet none of you fought in the war and you guys are trying to throw me out of the convention. I've got just as much right to be up front here as any of these delegates. I fought for that right and I was born on the Fourth of July."

I was really shouting now and another officer came over. I think he might have been in charge of the hall. He told me I could stay where I was if I was quiet and didn't move up any farther. I agreed with the compromise. I locked my brakes and looked for other veterans in the tremendous crowd. As far as I could tell, I was the only one who had made it in.

People had begun to sit down all around me. They all had Four More Years buttons and I was surprised to see how many of them were young. I began speaking to them, telling them about the Last Patrol and why veterans from all over the United States had taken the time and effort to travel thousands of miles to the Republican National Convention. "I'm a disabled veteran!" I shouted. "I served two tours of duty in Vietnam and while on my second tour of duty up in the DMZ I was wounded and paralyzed from the chest down." I told them I would be that way for the rest of my life. Then I began to talk about the hospitals and how they treated the returning veterans like animals, how I, many nights in the Bronx, had lain in my own shit for hours waiting for an aide. "And they never come," I said. "They never come because that man that's going to accept the nomination tonight has been lying to all of us and spending the money on war that should be spent on healing and helping the wounded. That's the biggest lie and hypocrisy of all—that we had to go over there and fight and get crippled and come home to a government and leaders who could care less about the same boys they sent over."

I kept shouting and speaking, looking for some kind of reaction from the crowd. No one seemed to want to even look at me.

"Is it too real for you to look at? Is this wheelchair too much for you to take? The man who will accept the nomination tonight is a liar!" I shouted again and again, until finally one of the security men came back and told me to be quiet or they would have to take me to the back of the hall.

I told him that if they tried to move me or touch my chair there would be a fight and hell to pay right there in front of Walter Cronkite and the national television networks. I told him if he wanted to wrestle me and beat me to the floor of the convention hall in front of all those cameras he could.

By then a couple of newsmen, including Roger Mudd from CBS, had worked their way through the security barricades and begun to ask me questions.

"Why are you here tonight?" Roger Mudd asked me. "But don't start talking until I get the camera here," he shouted.

It was too good to be true. In a few seconds Roger Mudd and I would be going on live all over the country. I would be doing what I had come here for, showing the whole nation what the war was all about. The camera began to roll, and I began to explain why I and the others had come, that the war was wrong and it had to stop immediately. "I'm a Vietnam veteran," I said. "I gave America my all and the leaders of this government threw me and the others away to rot in their V.A. hospitals. What's happening in Vietnam is a crime against humanity, and I just want the American people to know that we have come all the way across this country, sleeping on the ground and in the rain, to let the American people see for themselves the men who fought their war and have come to oppose it. If you can't believe the veteran who fought the war and was wounded in the war, who can you believe?"

"Thank you," said Roger Mudd, visibly moved by what I had said. "This is Roger Mudd," he said, "down on the convention floor with Ron Kovic, a disabled veteran protesting President Nixon's policy in Vietnam."

The security agents were frantically trying to stop other cameras from getting through and later I was to learn that Press Secretary Ronald Ziegler had almost flipped out when he heard Mudd had interviewed me and it had gone nationwide for almost two minutes.

By this time a few other veterans had managed to get into the hall. One of them came to tell me that my old friend Bobby Muller and Bill Wieman, a double amputee, had gotten passes from Congressman McCloskey and had managed to get into the center aisle in direct line with the podium almost two hundred feet back. "Get me up there quick," I said. He turned me around and wheeled me toward the back past the smiling security officers who must have thought I was leaving. What are you smiling at? I thought to myself. I'm just warming up.

"There, up there," the vet said, pointing to the front of the aisle where Bobby and Bill were sitting in their wheelchairs.

"Where you been?" Wieman said to me, as I shook their hands.

"I've been over there," I said, pointing to the other aisle. "I wanted to get all the way to the front, but this place is great."

We lined ourselves up together, wheelchair to wheelchair, facing the platform where Nixon would speak. They had brought in a couple of Stop the War signs, and I grabbed one and held it above my head.

There was an announcement at the podium and then a tremendous roar. It was the vice president of the United States, Spiro T. Agnew. The delegates stood chanting and shaking their clasped hands over their heads, stamping their feet up and down until it seemed as though the whole convention hall was going to explode. "Four more years," the crowd shouted. "Four more years, four more years."

Agnew stood rigid at attention, accepting the tumultuous applause. Finally he raised both of his palms, signaling them all to stop so he could give his speech. Every time he spoke a few words, he was interrupted by the wild crowd, wild and enthusiastic. "Agnew in 'seventy-six!" a fat woman yelled next to me. "Agnew in 'seventy-six!"

I pulled myself up onto the siderail of my wheelchair and sat holding my sign as high as I could. I wanted everyone in the hall to be able to see it. A man came up suddenly from my blind side. Before I knew what hit me he had grabbed my sign and torn it into shreds in front of me. "You lousy commie sonofabitch!" he shouted.

Now there was only one sign left and we decided to hold on to it until it was Nixon's turn to speak. A few seconds before he was introduced, security agents began to move in all around us. We must have been an ugly sight to the National Republican Party as we sat there in perfect view of all the national networks that were perched above us.

Suddenly a roar went up in the convention hall, louder than anything I had ever heard in my life. It started off as a rumble, then gained in intensity until it sounded like a tremendous thunderbolt. "Four more years, four more years," the crowd roared over and over again. The fat woman next to me was jumping up and down and dancing in the aisle. It was the greatest ovation the president of the United States had ever received and he loved it. I held the sides of my wheelchair to keep my hands from shaking. After what seemed forever, the roar finally began to die down.

This was the moment I had come three thousand miles for, this was it, all the pain and the rage, all the trials and the death of the war and what had been done to me and a generation of Americans by all the men who had lied to us and tricked us, by the man who stood before us in the convention hall that night, while men who had fought for their country were being gassed and beaten in the street outside the hall. I thought of Bobby who sat next to me and the months we had spent in the hospital in the Bronx. It was all hitting me at once, all those years, all that destruction, all that sorrow.

President Nixon began to speak and all three of us took a deep breath and shouted at the top of our lungs, "Stop the bombing, stop the war, stop the bombing, stop the war," as loud and as hard as we could, looking directly at Nixon. The security agents immediately threw up their arms, trying to hide us from the cameras and the president. "Stop the bombing, stop the bombing," I screamed. For an instant Cronkite looked down, then turned his head away. They're not going to show it, I thought. They're going to try and hide us like they did in the hospitals. Hundreds of people around us began to clap and shout "Four more years," trying to drown out our protest. They all seemed very angry and shouted at us to stop. We continued shouting, interrupting Nixon again and again until Secret Service agents grabbed our chairs from behind and began pulling us backward as fast as they could out of the convention hall. "Take it easy," Bobby sad to me. "Don't fight back."

I wanted to take a swing and fight right there in the middle of the convention hall in front of the president and the whole country. "So this is how they treat their wounded veterans!" I screamed.

A short guy with a big Four More Years button ran up to me and spat in my face. "Traitor!" he screamed, as he was yanked back by police. Pandemonium was breaking out all around us and the Secret Service men kept pulling us out backward.

"I served two tours of duty in Vietnam!" I screamed to one newsman. "I gave three-quarters of my body for America. And what do I get? Spit in the face!" I kept screaming until we hit the side entrance where the agents pushed us outside and shut the doors, locking them with chains and padlocks so reporters wouldn't be able to follow us out for interviews.

All three of us sat holding on to each other shaking. We had done it. It had been the biggest moment of our lives, we had shouted down the president of the United States and disrupted his acceptance speech. What more was there left to do but go home?

I sat in my chair still shaking and began to cry.

7

ALL HIS LIFE he'd wanted to be a winner. It was always so important to win, to be the very best. He thought back to high school and the wrestling team and out on Lee Place and Hamilton Avenue when he and the rest of the boys had played stickball or football. He thought back to that and remembered how hard he'd tried to win even in those simple games.

But now it all seemed different. All the hopes about being the best marine, winning all those medals. They all seemed crushed now, they were gone forever. Like the man he had just killed with one shot, all these things had disappeared and he knew, he was very certain, they would never come back again. It had been so simple when he was back on the block with Richie or running down to the deli to pick up a pack of Topps baseball cards, even working in the food store that summer before he went to the war now seemed like a real nice thing. It seemed like so much nicer a thing than what was happening around him now, all the faces, the torn green fatigues, and just below his foot was the guy's head with a gaping hole through his throat.

The Amtrac was heading back to the thick barbed wire where the battalion lived and everyone around him was quiet. There was no question in his mind they all knew what had happened—that he had just pulled the little metal trigger and put a slug through the corporal's neck.

Inside he felt everything sort of squeezing in on him. His hands kept rubbing up and down his leg. He was very nervous and his finger, the one that pulled the trigger, was sort of scratching his leg now.

Later, when they got back to the battalion area, he gave a quick report to a young lieutenant in the major's bunker. "They were attacking," he said, looking at the lieutenant's face, "and we moved backward."

"You retreated," the lieutenant said.

"Yes, we retreated and he got shot. He lived a little while but then he died. He died there in the sand and we called for help. And then we put him in the Amtrac. He must have run away when they started firing. It was dark and I couldn't tell."

"Okay," said the young-looking lieutenant. "Come back again in the morning and we can go over it again. Too bad about . . ." he said.

"Yeah," he said.

He was almost crying now as he turned and walked out of the big command bunker. There was sand all over the place outside and a cold monsoon wind was blowing. He looked out into the darkness and heard the waves of the China Sea breaking softly far away.

There was a path made of wooden ammo casings that led back to his tent. He walked on it like a man on a tightrope, it was so dark and so very hard to see. A couple of times he stumbled on the wooden boxes. It was quiet as he opened the tent flap, as quiet and dark as it had been outside the major's bunker. He dragged in carrying his rifle in one hand and the map case in the other. They were all asleep, all curled up on their cots, inside their mosquito nets. He walked up to his rack and sat down, his head sinking down to the floor. Panic was still rushing through him like a wild train, his heart still raced through his chest as he saw over and over again the kid from Georgia running toward him and the crack of his rifle killing him dead.

I killed him, he kept repeating over and over to himself.

He's dead, he thought.

Gripping his rifle, holding the trigger, he went through the whole thing again and again, tapping, touching the trigger lightly each time he saw the corporal from Georgia running toward him just as he had out there in the sand when everything seemed so crazy and frightening. Each time he felt his heart racing as the three cracks went off and the dark figure slumped to the sand in front of him.

"He's dead—go get him!" someone was yelling

to his right. "Go get him he's hit!" Someone was running now, running to the body and they were pulling the guy in. They were bringing him back to the trench where they all lay scared and shivering.

"Doc—Doc—where's the corpsman!" somebody was yelling.

"Hey Doc, hurry up!" Then somebody said it. Somebody shouted real loud, "It's corporal. They got corporal . . ."

"He's dead," somebody said. "He's gone."

Slowly he turned the rifle around and pointed the barrel toward his head. Oh Jesus God almighty, he thought. *Why*? Why? Why? He began to cry slowly at first. *Why*? I'm going to kill myself, he thought. I'm going to pull this trigger. He was going mad. One minute he wanted to pull the trigger and the next he was feeling the strange power of a man who had just killed someone.

He laid the weapon down by the side of his rack and crawled in with his clothing still on. I killed him, he kept thinking, and when I wake up tomorrow, he thought, when I wake up tomorrow it will still be the same. He wanted to run and hide. He felt like he was in boot camp again and there was no escape, no way off the island. He would wake up with the rest of them the next day. He would get up and wash outside the tent in his tin dish, he would shave and go to chow. But everything would not be all right, he thought, nothing would be all right at all. It was starting to be very different now, very different from what he had ever thought possible.

He opened his eyes slowly as the light came into the tent like a bright triangle. They were all starting to stir, the other men, starting to get up. And then he remembered again what had happened. He hadn't killed any Communist, he thought, he hadn't killed any Communist. Panic swept through his body. In some wild and crazy moment the night before he had pulled the trigger and killed one of his own people.

He tried to slow everything down. He had to think of it as an accident. A lot of guys were firing their guns, there was so much noise and confusion going on. And maybe, he tried real hard to think, maybe he didn't kill the corporal at all, maybe it was someone else. Didn't everyone else start firing after his first three shots? Didn't they all start screaming and shooting after that? Yes, he thought, that's exactly what happened. They were all firing too, he thought. I wasn't the only one. It could have been any of them. Any of them could have put the slug through the corporal's neck. Maybe it was the Communists who killed him. Maybe. But that was awfully hard to believe, that was even harder now to believe than the other men shooting the corporal. Something had gone wrong, something crazy had happened out there and he didn't want to think about it. He was getting tired of turning it over in his mind, over and over again. He was getting real tired of the whole thing. It was all playing so fast and so hard. It all hurt too much. It wasn't right. It wasn't fair. He wanted to forget it, but it wouldn't stop.

He went back to the big sandbagged bunker to see the major.

"That was a pretty rough night, sergeant," the major said, looking up from the green plastic maps on his desk.

"Yes sir," he said. "It was pretty bad."

"Ran into a lot of them, didn't you?" the major said, almost smiling.

"Yes, we sure did. I mean they just sort of popped up on us and started firing."

The major looked down at the maps again and frowned slightly. "What happened?" he said. "What happened out there?"

"Well, major, like I said, we were moving toward the village and we had just grabbed the woman."

"The woman?" the major said.

"Yes, we had just grabbed the pregnant woman."

"She was pregnant?"

"Well yes sir, but we didn't find out until later. We didn't even think she was a woman. She didn't have any chest major, she was flat like a board and we tied her hands behind her back. And there was a boy with her, maybe her small son. We tied his hands too."

"And then?" said the major.

"And then," he said, "we took them up on top of a big sand dune that was a few hundred yards from the village."

"Didn't anybody see you?"

"Yeah," he said. He could feel himself sort of relaxing now. "I think a couple of people in the village. They were going to get water or something. They saw us and one of them started running back to the village. The others just made believe they hadn't seen us at all. I knew they had but they made believe and kept walking back to the village. We set up a perimeter on top of the hill. We set it up so we could watch all around us and see if anyone was coming out of the village after the woman."

"What time was this?" said the major.

"Well—" he looked carefully at his watch. "I think it was about four. It was starting to get dark and I told all the men to eat their rations. Then it became very dark and there were a few small lights in the village and then the shooting started to the left. It was maybe a hundred meters from the big sand dune and I ran to the woman and the kid. I knew she was a woman now and pregnant. Then men started running toward the ocean, away from the dune. Some of them were very frightened. I kept yelling for them to stay, but everyone sort of scattered. Then they all seemed to be running in a line toward a long trench near the ocean. Most of them got back."

"Most of them?" said the major.

"Yeah," he said, "they all got back in the trench except one."

"Who was that?"

"That was corporal, he was the last to come back. And that was when it happened," he said.

"What happened?" said the major.

"That was when the corporal was killed."

The bald sergeant who worked for the major

walked in just as he told the major the thing that had been rolling around in his head all night.

"What happened?" said the major.

The bald sergeant was putting some papers on the major's desk. He did that and walked out.

"There were a bunch of shots," he said carefully. "Everybody was shooting, it was a bad fire-fight." He paused. "It was pretty bad and then corporal was shot. He was shot and he fell down in front of us and a couple of the men ran out to get him. They pulled him back in. I think the others were still firing. The corpsman tried to help . . . the corporal was shot in the neck . . . The corpsman tried to help . . ."

It was becoming very difficult for him to talk now. "Major," he said, "I think I might have . . . I think I might have killed the corporal."

"I don't think so," said the major quickly.

"It was very confusing. It was hard to tell what was happening."

"Yes I know," said the major. "Sometimes it gets very hard out there. I was out a couple of weeks ago and sometimes it's very hard to tell what's happening."

He stared down at the floor of the bunker until he could make himself say it again. He wasn't quite sure the major had heard him the first time.

"But I just want you to know, major, I think I was the one who killed him. I think it might have been me."

There, he had said it. And now he was walking away.

For some reason he was feeling a lot better.

He had told the major everything and the major hadn't believed it. It was like going to confession when he was a kid and the priest saying everything was okay. He walked by the men outside the radio shack. They turned their faces away as he passed. Let them talk, he thought. He was only human, he had made a mistake. The corporal was dead now and no one could bring him back.

The chaplain held a memorial service that afternoon for the man he had killed and he sat in the tent with the rest of the men. There was a wife and a kid, someone said. He tried to listen to the words the chaplain was saying, the name he kept repeating over and over again. Who was this man he'd just killed? Who had he been? He wanted to scream right there in the church tent, right there during the ceremony. He kept hearing the name too many times, the name of the dead man, the man with the friends, the man with the wife, the one he didn't know or care to know, the kid from Georgia who was now being carefully wrapped up in some plastic bag and sent back in a cheap wooden box to be buried in the earth at nineteen.

He had panicked with the rest of them that night and murdered his first man, but it wasn't the enemy, it wasn't the one they had all been taught and trained to kill, it wasn't the silhouette at the rifle range he had pumped holes in from five hundred yards, or the German soldiers with plastic machine guns in Sally's Woods. He'd never figured it would ever happen this way. It never did in the movies. There were always the good guys and the bad guys, the cowboys and the Indians. There was always the enemy and the good guys and each of them killed the other.

He went back to his tent after the ceremony was over and sat down. There was some mail but he couldn't get interested in it. Someone had sent him a Sergeant Rock comicbook. But it wasn't funny anymore. The good guys weren't supposed to kill the good guys.

The next few weeks passed in a slow way, much slower than any time in his whole life. Each day dragged by until the night, the soft soothing night, when he could close himself off from the pain, when he could forget the terrible thing for a few hours. Each night before he slept he prayed to his god, begging for some understanding of why the thing had happened, why he had been made into a murderer with one shot. Why him? he thought over and over again. He first pleaded with God, then he became angry, demanding. Oh God, he thought, why did this happen, for what reason? What kind of god, he thought, would do this to him? What kind of god would give him these terrible feelings and nightmares for what seemed to be the rest of his life?

The time passed in big gaps of deadness. Nights when he could sleep and forget and mornings when it all came back and the men stood by the tents looking at him in their peculiar way, whispering on the chow line. He found himself reading a small pocket Bible so he would not have to look

at them and writing long letters to his mother ar
father. He wrote in his diary that he wanted
become a priest, and that was what he told h
parents in the letter about the corporal that h
finally wrote home. He told them the story he ha
told the major, the story about the firefight. Ar
the whole thing in the letter took on a new ar
beautiful meaning. He had seen a man killed ar
something, something very deep and wonderfu
had happened to him. In some wonderful way, h
wrote to them, he had become something ve
different than he had ever been before. And nov
he told them, he wanted to be a priest. He wante
to be like the guy up on the altar, the healer ar
the guy who gave communion.

He finished the letter and he sent it. There, h
thought, it's through. And now deep down insic
him he still felt the angry pain, but it became
little easier to live now, easier to live—eve
though the war was going on a little worse tha
before, artillery and rockets were hitting the cam
almost every day, sending the men into the litt
bunkers they had built. The major was still sittir
behind his desk in the big sandbagged battalio
bunker, and whenever he walked past him th
major would return his sharp salute with a ve
confident smile on his face. He thought of th
major as his friend. He had understood the who
terrible thing. He had said that maybe it didn
happen, things got confusing out there, and th
major said he knew, that he had been out the
himself under heavy fire and he knew.

He knew the major understood everything, like the men who whispered softly on the chow line and the men who stood talking by their tents. No one wants to say, he thought, no one wants to talk about it. Who wanted to approach him and ask if he had done it, if he had killed the corporal that night? No one. No one would ever do it, he thought.

There was a night not long after he had killed the corporal when he was walking on the wooden path that snaked around all the tents past the bunkers like a sidewalk. He was sort of tiptoeing along the casings and he opened up what seemed to be his tent. He had seen this light in the long crack at the bottom of it and he walked in to find he had just walked into the battalion commander's tent. It was very dark, so dark somebody, anybody, could get lost in a place like that, he thought. Just like that goddamn patrol a few months ago when he had read the map wrong, when he had led the men in the wrong direction. He had been a thousand meters off. He was a mile from where he was supposed to be, and now he was doing it again. He was walking in on the goddamn battalion commander who was in his pajamas getting ready to go to bed or something.

"Yes, what do you want, sergeant?" he heard the battalion commander saying to him.

"Ahhh, nothing," he said. "I made a mistake, sir. I thought this was my tent."

The battalion commander looked at him for a

moment, looked at him like he had done a ve
stupid thing. "Well, carry on," he said.

It was his friend the major who gave him h
second chance. He called him into the comman
bunker one day and told him he wanted him
become the leader of his new scout team. Th
major who understood him told him he liked th
way he operated and said he knew the sergean
could do a good job.

Here was his chance, he thought, to mak
everything good again. This young, strong marin
was getting a second crack at becoming a hero
He knew, he understood, the thing the major wa
doing for him, and he left the tent feeling stronge
and better than he'd felt for a long time. Her
was his chance, he thought over and over again

He walked down the twisting ammo-box sid
walk and saluted one of the officers as smartly a
ever, much too smartly for anyone who had bee
over there as long as him. The thoughts of th
night he'd killed the corporal were already be
coming faded as he began to think more and mor
about the scout team, how he would train them
and the things they would do to make up for a
the things that had come before.

He wrote in his diary that night how proud h
was to have been made the leader of the scout
to be serving America in this its most critical hou
just like President Kennedy had talked about. H
might get killed, he wrote, but so had a lot o
Americans who had fought for democracy. It wa

very important to be there putting his life on the line, to be going out on patrol and lying in the rain for Sparky the barber and God and the rest. He was proud. He was real proud of what he was doing. This, he thought, is what serving your country is supposed to be about.

HE WENT OUT on patrol with th
others the night of the ambush at exactly eigh
o'clock, loading a round into the chamber of hi
weapon before he walked outside the tent and int
the dark and rain. As usual he had made all th
men put on camouflage from head to toe, mad
sure they had all blackened their faces, and a
tached twigs and branches to their arms and leg
with rubber bands.

One by one the scouts moved slowly past th
thick barbed wire and began to walk along th
bank of the river, heading toward the graveyar
where the ambush would be set up. They wer
moving north exactly as planned, a line of sha
ows tightly bunched in the rain. Sometimes
would stop raining and they would spread o
somewhat more, but mostly they continued
bunch up together, as if they were afraid
losing their way.

There was a rice paddy on the edge of th
graveyard. No one said a word as they walke

through it and he thought he could hear voices from the village. He could smell the familiar smoke from the fires in the huts and he knew that the people who went out fishing each day must have come home. They were the people he watched every morning moving quietly in their small boats down toward the mouth of the river, heading out to the sea. Some of the older men reminded him of his father, going to work each morning and coming back home every night to sit by their fires with their children cooking their fish. They must talk about us sometimes, he thought. He wondered a lot what it was they thought about him and the men.

He remembered how difficult it had been when he had first come to the war to tell the villagers from the enemy and sometimes it had seemed easier to hate all of them, but he had always tried very hard not to. He wished he could be sure they understood that he and the men were there because they were trying to help all of them save their country from the Communists.

They were on a rice dike that bordered the graveyard. The voices from the huts nearby seemed quite loud. He looked up ahead to where the lieutenant who had come along with them that night was standing. The lieutenant had sent one of the men, Molina, on across the rice dikes almost to the edge of the village. The cold rain was still coming down very hard and the men behind him were standing like a line of statues waiting for the next command.

But now something was wrong up ahead. He

could see Molina waving his hands excitedly trying to tell the lieutenant something. Stumbling over the dikes, almost crawling, Molina came back toward the lieutenant. He saw him whisper someting in his ear. And now the lieutenant turned and looked at him. "Sergeant," he said, "Molina and I are going to get a look up ahead. Stay here with the team."

Balancing on the dike, he turned slowly after the lieutenant had gone, motioning with his rifle for all of the men in back of him to get down. Each one, carefully, one after the other, squatted along the dike on one knee, waiting in the rain to move out again. They were all shivering from the cold.

They waited for what seemed a long time and then the lieutenant and Molina appeared suddenly through the darkness. He could tell from their faces that they had seen something. They had seen something up ahead, he was sure, and they were going to tell him what they had just seen. He stood up, too excited to stay kneeling down on the dike.

"What is it?" he cried.

"Be quiet," whispered the lieutenant sharply, grabbing his arm, almost throwing him into the paddy. He began talking very quickly and much louder than he should have. "I think we found them. I think we found them," he repeated, almost shouting.

He didn't know what the lieutenant meant. "What?" he said.

"The sappers, the sappers! Let's go!" The lieutenant was taking over now. He seemed very sure of himself, he was acting very confident. "Let's go, goddamn it!"

He clicked his rifle off safety and got his men up quickly, urging them forward, following the lieutenant and Molina toward the edge of the village. They ran through the paddy, splashing like a family of ducks. This time he hoped and prayed it would be the real enemy. He would be ready for them this time. Here was another chance, he thought. He was so excited he ran straight into the lieutenant, bouncing clumsily off his chest.

"I'm sorry, sir," he said.

"Quiet! They're out there," the lieutenant whispered to him, motioning to the rest of the men to get down on their hands and knees now. They crawled to the tree line, then along the back of the rice paddy through almost a foot of water, until the whole team lay in a long line pressed up against the dike, facing the village.

He saw a light, a fire he thought, flickering in the distance off to the right of the village, with little dark figures that seemed to be moving behind it. He could not tell how far away they were from there. It was very hard to tell distance in the dark.

The lieutenant moved next to him. "You see?" he whispered. "Look," he said, very keyed up now. "They've got rifles. Can you see the rifles? Can you see them?" the lieutenant asked him.

He looked very hard through the rain.

"Can you see them?"

"Yes, I see them. I see them," he said. He was very sure.

The lieutenant put his arm around him and whispered in his ear. "Tell them down at the end to give me an illumination. I want this whole place lit up like a fucking Christmas tree."

Turning quickly to the man on his right, he told him what the lieutenant had said. He told him to pass the instructions all the way to the end of the line, where a flare would be fired just above the small fire near the village.

Lying there in the mud behind the dike, he stared at the fire that still flickered in the rain. He could still see the little figures moving back and forth against it like small shadows on a screen. He felt the whole line tense, then heard the WOOOORSHH of the flare cracking overhead in a tremendous ball of sputtering light turning night into day, arching over their heads toward the small fire that he now saw was burning inside an open hut.

Suddenly someone was firing from the end with his rifle, and now the whole line opened up, roaring their weapons like thunder, pulling their triggers again and again without even thinking, emptying everything they had into the hut in a tremendous stream of bright orange tracers that crisscrossed each other in the night.

The flare arched its last sputtering bits into the village and it became dark, and all he could see were the bright orange embers from the fire that had gone out.

And he could hear them.

There were voices screaming.

"What happened? Goddamn it, what happened?" yelled the lieutenant.

The voices were screaming from inside the hut.

"Who gave the order to fire? I wanna know who gave the order to fire."

The lieutenant was standing up now, looking up and down the line of men still lying in the rain.

He found that he was shaking. It had all happened so quickly.

"We better get a killer team out there," he heard Molina say.

"All right, all right. Sergeant," the lieutenant said to him, "get out there with Molina and tell me how many we got."

He got to his feet and quickly got five of the men together, leading them over the dike and through the water to the hut from where the screams were still coming. It was much closer than he had first thought. Now he could see very clearly the smoldering embers of the fire that had been blown out by the terrific blast of their rifles.

Molina turned the beam of his flashlight into the hut. "Oh God," he said. "Oh Jesus Christ." He started to cry. "We just shot up a bunch of kids!"

The floor of the small hut was covered with them, screaming and thrashing their arms back and forth, lying in pools of blood, crying wildly, screaming again and again. They were shot in the face, in the chest, in the legs, moaning and crying.

"Oh Jesus!" he cried.

He could hear the lieutenant shouting at them, wanting to know how many they had killed.

There was an old man in the corner with his head blown off from his eyes up, his brains hanging out of his head like jelly. He kept looking at the strange sight, he had never seen anything like it before. A small boy next to the old man was still alive, although he had been shot many times. He was crying softly, lying in a large pool of blood. His small foot had been shot almost completely off and seemed to be hanging by a thread.

"What's happening? What's going on up there?" The lieutenant was getting very impatient now.

Molina shouted for the lieutenant to come quickly. "You better get up here. There's a lot of wounded people up here."

He heard a small girl moaning now. She was shot through the stomach and bleeding out of the rear end. All he could see now was blood everywhere and he heard their screams with his heart racing like it had never raced before. He felt crazy and weak as he stood there staring at them with the rest of the men, staring down onto the floor like it was a nightmare, like it was some kind of dream and it really wasn't happening.

And then he could no longer stand watching. They were people, he thought, children and old men, people, people like himself, and he had to do something, he had to move, he had to help, do something. He jerked the green medical bag off his back, ripping it open and grabbing for bandages, yelling at Molina to please come and help him. He knelt down in the middle of the screaming bodies and began bandaging them, trying to cover the holes where the blood was still spurting out. "It's gonna be okay. It's gonna be okay," he tried to say, but he was crying now, crying and still trying to bandage them all up. He moved from body to body searching in the dark with his fingers for the holes the bullets had made, bandaging each one as quickly as he could, his shaking hands wet with the blood. It was raining into the hut and a cold wind swept his face as he moved in the dark.

The lieutenant had just come up with the others.

"Help me!" he screamed. "Somebody help!"

"Well, goddamn it sergeant! What's the matter? How many did we kill?"

"They're children!" he screamed at the lieutenant.

"Children and old men!" cried Molina.

"Where are their rifles?" the lieutenant asked.

"There aren't any rifles," he said.

"Well, help him then!" screamed the lieutenant to the rest of the men. The men stood in the entrance of the hut, but they would not move. "Help him, help him. I'm ordering you to help him!"

The men were not moving and some of them were crying now, dropping their rifles and sitting down on the wet ground. They were weeping now with their hands against their faces. "Oh Jesus, oh God, forgive us."

"Forgive us for what we've done!" he heard Molina cry.

"Get up," screamed the lieutenant. "What do you think this is? I'm ordering you all to get up."

Some of the men began slowly crawling over the bodies, grabbing for the bandages that were still left.

By now some of the villagers had gathered outside the hut. He could hear them shouting angrily. He knew they must be cursing them.

"You better get a fucking chopper in here," someone was yelling.

"Where's the radio man? Get the radio man!"

"Hello Cactus Red. This is Red Light Two. Ahhh this is Red Light Two. We need an emergency evac. We got a lot of wounded . . . ahh . . . friendly wounded. A lot of friendly wounded out here." He could hear the lieutenant on the radio, trying to tell the helicopters where to come.

The men in the hut were just sitting there crying. They could not move, and they did not listen to the lieutenant's orders. They just sat with the rain pouring down on them through the roof, crying and not moving.

"You men! You men have got to start listening to me. You gotta stop crying like babies and start acting like marines!" The lieutenant who was off the radio now was shoving the men, pleading with them to move. "You're men, not babies. It's a mistake. It wasn't your fault. They got in the way. Don't you people understand—they got in the goddamn way!"

When the medivac chopper came, he picked up the little boy who was lying next to the old man. His foot came off and he grabbed it up quickly and bandaged it against the bottom stump of the boy's leg. He held him looking into his frightened eyes and carried him up to the open door of the helicopter. The boy was still crying softly when he handed him to the gunner.

And when it was all over and all the wounded had been loaded aboard, he helped the lieutenant move the men back on patrol. They walked away from the hut in the rain. And now he felt his body go numb and heavy, feeling awful and sick inside like the night the corporal had died, as they moved along in the dark and the rain behind the lieutenant toward the graveyard.

IT WAS GETTING very cold and it was raining almost every day now. Some guy was sent back home because a booby trap had blown up on him. And it was about then I started looking for booby traps to step on, taking all sorts of crazy chances, trying to forget about the rain and the cold and the dead children and the corporal. I would go off alone sometimes on patrol looking for the traps, hoping I'd get blown up enough to be sent home, but not enough to get killed. It was a rough kind of game to play. I remember walking along, knowing goddamn well exactly what I was doing, just waiting for those metal splinters to go bursting up into my testicles, sending me home a wounded hero. That was the only way was getting out of this place. I took more chances than ever before, daydreaming as I strolled through the minefields, thinking of the time I saw a guy named Johnny Temple play in Ebbets Field or the time Duke Snyder struck out and tossed that old bat of his up in the air when the umpire threw him out of the game.

One morning the battalion was blown almost completely apart by an artillery attack. We had been out on patrol most of the night lying in the rain. We weren't even awake when the first couple of rounds began to pound in all around us. There was a whistle, then a cracking explosion. They had us right on target. We all ran for our lives, trying to make it to the bunker we had dug for ourselves. I was still half-asleep and not quite conscious of what was happening to me. All I remember was that I had to get to the bunker. Finally, after what seemed a long time, we all crawled down into the sandbags. We huddled together like children and I heard myself saying "Oh God please God I want to live." Artillery rounds kept crashing in and there was a tremendous explosion in the tent right next to ours. I wondered if anyone had been in it. I continued to pray with all the strength in me that I wouldn't be killed.

When the barrage finally lifted we all looked at each other feeling a little embarrassed for acting so frightened and praying behind the sandbags. Outside the bunker there was a sharp smell of gunpowder and people were beginning to move. I grabbed my green medical bag and told the rest of the men to stay in the bunker and I went out into the sand looking for anyone who was wounded. The first thing I saw was our tent all blown to shit. Big chunks of shrapnel had torn gaping holes through the corrugated tin roof and slashed through the tent like the thin stabs of a knife. We had been hit by almost 150 rounds in only a few minutes. Everyone was walking around in a daze.

There were a bunch of men over at the motor pool kneeling around someone on the ground. I ran over there as fast as I could, my dog tags jangling around my neck. They were kneeling around a guy I knew pretty well. Mac.

I looked down and saw that he was dead. His neck was almost off and his right arm had been severed. He had hundreds of silver holes in his face and chest, looking like little puncture points. MacCarthy was dead, bleeding in the sand, his dark blue Boston eyes open and staring up at the sky. I had just seen him the morning before on the chow line after we had come in from patrol. He had smiled at me and told me how everything was down at the motor pool. But now he was dead and I picked up my bag and walked back to the bunker, thinking how MacCarthy had just looked like a thing, a mannequin. *The dead, he thought looked kind of funny in a way, kind of very ridiculous.* I felt almost like laughing and when I came up to the bunker there was the short kid from New Jersey who was taking pictures of the demolished tent. He was taking pictures with a little camera with the care and precision of a guy who should be shooting some pretty trees back home. I could see that a lot of the men were laughing and joking now, laughing and joking about the same thing. *It was like the boy scouts, like the boy scouts getting all chopped up in their pajamas while having a nightmare.*

Another crowd had gathered around a trench. It was hard to tell what had happened there, how many bodies there were. Maybe three all mangled together in a heap, a bunch of arms and legs. There was a smell of gunpowder and blood mixed with burning flesh. One of the heads was completely severed, chopped off, with the exception of a strand of muscle—that was the only thing that continued to connect the head to the stinking corpse. There was nothing any of us could do but pick up the pieces. They seemed very cold and gray and someone in back of me was taking pictures. I fished around for identification in one corpse's dead back pocket and found a wallet. It was Sergeant Bo, one of my friends. He was the supply sergeant and had a wife somewhere. He was sort of the Sergeant Bilko of the battalion. He never went on patrol and had the most comfortable quarters of anyone, with a rug and a desk and a picture of his pretty wife. He had a very young face and now he was in that hole, mangled in that hole, stinking with the others.

The lieutenant came by and ordered the men to put the pieces on a stretcher. Sergeant Bo was my friend and now he was dead. They were going to put him in a plastic bag. They were going to do that with the pieces just like they were going to do with MacCarthy and like they'd done with the corporal from Georgia whom I'd killed the month

before. Out by the command bunker they had al
the dead lined up in a neat long line. They wer
all stripped of their clothes and staring up at th
sky. Bo and Mac were there with a lot of other
I hadn't seen before. About eleven men had bee
killed in the attack.

There were scores of wounded. Sergeant Peter
had been hit in the eye and Corporal Swanso
was lying in the command tent with a large piec
of metal still stuck in his head. I went up to hir
and held his hand, telling him everything wa
going to be all right. He told me to send a lette
right away to his wife in California and tell he
what had happened. I promised him I'd do it tha
night but I never did and I never heard from hi
again.

The men were beginning to relax a little mor
now. Everyone was smoking cigarettes and feelin
a little closer to everyone else. Maybe, I though
the men would stop talking about me behind m
back now. Maybe with all that blown-away fles
the killing of the corporal from Georgia wouldn
mean that much anymore.

He was just another body, he thought, just lik
the rest of them, the ones who had all been blow
to pieces. For some crazy reason he began feelin
a lot better about everything. The more the bette
he thought, the more that looked like the corpor
the better. Maybe, he thought, they would get co
fused and forget in all the madness that he ha
murdered the kid from Georgia. Maybe they wou

nderstand the mistake of putting the slug in the orporal's neck. He wanted to cry for all his riends who had died that day but he couldn't. Ie couldn't feel too much anymore.

WE STOPPED GOING out on patrol in the beginning of the new year. We began t take showers every morning and even eat thre meals a day again. It seemed like the perfect tim to fix up the tent. Michaelson brought in a can c dark oil that we swept all over the wood floo Even more work was put in on the bunker.

There was news one morning of a big fight little up north and we began getting restless an edgy. A lieutenant from the battalion had bee killed there. I knelt over him with the chaplai when they brought his body in. He was covere with a raincoat. There was a small bullet hole i his forehead and the whole back of his head ha been shot out. He was dead like all the rest, an for some reason right then I felt something bi was about to happen.

The major called me over and told me to get th men ready to move out. We were going nort across the river.

When I got back to the tent, Michaelson tol

me he would see me in heaven after today. He was to die that afternoon. Every one of us seemed to have a funny feeling. I kept thinking over and over that I was going to get hit—that nothing would be quite the same after this day.

We went to get some chow and I remember the major yelled at me for not putting helmets on the men. We'd never used them in the past and I couldn't understand why on this day the major wanted us to wear helmets and flak jackets. We had to walk all the way back to our tents and put the stuff on. We felt like supermen in the cumbersome jackets as we got into the truck that took us to the southern bank of the river. We all got out and waited for a while and then a small boat took us to the other side, where everybody else was getting ready to sweep up north to where the lieutenant's squad had been wiped out.

I remember moving along the beach beside the ocean later. There were sand dunes that reminded me of home and lots of scrub pine trees. The men were in a very sloppy formation. It seemed everyone was carrying far too much equipment. The sky was clear and the Vietnamese were walking and fishing. Except for the noise of the tanks and Amtracs that were moving slowly along with us, it seemed like a Sunday stroll with everyone dressed up in costume. It was hard to remember that at any moment the whole thing might bust wide open and you might get killed like all the other dead losers. There was that salt air that smelled so familiar.

Then the whole procession suddenly came to a

stop and we were told to go back. There was something happening in the village on the north bank of the river. A big fight was going on and the Popular Forces were pinned down and in lots of trouble. I ran up to the captain who had given the order and asked him was he sure we weren't supposed to continue going up north. The men didn't want to go back, I said. Was it the major who had given the order? I asked. The captain said he'd try to get confirmation. I waited with the Amtrac engines roaring in my ears while he radioed the rear. When he got off the radio, he told me the major had changed his mind. The scouts would now lead the attack into the village.

I climbed on one of the Amtracs to talk to the men. They seemed very quiet. They had the same feeling I did that it was all about to come down, that this walk in the sand might be the last one for all of us.

There was going to be some kind of crazy tactical maneuver where we were going to march west along the bank of the river and make a direct assault on the village after crossing the razorback, which was the biggest sand dune in the area. A group of us would dismount from one of the Amtracs and lead the primary assault and the other two Amtracs would sweep from north to south through the graveyard and attack from another flank. It all sounded so crazy and simple I kept trying to get my thoughts together, trying to think how much I wanted to prove to myself that I was a brave man, a good marine. No matter what happened out there, I thought to myself, I could never retreat. I had to be courageous. Here was my chance to win a medal, here was my chance to fight against the real enemy, to make up for everything that had happened.

This was it, he thought, everything he had been praying for, the whole thing up for grabs.

There were ten of them walking toward the village, and he felt the rosary beads in his top pocket and knew that the little black Bible they had given them all on the planes coming in was in his other pocket too. The other men were getting off the 'tracs in the graveyard. He could see the heat still coming up from the big engines and the men looked real small in the distance, like little toy soldiers jumping off tanks. He looked to the left and they were all there, it was a perfect line. He had trained the scouts well and everything looked good. There was a big pagoda up ahead and a long trench full of Popular Forces. There wasn't any firing going on and he asked the commander of the Viet unit to help him in the assault that was about to take place. The Viet officer said they were staying put and none of them was even going to think about attacking the village. He was angry as he moved the scouts over the top of the long trench line. They're a bunch of fucking cowards, he thought. "Look at them!" he shouted to the scouts. "They're sitting out the war in that trench like a bunch of babies."

"Let's go!" he said. And now they began to move into a wide and open area. They were ten men armed to the teeth, walking in a sweeping line toward the village. It was beautiful, just like the movies.

The firing first started in the graveyard. There were loud cracks, and then the whole thing sounded like someone had set off a whole string of fireworks. He could hear the mortars popping out, crashing like cymbals when they landed on top of the 'tracs. The whole graveyard was being raked by mortars and heavy machine-gun fire coming out of the village.

I remember we all sort of stopped and watched for a moment. Then all of a sudden the cracks were blasting all around our heads and everybody was running all over the place. We started firing back with full automatics. I emptied a whole clip into the pagoda and the village. I was yelling to the men. I kept telling them to hold their ground and keep firing, though no one knew what we were firing at. I looked to my left flank and all the men were gone. They had run away, all run away to the trees near the river, and I yelled and cursed at them to come back but nobody came. I kept emptying everything I had into the village, blasting holes through the pagoda and ripping bullets into the tree line. There was someone to my right lying on the ground still firing.

I had started walking toward the village when the first bullet hit me. There was a sound like firecrackers going off all around my feet. Then a real loud crack and my leg went numb below the knee. I looked down at my foot and there was blood at the back of it. The bullet had come through the front and blew out nearly the whole of my heel.

I had been shot. The war had finally caught up with my body. I felt good inside. Finally the war was with me and I had been shot by the enemy. I was getting out of the war and I was going to be a hero. I kept firing my rifle into the tree line and boldly, with my new wound, moved closer to the village, daring them to hit me again. For a moment I felt like running back to the rear with my new million-dollar wound but I decided to keep fighting out in the open. A great surge of strength went through me as I yelled for the other men to come out from the trees and join me. I was limping now and the foot was beginning to hurt so much, I finally lay down in almost a kneeling position, still firing into the village, still unable to see anyone. I seemed to be the only one left firing a rifle. Someone came up from behind me, took off my boot and began to bandage my foot. The whole thing was incredibly stupid, we were sitting ducks, but he bandaged my foot and then he took off back into the tree line.

For a few seconds it was silent. I lay down prone and waited for the next bullet to hit me. It was only a matter of time, I thought. I wasn't retreating, I wasn't going back, I was lying right there and blasting everything I had into the pagoda. The rifle was full of sand and it was jamming. I had to pull the bolt back now each time trying to get a round into the chamber. It was impossible and I started to get up and a loud crack went off next to my right ear as a thirty-caliber slug tore through my right shoulder, blasted through my lung, and smashed my spinal cord to pieces.

I felt that everything from my chest down was completely gone. I waited to die. I threw my hand back and felt my legs still there. I couldn't feel them but they were still there. I was still alive. And for some reason I started believing, I started believing I might not die. I might make it out of there and live and feel and go back home again. I could hardly breathe and was taking short little sucks with the one lung I had left. The blood was rolling off my flak jacket from the hole in my shoulder and I couldn't feel the pain in my foot anymore, I couldn't even feel my body. I was frightened to death I didn't think about praying, all I could feel was cheated.

All I could feel was the worthlessness of dying right here in this place at this moment for nothing.

THE BACK YARD, that was the place to be, it was where all the plans for the future, the trips to Africa, the romances with young high-school girls, it was where all those wonderful things took place. Remember the hula hoop, everyone including my mother doing it and my sister, yes my sister, teaching me the twist in the basement. Then out on the basketball court with all the young fine-looking girls watching. Then back on the fence for a walk around the whole back yard. Up there! Can you see me balancing like Houdini? Can you see me hiding in a box, in a submarine, on a jet? Can you see me flying a kite, making a model, breeching a stream?

It was all sort of easy, it had all come and gone, the snowstorms, the street lamps telling us there was no school at midnight, the couch, the heater with all of us rolled up beside it in the thick blankets, the dogs, it was lovely. Getting nailed at home plate, studying the cub scout handbook, tying knots, playing Ping-Pong, reading National

Geographic. *Mickey Mantle was my hero and Joan Marfe was the girl I liked best. It all ended with a bang and it was lovely.*

There was a song called "Runaway" by a guy named Dell Shannon playing one Saturday at the baseball field. I remember it was a beautiful spring day and we were young back then and really alive and the air smelled fresh. This song was playing and I really got into it and was hitting baseballs and feeling like I could live forever.

It was all sort of easy.
It had all come and gone.